THE PHYSICS OF MUSICAL SOUNDS

APPLIED PHYSICS GUIDES

General Editor:

SIR GRAHAM SUTTON
C.B.E., D.Sc., F.R.S.

Chairman of the National Environmental Research Council.
Director-General Meteorological Office, formerly Dean of the Royal Military College of Science Shrivenham
and Bashforth Professor of Mathematical Physics.

Technology of Instrumentation
E. B. PEARSON
M.Sc., F.Inst.P., M.I.E.E., A.F.R.Ae.S.

Feedback Theory and its Applications
P. H. HAMMOND
B.Sc., A.M.I.E.E.

High Speed Computing, Methods and Applications
S. H. HOLLINGDALE
M.A., Ph.D.

The Technique of Optical Instrument Design
R. J. BRACEY
M.B.E., F.Inst.P., F.R.M.S.

The Physics of Lightning
D. J. MALAN
D.Sc., F.R.S.S.Af.

Elements of Hypersonic Aerodynamics
R. N. COX   L. F. CRABTREE
B.Sc., M.A., Ph.D.   B.Sc., D.I.C., Ph.D.

The Environment in Modern Physics
C. W. KILMINSTER
M.Sc., Ph.D.

THE PHYSICS OF
MUSICAL SOUNDS

C. A. TAYLOR

D.Sc., F.Inst.P.   Professor of Physics, University College, Cardiff

*Formerly Reader in Physics in the Faculty
of Technology of the University
of Manchester*

NEW YORK
AMERICAN ELSEVIER PUBLISHING COMPANY, INC.

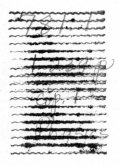

First published 1965

AMERICAN ELSEVIER PUBLISHING COMPANY, INC.
52 Vanderbilt Avenue,
New York 17, New York

Thielmon 19 Ja 66 - Physics

LIBRARY OF CONGRESS CATALOG CARD NUMBER: 65–14698

PRINTED IN GREAT BRITAIN

Foreword

To-day, more people listen to music than ever before. Yet the study of sound, as a distinct branch of physics, in recent years has languished in our schools and universities. Professor Taylor's book should go a long way to restore the situation. In this volume the classical treatment of sound waves is brought up to date by modern mathematical methods, and the results are applied to clarify the design and performance of musical instruments, most of which were brought to their final form long before their characteristics could be examined in a manner that would satisfy a modern physicist. Yet music is more than a succession of pressure waves in air, and this book not only describes the analysis of musical sounds by modern techniques but also approaches the extremely interesting but extraordinarily difficult problem of explaining why certain sounds appeal to us and excite our imagination, whereas others are dull or even repellent.

When I read Professor Taylor's book in manuscript I found it fascinating. I feel certain that others, whether they are skilled performers, sound reproduction engineers or, like myself, simply people who enjoy music, will find it equally stimulating.

O. G. S.

Preface

The absorbing interest that I have always found in this subject has been inspired mainly by three people and, in a real sense, the book owes its existence to them. I was fortunate in attending a school at which both Physics and Music were taught by the same master, and I grew up with the notion that this was not only a satisfactory arrangement but a normal one; it was some time before I realized that in most schools the two subjects were entirely divorced. That master, the late Mr. C. Early, head of the Physics Department at the Kingston High School, Hull, gave me a remarkable grounding in experimental physics and inspired enthusiasm for both physics and music that has never left me. He was able, during his last illness, to read most of the manuscript and made many invaluable comments and suggestions. The book is gratefully dedicated to his memory.

I was also fortunate that, through the vagaries of the war, I was enabled to attend Dr. Alexander Wood's lectures on sound and they, together with his delightful book *The Physics of Music*, have been the conscious and unconscious sources of many ideas.

Finally when I joined the staff of the Physics Department of the Manchester College of Science and Technology my interest was further stimulated by my being given the task of lecturing on sound to budding physicists who were supposed to have completed an "A"-level course; it soon became apparent that, for most of them, sound had been missed out and the problem of teaching the subject at the higher level became more challenging. Professor H. Lipson was responsible for this assignment and he has supported and encouraged my interest ever since.

The book is intended to be read by anyone who is fascinated by the relationship between physics and music. I suppose that the overall level is about that of a first-year University course, but I have tried to write it so that less-mathematically-minded readers can omit the sections marked with an asterisk without loss of continuity. I have also included considerable reference to Fourier transformation because it is a subject of growing importance which is usually treated in a highly mathematical way; my treatment is experimental, practical and non-rigorous. It also happens to be a subject whose universality of application I find elegant and satisfying.

I should like to express thanks to many people in addition to the three already mentioned. My wife and family have endured much during the preparation of the book with great patience and have given me constant encouragement; Miss M. W. Allen typed the manuscript and gave valuable assistance in checking and preparing material for the printer; Dr. R. P. Williams read the proofs with great care; Mr. F. Kirkman prepared most of the photographs; Dr. E. C. Yeadon carried out some of the experimental work on optical harmonic analysis; Mr. F. Merry of Leigh Central County Secondary School drew my attention to his "milk-straw" models for demonstrating wave summation; Mr. L. L. Ardern gave generous help in tracing elusive references; the Principal of the Royal Manchester

College of Music allowed some of his students to take part in experiments; M. F-Baschet and his colleagues discussed their new instruments with me, and many other colleagues took part in experiments and discussions.

Finally, I should like to thank the Editor, Sir Graham Sutton, for giving me the opportunity to write the book, and the publishers and printers for their co-operation.

Manchester, April 1965   C. A. T.

Acknowledgment is due to the following for permission to reproduce the figures mentioned:

Figure 6.11. Dr. G. B. Brown and the Institute of Physics and the Physical Society.

Figure 6.12. Professor J. Backus and the American Institute of Physics.

Figures 10.1, 10.3, 10.5. Messrs. Boosey & Hawkes Ltd., London.

Figure 10.4. The McGraw-Hill Book Company, New York.

Figure 11.3. The British Broadcasting Corporation.

and to the John Compton Organ Co. and the Hammond Organ Co. for making available technical information.

Contents

* Sections marked with an asterisk contain the more mathematical material and may be omitted.

CHAPTER 3

The Origin of Differences in Tonal Quality

CHAPTER 4

Harmonic Analysis and Fourier Transformation

CHAPTER 5

Amplification, Matching and Coupled Systems

CHAPTER 6

Starting Transients and the Initiation of Vibrations

CHAPTER 7

Miscellaneous Other Influences on the Character of a Musical Sound

CHAPTER 8

Combinations of Notes

CHAPTER 9

Influences on the Perception of Sound

9.2.   Room acoustics   136

       9.2.1. The basic conditions for good acoustics   138
              (i) acceptable reverberation

       9.2.2. The basic conditions for good acoustics   139
              (ii) Uniform distribution

       9.2.3. The effect of acoustic characteristics on the quality of sound perceived   140

9.3.   Perception via electrical reproduction   143

       9.3.1. Introduction   143

       9.3.2. Imperfections in reproduction systems   144

CHAPTER 10

The Physical Characteristics of Conventional Instruments

CHAPTER 11

The New Instruments

CHAPTER 1

Introduction

1.1 The theme of the book—the design of a new musical instrument

Music seems to have a special fascination for physicists and mathematicians. There have been many attempts to explain this fact, with Pythagoras himself one of the early thinkers who recognised the kindred perfection of mathematical ratios and musical intervals. Whatever the true underlying explanation may be there are many good practical reasons why physicists should know something about music; musicians have recognised for some time the value of some understanding of physical principles in getting the best performance from their instruments. Why then is sound the "Cinderella" subject of school physics? The easy answer is that it does not account for many questions in the Advanced-level G.C.E. examination! But this is only a symptom; obviously the small place given to sound in the G.C.E. syllabus reflects an earlier lack of interest on the part of School and University physicists. Here then is the paradox: on the one hand physicists are fascinated by music and on the other hand they rate the study of sound so low that many schools ignore it altogether.

Sound, however, is an extraordinarily useful subject. Wave motion is one of the really important concepts in physics and sound provides a useful one-dimensional introduction to it. Fourier transformation is a subject of growing importance in many different spheres of physics—radio-communication, radio-astronomy, optics, X-ray, electron and neutron diffraction, to mention just a few—and again sound provides an excellent one-dimensional introduction. Audio and visual aids are widely recognised as powerful teaching tools, and sound is an ideal subject for demonstration.

The study of sound also brings one face to face with the problems of individual psychology, of the relationships between physiological sensations and physical stimuli, and of the extremely complex mixture of emotion, taste, training and background which is at work, making our attempts at objective judgment in any field dangerously subjective. All physicists must be aware of such limitations and be prepared to design experiments which will minimise the subjective effects.

All these are excellent reasons why the study of sound should be part of every physicist's training. Can we therefore resolve the paradox and make use of the fascination of music as a vehicle? Basically there is probably little that is new in this book except the method of presentation; all the various aspects of the study of sound covered are linked together by a musical theme. This theme is the possibility of designing a completely new musical instrument. The various chapters follow through all the basic investigations necessary to obtain design data and to discover the essential features of an instrument; the last chapter ought therefore to contain an account of the completely new instrument. The theme, however, is clearly an unfinished one and only partial answers can be given in the final summing-up.

1.2   What is a musical instrument?

We must start with a definition of a musical instrument. Dictionaries and encyclopaedias on the whole are not very helpful and often include in the definition the idea that the sound is produced by mechanical vibration; this would, of course, exclude many instruments, particularly electronic devices. For the purpose of our investigation it will be sufficient to say that a musical instrument is a device for producing musical sounds that can be varied in order to play tunes. There could, of course, be considerable argument about this; it immediately excludes the triangle, drums, etc. on which tunes in the ordinary sense of the word are not played, and it includes such devices as the saw, the tuned motor-horn, and the siren whose value as musical instruments might be doubted in some quarters. However, it gives us a starting point and immediately raises the questions "What is a musical sound?" and "What is the nature of the variation which enables us to play tunes?"

1.3   What is a musical sound?

The Oxford dictionary defines musical sounds as "such as are used in music and having the nature of 'tones' as distinguished from mere noises". Tone again is defined as "a sound of definite pitch and character produced by regular vibration of a sounding body".

We shall take it as common ground that sound is transmitted from point to point as compression waves in the air. We therefore need to study the pressure variation with time, at some fixed point in order to discover the significant differences between sounds of different kinds. This is, of course, most easily done with a microphone and cathode-ray oscillograph. We shall have to assume for the moment that the microphone, amplifiers, etc., do not modify the form of the variation—an assumption which we shall re-examine in Chapter 9. In Fig. 1.1 are shown the oscillograph traces of various kinds of sounds. Figure 1.1a is for a miscellaneous collection of clicks, bangs and crashes, none of which is to the slightest extent musical. Figure 1.1b is for a brief extract of a full orchestra playing a fragment of Beethoven's 7th Symphony. Obviously both are extremely complex forms of variation, and both would be extremely difficult to describe in either artistic or mathematical terms. Figure 1.1c a trace for a piece of "pop" guitar music, Fig. 1.1d the trace for a fragment of jazz, and Fig. 1.1e the trace for the sound of a full orchestra tuning-up—musical in the sense that it is made by musical instruments, but hardly music in the aesthetic sense. These are visually much more alike than the corresponding sounds and are all equally difficult to describe. It is, of course, apparent that, just as at the beginning of most physical investigations, we need to make a great many simplifications if we are to make progress in understanding the scientific difference between music and noise.

The two simplest sounds that can be considered are "white" noise and a pure tone. White noise is the kind of sound which one can imagine continuing indefinitely, never changing in intensity or quality and yet having no musical character at all; it sounds very much like prolonged applause, and its trace is shown in Fig. 1.1f. A pure tone, on the other hand, is a plain, steady single note of constant pitch and intensity; it sounds like a rather characterless flute and its trace is shown in Fig. 1.1g. It is perhaps tempting to refer to it as an "ideal" musical note. Clearly, from its trace, it involves perfect repetition, whereas the white noise seems to be a completely random collection of pulses with no suggestion of regularity. One might even say that the Beethoven, the jazz and the orchestra tuning-up all lie—scientifically speaking—between these two extremes, involving some regularity and some irregularity. It is important, however, in describing the pure tone, to avoid the term "ideal"; its use would imply that all other sounds are imperfect and in some way trying to achieve the perfection of the ideal. It also means that as each new complication is introduced the impression is given that we are moving further and further away from an ideal and that the necessity for correction and reassessment of ideas arises in some way from an imperfection of nature. Musically speaking, of course, the pure tone is the dullest of all sounds. It is better, as in other physical discussions, to make it clear that the simplification is necessary because of our human inability to deal immediately with the complex realities of interesting sounds; the gate is then left wide open for us, as the book progresses, to develop our physical

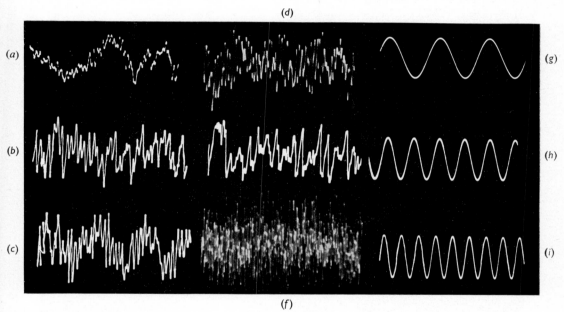

Figure 1.1   Oscillograph traces of various sounds: (*a*) Clicks and bangs. (*b*) Fragment of a Beethoven symphony. (*c*) Fragment of "pop" guitar music. (*d*) Fragment of modern jazz. (*e*) Orchestra tuning-up. (*f*) White noise. (*g*) Pure tone, 440 c.p.s. (*h*) Pure tone, 880 c.p.s. (*i*) Pure tone, 1,320 c.p.s.

and mathematical ideas from the pure tone nearer and nearer to the realities of a full orchestra.

It does appear, then, that we must start our investigation into the possible sources of musical sounds from the simple idea of *regularity*. This is perhaps all too obvious; indeed, the dictionary definitions already quoted involve the idea of regularity or vibration.

1.4 Pure musical tones: pitch and frequency

The simplest possible musical instrument is clearly one which by some means produces perfectly regular sinusoidal compressions and rarefactions of the air. Part of the definition of an instrument given in 1.2, however, involved the idea of variation in order to play tunes.

The idea of pitch—higher and lower notes—is a familiar one, and to make our investigation really complete we should now establish the physical characteristic (or characteristics) of the sound wave which determines the pitch perceived.

It is easily established by means of the cathode-ray oscillograph and tones of different pitches (or gliding tones) that the frequency of repetition of the regular variations of the pure tone is the primary factor determining the pitch, and further that the relationship is a logarithmic one. Musically, notes an octave apart seem to have a great deal in common, and a succession of notes spaced at octave intervals appear to be equally spaced to the ear; their frequencies, however, are found to be in the ratio 1:2:4:8 etc. (Figs. 1.1(g, h)). Thus the apparently-arithmetic progression in perception corresponds to a geometrical progression in frequency. We shall see later (section 9.4.5) that there are other factors—such as loudness—which affect the estimation of the pitch of a note and that it is to some extent a subjective quantity.

Many simple devices can be made to produce sounds which are relatively pure tones and we shall devote the whole of Chapter 2 to the various possible sources of pure or nearly pure tones, including a theoretical section on vibrating systems.

It is clear that in order to produce a musical sound we need to produce a succession of compressions and rarefactions at regular intervals, and that to play tunes we must vary the rate of repetition. The most common natural source of such regularity is some kind of vibrating system. The pitch may be varied either by using a separate vibrator for each note (cf. piano, harp, etc.), by varying the shape or other constants of the vibrator (cf. violin, woodwind, etc.), or by varying the form or mode of vibration (cf. brass instruments). There are, of course, various other ways of producing regular variations of pressure derived from rotation or electrical oscillation and these will also be discussed.

1.5   Comparison between pure tones and instrumental tones

Some of the simpler vibrators described produce oscillograph traces very like those of the pure tone. If, however, the trace of a note of a "real" instrument is observed there are obvious differences (see, for example, Fig. 3.1); it shows regular repetition, but the form of variation which repeats is clearly quite different.

Just as it is possible for simple vibrators to be made to vibrate in different modes it seems reasonable to suppose that a system might vibrate in several modes at once. We thus need to investigate the relationships between the frequencies of the modes and for many—but not all—systems these partial vibrations (partials or overtones) turn out to be harmonic in their frequency relationship—that is, their frequencies are in simple numerical ratios 1, 2, 3, 4 etc. The addition of these harmonics in various proportions, studied in Chapter 3, can be shown to give rise to wave traces like those of Figs. 3.1 (c and d) and to sound more like an orchestral instrument than a pure tone.

The next logical step is to attempt to analyse the tones of real instruments into component simple vibrations; Chapter 4 is devoted to this study and leads to the introduction of a theoretical section on Fourier analysis.

1.6   Comparison between harmonic mixtures and instrumental tones

We have now arrived at the stage where we should be able to produce synthetically—either mechanically or electrically—a wave form resembling very closely that of any given orchestral instrument; the earlier analysis into harmonic components gives the data from which the synthesis may be performed. Certain pre-war electronic organs involved this kind of synthesis; stops labelled "oboe" or "clarinet" gave tolerable wave forms but would certainly not deceive anyone into believing that an oboe or clarinet was being played. Experience of this sort soon shows that there are factors other than harmonic mixture which control the quality of tone perceived. A further study of the needs of an actual instrument—particularly the requirement of adequate loudness and the need for amplification of some kind, and the consequent study of the effects of coupled vibrating systems on each other—leads to a study of transient phenomena. In particular, the way in which a note starts and "builds up" turns out to have a very powerful influence on the quality and especially on the recognition of a single instrument playing in a group. Chapter 5 is devoted to the effects arising from coupled systems and mechanical amplification; Chapter 6 deals with the many ways of initiating vibrations—bowing, blowing, reeds, edge tones, etc.—and leads on to further theoretical discussions of the equivalent of Fourier analysis of periodic wave forms—Fourier transformation of non-periodic functions.

1.7 Miscellaneous influences on the sound produced by an instrument

Even the right harmonic mixture with the right starting transient and "build-up" still does not produce a sound indistinguishable from a real instrument. In Chapter 7 some of the other influences are discussed. They include noise (particularly in wind instruments and from bowed strings), terminal effects—the piano, for example, is practically all starting transient and termination with no "steady state" in the middle—formants (harmonics of specific pitch which are emphasized regardless of the particular note being played) and vibrato effects, both accidental and deliberate.

So far, of course, we have been considering single notes and have not studied the possible effect of one note on another. Chapter 8 is devoted to discussions of beats and combination tones and of various theories of dissonance and harmony. There seems to have been a certain amount of confusion over combination tones and some attempt will be made to clarify the issues using the Fourier-transform concept already introduced.

1.8 Miscellaneous influences on sound perception by the hearer

After the sound has been generated by the instrument or group of instruments there are still several stages through which the sound wave must pass before becoming the sensation of sound in the mind of the hearer. The three principal steps studied in Chapter 9 are first the acoustical properties of the room in which the performer and observer are placed. Secondly, it is useful to consider perception via electrical reproducing systems. Both broadcasting and recordings make up a very large proportion of our sources of music, and the study of the requirements and performance of modern electronic systems is really a suitable subject for several books rather than for a section of one chapter; a brief outline only will be presented. Finally, the fascinating and complicated mechanism of hearing—in which physiology, psychology and physics are very closely interwoven—is discussed, and we shall see that there are still many unanswered questions in this field.

1.9 Actual and proposed instruments

At this stage we should have much of the design data necessary to produce a musical instrument, which was the original aim of the connecting theme. In the last two chapters we shall study first existing conventional instruments in order to see how the various factors play their part, and then modern electrical and mechanical developments in which attempts have been made to produce new kinds of musical sounds. Included in this chapter are some of the computer-controlled instruments which, though perhaps at present of doubtful value artistically, have tremendous possibilities as controlled sources of complex sounds for psychological and physiological studies.

It is clear that the performance of an orchestral work by seventy or so players can be said to involve tremendous artistry on the part of the composer, conductor and players; it involves superb craftsmanship on the part of the instrument-makers, but it can also be regarded as an immense experiment in practical physics. Each player is required to produce vibrations of the right frequency at the right time, to produce the right mixture of harmonics or modes of vibration, to achieve the right starting transients, the right admixture of noise, vibrato, etc. It is probable that an understanding of the underlying physics would be of great help to the performers; it is certain that a study of musical instruments will be of immense value to physicists both in introducing ideas of basic importance in physics and in consolidating an understanding of the ways in which different branches of physics—and of other sciences—become inextricably interwoven whenever a close study of a natural phenomenon is begun.

CHAPTER 2

Generation of Simple Tones

2.1 Basic methods of tone generation

In Chapter 1 the essential feature of a musical sound was shown to be the regular periodic repetition of the pressure variations in the wave transmitting it to the ear. In the most elementary kind of musical sound—the pure tone—the form of the variation is extremely simple; it is, of course, sinusoidal, that is the pressure variation at a particular point in space is proportional to the sine or cosine of some simple function of the time. We shall return to this point a little later in the chapter to discuss the reasons why sinusoidal variation should be so common in nature and why it makes such an important and useful starting point for our discussions. First, however, it will be helpful to survey the possible ways of producing regular trains of sound waves without worrying too much about how they work or about the precise form of the waves produced.

Perhaps the most obvious source of regularity is vibration of some kind; vibration of solid bodies or in air cavities is the source of sound in the vast majority of conventional

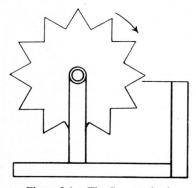

Figure 2.1. The Savart wheel.

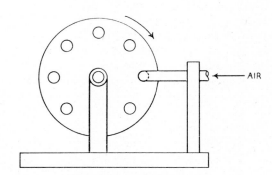

Figure 2.2 The simple siren.

musical instruments, and its study will form a major portion of this chapter. A regular periodicity can also be derived from rotation. The crudest method of conversion is the Savart wheel (Fig. 2.1) which consists essentially of a toothed wheel, capable of rotation at various speeds, against which is held a thin sheet of cardboard or plastic; the note produced is very harsh and noisy. The siren (so called because it is said to be capable of "singing under water") is more effective as a rotary converter; in its simplest form (Fig. 2.2) it consists of a rotating wheel with regularly-spaced holes in its periphery. As the wheel rotates the holes interrupt a stream of air issuing from a nozzle, thereby producing the required periodic compressions; a more efficient application of the same principle will be described in section 2.11. More recently electrical systems for deriving tones from rotation have been developed; they use the interruption of light falling on to a photocell, the change in capacity of a rotary capacitor, or periodic variations in a magnetic field. Details of these systems and of the resulting wave forms will be given in section 2.11.

The remaining source of sound to be considered is the loudspeaker which can convert into sound the oscillation of the current in an electrical circuit. Various devices have been developed using electrical oscillations as a practical source of musical sounds; we shall be concerned (section 2.12) mainly with the wave form that can be generated in this way, and with the close parallel that exists between electrical and mechanical oscillations.

2.2 Basic methods of pitch-changing

Included in the original definition of a musical instrument adopted in section 1.2 was the idea of variation in order to play tunes. Variations in the loudness of sound, which are related to variations in the amplitude of the disturbance, are important, but the pitch is, of course, the primary variable in playing tunes. The pitch of a note depends almost entirely on its frequency (section 1.4); pitch-changing is thus for the present purpose synonymous with frequency-changing.

The simplest method of frequency-changing to permit the playing of tunes is to use a separate source for each note, the frequency of each being pre-set. This method applies equally well to all sources; it is the method used in the piano, harp and in all kinds of organs, both traditional and electronic.

The alternative is to use one source and to place its frequency under the control of the player; sometimes a small number of sources is needed to cover the required frequency range. For vibration sources there are three methods of controlling the frequency; one is to alter the shape of the vibrator, the second is to vary the stress applied to it, and the third is to alter the mode or pattern of vibration. Alteration in the shape provides the most rapid changes and is used as the primary control in many instruments—the strings and woodwind for example. Changes in applied stress are more difficult to control rapidly and are used chiefly for pre-tuning, for example in the piano and harp. Mode-changing gives only discontinuous jumps but is in common use; it is, of course, the basic process of pitch control in the brass instruments.

In rotation sources, change of speed of the rotor is the obvious method of pitch-changing; in electrical oscillation the constants of the circuit may be changed in a way analogous to the change of shape or stress in mechanical vibrators.

2.3 Vibrating systems—general survey

What kind of bodies vibrate? Let us start with solid matter and consider first of all "three-dimensional" objects, that is objects in which no one dimension is of a different order of magnitude from the others. Such solid lumps of matter are not promising as sources of sound. If they are made of hard material—glass or steel—it is possible that a note of specific pitch may be emitted if the object is struck with a hammer; the characteristic "ring" of an anvil is perhaps an example. The notes of such objects are usually of relatively high pitch and, since it is not easy to change either the shape or the state of stress, the pitch is fixed. It is usually only practicable to excite vibrations by striking, and this gives little control over the mode. They must therefore be regarded as fixed-frequency sources if used at all.

If, however, we allow one of the dimensions to become much smaller than the other two, vibrations, and hence musical sounds, are much more readily obtained. The object has become recognisable as a flat plate and may be made to vibrate either by striking with a hammer or by bowing with, for example, a double-bass bow. (The mechanism of bowing will be discussed in Chapter 6.) Experiment soon shows that in order to produce sustained vibrations, and hence a prolonged note of acceptable intensity, the precise way in which the plate is held or clamped is as important as the method of initiating the note. Three examples of "plate" vibrators are worthy of mention, though, as we shall see later on, the vibrations of plates play important secondary roles in many instruments. In the Glockenspiel (or Celeste—which is merely a keyboard version of the same thing) the notes are produced by striking small metal plates with a hard hammer. The plates are usually made of steel and are thick enough to be rigid; the pitch of each is determined by its dimensions and remains fixed. The musical saw is essentially a flat metal plate; it is played by bending it into an "S" shape, usually with the wooden handle clamped between the player's knees (see Fig. 2.3). Notes of surprising purity and intensity can be produced either by striking the flat surface or by bowing the edge somewhere near the mid-point. The pitch of the note can be changed over fairly wide limits by altering the curvature; changes in the shape and applied stress are thus made simultaneously. Any flat sheet of metal may be made to produce a note in this way; other materials too will respond, though with less purity and intensity—even stiff cardboard may be made to give a recognisable note.

Figure 2.3   Method of holding the musical saw.

If one attempts to produce a gliding note, starting at a low pitch and then moving smoothly upwards, the saw or other flat plate usually exhibits discontinuities; the pitch suddenly changes by quite a large amount and one may find an unstable state in which minute changes in bow pressure will change the note (Gentil, 1957). This provides an excellent example of mode-change, which has already been mentioned as a means of changing pitch. It is easier to investigate precisely what is happening by using the third application of flat-plate vibration which is to be discussed—the Chladni Plate (Waller, 1960). A flat plate of steel or hard-rolled brass, usually circular or square (though other shapes have been used) from 3 in. to 18 in. across, is supported on a firm stand at its mid-point. A wide range of notes can be obtained by bowing at different points of the periphery and lightly damping various other portions of the plate (Fig. 2.4). Sand scattered on the plate congregates in the regions where the amplitude of vibration is a minimum, and the pattern of vibration can be clearly seen.† A fuller discussion of methods of exciting the plates and of the results is given

----

†Andrade & Smith (1931) showed that the sand actually collects along lines for which the maximum acceleration of the plate is g; for very vigorous vibrations these lines are very close to, and on either side of, the nodal lines and visually become identical with them.

in section 2.5. It should perhaps be mentioned that for the purposes of our present classification a bell would be regarded as a derivation from a flat plate; the distortion has important effects on the possible modes of vibration.

If a second dimension is allowed to become very small the ease with which the vibrations may be produced increases enormously; strings are perhaps the commonest sources of musical sounds, and rods of various kinds are also useful. It is interesting to speculate on the circumstances which led to the discovery of various potential musical instruments, and it is usually held that the archer's bow was the forerunner of the string section of the orchestra. Early hunters probably noticed that the "twang" of the released string was characteristic of the bow and may even have used the pitch intuitively as a means of judging the correct tension. Recent workers (e.g. Baines, 1961) have suggested that the development may have been the other way round or perhaps even that the weapon and the instrument developed independently. Whatever the true origin it is clear that many of the essential properties of vibrating strings were known even by the time of Pythagoras. The shape (i.e. length) can be varied quite independently of the state of stress (tension) and both of these variables are used to change the pitch in actual instruments; the length is usually used as the immediate control during performance and the tension as a more permanent change for tuning purposes. The physical characteristics of the string, of course, play an important part. One of the most obvious features is that the intensity of sound that can be produced by a string completely on its own is very small indeed, and it is quite useless as an instrument. This is simply because the disturbance of the air that can be produced is very much less than that produced by a large vibrating plate. We shall return to this important point in Chapter 5. The transverse vibrations of strings may be excited in various ways, bowing,

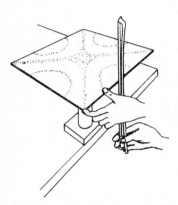

Figure 2.4 Method of exciting a particular mode of a Chladni plate.

plucking, striking, etc., and the mode can be changed by altering the point of excitation and the auxiliary damping in the same way as for the Chladni plate. Rods are of less importance in instruments, although the transverse vibrations of solid rods are the source of the bell-like tones of many chiming clocks. In scientific studies the longitudinal vibrations of a solid rod were a useful steady source of notes of high pitch required for velocity of sound experiments (e.g. Kundt's tube) before the days of electronic sources. A solid brass rod a metre or so long and about half a centimetre in diameter can be made to emit a loud note, which will persist for ten to fifteen secs; it must be held exactly at its mid-point between the finger and thumb of one hand, and stroked with a heavily-resined cloth from a point about one-third of the length from one end towards the nearest end. It is helpful if the whole rod is rubbed with powdered resin before the experiment begins. Again, this kind of vibration is not confined to metals; hardwood or glass rods both give clear notes. The pitch depends on the physical properties of the rod and also, of course, on its dimensions. Clamping the rod at the mid-point as suggested results in only one or two modes of vibration which depend on the precise method of stroking. Other modes may be produced by changing the clamping position as well. A tuning-fork is to be regarded for our purposes as a rod forced into a single transverse mode by its shape and the addition of the stem.

So much for solid matter. Liquids are exceedingly unprofitable as direct sources of sound. Water dropping into a reservoir or vessels full of water, may produce musical notes, but investigation usually shows that the container is the dominant factor and the principal vibrator is either the air in a cavity or the container itself. We shall therefore ignore liquid vibration as a possible source of sound.

After the strings, the vibration of air in cavities forms the next most common source of musical sounds. Again, we may classify according to dimensions. Cavities in which all three dimensions are comparable do not often function as a *primary* source of musical sounds. The possible exceptions are the percussion instruments such as the tympani, in which it could be argued that the volume of air in the drum is the source. They do, however, play a large part as auxiliary components of instruments; the body cavities of the string family are obvious examples. Scientifically the Helmholtz resonator—the standard means of frequency analysis before electronic devices—is perhaps the most important vibrating cavity, though this again is not a primary source. Its natural frequency is dependent in quite a complicated way on the shape and volume and particularly on the conditions near the aperture; the only instrumental application appears to be the "ocarina".

"Two-dimensional" cavities can be ignored almost completely but "one-dimensional" cavities—i.e. cavities in which one dimension is much greater than the other two—occur in many instruments. All the woodwinds and the brass involve the vibrations of air in such a cavity. It is again interesting to make historical speculations, and it seems much more likely that the three-dimensional cavity—the wind blowing across the mouth of a bottle or hollow skin—was discovered before the pipe. The pipe, however, behaves much more predictably when attempts are made to change pitch, as we shall see in a later section.

We have thus found that a great variety of objects may be made to vibrate if subjected to the right kind of treatment—or, in other words, if we learn to "play" the instrument. We soon meet the need for compromise, however, as the most conveniently-controlled sources —the strings—turn out also to be the weakest. Nevertheless, it is clear that we shall need to study plates, rods, strings and "one-dimensional" cavities (i.e. pipes) as potential primary sources, and three-dimensional cavities for auxiliary duties.

*2.4 Characteristics of vibrating systems

So far we have not considered the fascinating question of why there should be so many natural sources of vibration suitable for producing musical sounds. What are the necessary characteristics? Clearly, precision in repetition is the outstanding one. Once a vibration has started its frequency must remain constant over a fairly long period—the duration of the note. It is certainly not obvious, if one reflects for a moment, that all the vibrating systems we have been considering should obey this condition. Why should the vibrations be iso-chronous? It might seem more reasonable to suppose that they would become slower as the vibration died out—or, in other words, that the pitch would go down with time. The simplest way of approaching this general problem is through dimensional analysis.

There are two essential components in any vibrating system. First, restoring forces must exist which tend to return the system to its equilibrium position after a disturbance; and secondly, there must be inertia which tends to delay the return at first, and later to carry the system beyond the neutral point in order to maintain the motion. The factors likely to influence the periodic time are thus the restoring force F, the amount of displacement from the neutral position d, and the inertial mass M. Let us suppose that the periodic time is a simple function of these three,

$$\tau \propto (F)^a(d)^b(M)^c. \qquad [2.1]$$

If we now insert the dimensions of all the quantities in length, mass and time we find

$$T \propto (MLT^{-2})^a(L)^b(M)^c,$$

whence by equating the dimensions of time, length and mass successively we arrive at the solution $a = -\frac{1}{2}$, $b = \frac{1}{2}$, $c = \frac{1}{2}$. That is

$$\tau \propto \sqrt{\frac{Md}{F}}. \qquad [2.2]$$

Now, for a given system, the inertial mass M will remain constant during vibrations; the vibration will therefore be isochronous if d and F vary together, that is, if the restoring force is always proportional to the displacement from the equilibrium position. In any perfectly elastic body the force required to produce a given displacement or distortion is proportional to the displacement, and hence any perfectly elastic bodies will tend to vibrate isochronously. Since it turns out in practice that many bodies behave as though perfectly elastic over at least a small range of displacements, we find a large number of naturally isochronous vibrators.

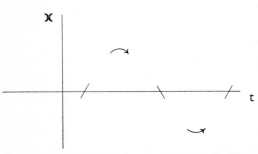

Figure 2.5   Steps in plotting a graph from the differential equation $-kx = m\dfrac{d^2x}{dt^2}$.

Let us now proceed a little further with the study of the motion of a body under the action of restoring forces proportional to the displacement from some fixed point. Since we are considering a *restoring* force it is clear that its sign must be opposed to that of the displacement and the normal equation of motion—force = mass × acceleration—will become

$$-kx = m\frac{d^2x}{dt^2} \qquad [2.3]$$

where k is the force per unit displacement, x is the instantaneous displacement, t the time and m the mass. How is this general equation to be interpreted?

Consider an attempt to plot a graph of x against t to conform to this equation. On such a graph d^2x/dt^2 would be a measure of the curvature, and the equation tells us that the curvature is proportional to x and opposite in sign. Thus when x is zero the graph must be a straight line. But if ever x begins to grow large positively the curvature increases negatively, and this will clearly result in bringing the value of x down towards zero again—with consequent straightening of the curve (see Fig. 2.5). It is clear that the solution is likely to be an oscillation of some kind and in fact that a solution of the form

$$x = a \sin \omega t \qquad [2.4]$$

or

$$x = a \cos \omega t \qquad [2.5]$$

would be satisfactory. If $x = a \sin \omega t$ then

$$\frac{dx}{dt} = a\omega \cos \omega t \quad \text{and} \quad \frac{d^2x}{dt^2} = -a\omega^2 \sin \omega t = -\omega^2 x.$$

Thus if we substitute in equation [2.3] we have

$$-kx = m(-\omega^2 x). \qquad [2.6]$$

In other words, $x = a \sin \omega t$ *is* a solution if $\omega = \sqrt{\dfrac{k}{m}}$; $x = a \cos \omega t$ may also be shown to be a solution subject to the same condition. These are just two particular solutions which are of interest at the moment; we shall consider a more general solution later.

If the oscillograph traces of many of the simple vibrators already discussed—the bowed Chladni plate, the saw, the solid rod, the tuning-fork, etc.—are examined they turn out to be nearly of the simple sinusoidal form just discussed and which we described in Chapter 1 as the "pure tone". We have therefore a variety of sources of relatively pure tones available as a starting point for our instrument.

Before leaving the simplest forms of vibration it will be useful to relate equations [2.4] and [2.5] with [2.2]—the prediction of the dimensional analysis. In equations [2.4] or [2.5] it is clear that the displacement x will complete a cycle of values every time t increases by $2\pi/\omega$; ω is thus the angular frequency measured in radians per second. The period of the motion—the time taken for one complete cycle—is $\tau = \dfrac{2\pi}{\omega} = 2\pi\sqrt{\dfrac{m}{k}}$ which agrees exactly with the equation [2.2] of the dimensional analysis except, of course, that we now have a value for the constant. Motion of this kind governed by equation [2.3] is often referred to as Simple Periodic or Simple Harmonic motion.

2.5 Modes of vibration

In discussing the vibrations of a musical saw in the last section-but-one, the occurrence of discontinuities when one attempts to change frequency smoothly over a wide range was mentioned. The occurrence of these discontinuities or changes of mode is of extreme importance, and we shall devote further attention to it now, in the later sections of this chapter, and again in the next chapter. The Chladni plate perhaps provides the most useful demonstration of the phenomenon of change of mode. Figure 2.6 shows some of the patterns that can be obtained. In each example the bow

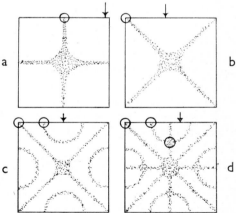

Figure 2.6 Four modes of a Chladni plate.

is applied to the edge at the position of the arrow with one hand, and the thumb or fingers of the other hand are applied to the plate at the points indicated by circles to damp out unwanted modes. Two facts emerge very clearly from this experiment. First, the pitch of the note, as one might expect, is higher the greater the number of divisions of the plate, that is the smaller the size of the individual vibrating portions between the nodal lines (lines of no displacement). Secondly, the frequencies of vibration of the various modes do not appear to be related by a simple rule and do not necessarily bear any simple ratio to each other.

Some modes which are only obtained with difficulty by bowing can be obtained more readily by holding a piece of solid carbon dioxide in contact with the plate at the bowing point. A third method of using the plate is particularly effective in demonstrating the frequency ratios involved. The plate is removed from its normal support and fixed to the armature of a vibration transducer. The transducer is fed from a variable-frequency signal generator and, if the frequency of the source is gradually increased, the plate responds in violent vibration each time the frequency of one of its modes of vibration is reached.

It usually simplifies matters if one reduces the number of dimensions involved in a problem and so we may find it simpler at this point to consider a one-dimensional solid. A very useful demonstration of the modes of a string can be performed with a large-scale model. A solid rubber cord (the type used for vacuum seals is ideal) about 5 mm. in diameter and 5–10 metres in length is fixed at one end and is held at the other in the operator's hand so that it rests more-or-less horizontally. If the end held in the hand is then made to oscillate in a vertical plane it is possible to find frequencies at which the string settles down into a definite mode of vibration with regularly-spaced nodes and anti-nodes (Fig. 2.7(a–f)). An electrically driven transducer from which a string is suspended under the tension produced by a small weight can also be used to demonstrate the relationships between frequency and mode.

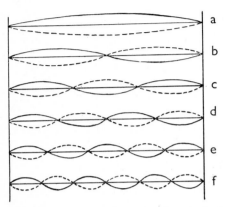

Figure 2.7 The first six modes of a stretched string.

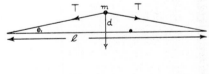

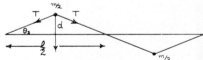

Figure 2.8 Over-simplified model for the first two modes of a stretched string.

Let us consider a very simple argument relating to the two simplest modes (Fig. 2.7(a) and (b)). The behaviour of one-half of the string in the mode of Fig. 2.7(b) will clearly resemble that of a string of half the length vibrating in the mode of Fig. 2.7(a). A very crude approach to the question of what happens to the frequency may be made by assuming the mass to be concentrated at the mid-point (see Fig. 2.8). The restoring force is then $2T \sin \theta$, and if the angle is small this is $\dfrac{4Td}{l}$ or $\dfrac{4T}{l}$ per unit displacement. Thus the period (equation [2.2]) $\propto \sqrt{\dfrac{Ml}{4T}}$. For the second mode the mass is halved but, for the same displacement, θ is doubled and the restoring force is now $\dfrac{8T}{l}$ per unit displacement; the period is thus propor-

tional to $\sqrt{\dfrac{M}{2} \cdot \dfrac{l}{8T}}$ which is exactly half that obtained before. This is a very unsound argu-

ment in many ways, but it does suggest a simple frequency relationship. In fact we find that the simple relationship holds experimentally over quite a wide range, and the ratios for the modes of Fig. 2.7(a–f) are simply $1:2:3:4:5:6$. It is clear, however, that our simple argument about the inertial mass and the restoring force proportional to displacement soon begins to lose rigour, and a much firmer basis for argument will be needed even to study strings, and certainly if we want to extend the discussion to plates.

The rubber rope again provides a key idea. If it is plucked at a point fairly close to one end one can see a wave or kink travelling up and down, successively reflected at one end and then the other. It is easy to demonstrate that the time taken for this wave to travel up and down is the same as that for one complete cycle of vibration in mode 1. That is the *funda-mental* period of the string. A little further thought shows that each mode can be con-sidered in terms of a wave travelling up and down the string, but, if certain conditions are satisfied concerning the frequency and velocity of the wave and the length of the string, the net result to *an outside observer* appears to be one or other of the simple vibrations illustrated in Fig. 2.7. The wave approach to modes of vibration is very helpful; one can see imme-diately how it can be extended to two and three dimensions and how much more compli-cated the boundary conditions for establishing a two- or three-dimensional mode are likely to be. It will be presented in the next four sections for specific applications that will be needed in our musical development. It is interesting to note that the possibility of vibration of a system in discrete modes of specific frequency can be a useful introduction to the wave-mechanical treatment of the quantisation of the emission of radiation.

*2.6 Wave treatment of vibrating systems

Let us consider first of all the propagation of some kind of condition in a particular direction in space. Let us represent the measure of the condition at a point distant x from

some arbitrary origin at an instant of time t_0 by the symbol ϕ. (ϕ may in fact be pres-sure, density, displacement along the direction of the wave, displacement per-pendicular to the wave, or any one of a host of other conditions.) Suppose that at the given instant t_0 we plot a graph of ϕ against x and assume that a short time later at t_1 the graph of ϕ against x remains un-changed in shape but has moved bodily

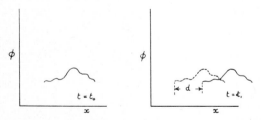

Figure 2.9   Translation of a constant wave profile.

along the x-axis by a certain distance d—that is, the wave is being propagated without modification; then a study of Fig. 2.9 will show that the equation of the wave can be de-rived as follows.

Let $\phi = f(x)$ be the equation at $t = t_0$.

Then at $t = t_1$

$$\phi = f(x - d). \qquad\qquad [2.7]$$

Now suppose the wave is travelling at a constant velocity c without change of shape. Then $d = ct$ and

$$\phi = f(x - ct). \qquad\qquad [2.8]$$

We may thus represent a wave of constant profile travelling from left to right by the equation $\phi = f(x - ct)$. It can easily be seen that a wave travelling from right to left would lead to the equation

$$\phi = f(x + ct). \qquad\qquad [2.9]$$

We have not so far said anything about the form of the function f, and it would clearly be useful to derive a more general equation which would not be tied down to a specific form of f. This may be done as follows.

Let $(x - ct) = z$, then $\phi = f(z)$

$$\left(\frac{\partial z}{\partial x}\right)_t = 1$$

and

$$\left(\frac{\partial z}{\partial t}\right)_x = -c$$

Thus

$$\left(\frac{\partial \phi}{\partial x}\right)_t = \frac{df}{dz}\left(\frac{\partial z}{\partial x}\right)_t = \frac{df}{dz}$$

$$\left(\frac{\partial^2 \phi}{\partial x^2}\right)_t = \frac{d^2f}{dz^2}\left(\frac{\partial z}{\partial x}\right)_t = \frac{d^2f}{dz^2}$$

and

$$\left(\frac{\partial \phi}{\partial t}\right)_x = \frac{df}{dz}\left(\frac{\partial z}{\partial t}\right)_x = -c\frac{df}{dz}$$

$$\left(\frac{\partial^2 \phi}{\partial t^2}\right)_x = -c\frac{d^2f}{dz^2}\left(\frac{\partial z}{\partial t}\right)_x = c^2\frac{d^2f}{dz^2}$$

hence

$$\left(\frac{\partial^2 \phi}{\partial t^2}\right)_x = c^2\left(\frac{\partial^2 \phi}{\partial x^2}\right)_t. \qquad\qquad [2.10]$$

Notice that $\phi = f(x + ct)$ leads to an identical equation. Equation [2.10] is evidently an equation relating ϕ, x and t, and the constant c which does not involve the function f. That is, it must represent any wave propagated with constant shape or profile at a constant velocity. It is in fact the one-dimensional form of the wave equation and is of enormous importance in physics.

Although of the second order, it is a linear differential equation—that is, it does not involve powers of any of the variables or their derivatives greater than one—and hence the principle of superposition applies. In other words, if any two expressions $\phi = f_1(x,t)$ and $\phi = f_2(x,t)$ are both solutions then $\phi = f_1(x,t) + f_2(x,t)$ is also a solution. The propagation of sound waves in air turns out to be governed by this kind of equation, and the principle of superposition is the mathematical expression of the fact that the instantaneous displacement or pressure at a particular point over which a number of waves pass is simply the algebraic sum of all the separate displacements or pressures which each wave would create independently. In other words, the waves pass through each other and are themselves unaffected by each other. The net effect, as it appears to an outside observer, is the algebraic sum of the individual effects and may appear to be very different. (See also sections 3.2 and 3.6)

We have already seen that a simple kind of vibration that occurs frequently in nature is sinusoidal, and we have also seen experimentally that a string or pipe vibrating in a simple mode gives rise to sinusoidal pressure variations. Let us check therefore that a sinusoidal function would satisfy equation [2.10]. A suitable function would be

$$\phi = a \sin p(x - ct).$$ [2.11]

Assuming a and p to be constants, independent of x and t, and also assuming c, the velocity, to be independent of x and t, we find

$$\left(\frac{\partial \phi}{\partial t}\right)_x = a(-pc) \cos p(x - ct) \qquad \left(\frac{\partial \phi}{\partial x}\right)_t = ap \cos p(x - ct)$$

$$\left(\frac{\partial^2 \phi}{\partial t^2}\right)_x = -a(p^2 c^2) \sin p(x - ct) \qquad \left(\frac{\partial^2 \phi}{\partial x^2}\right)_t = -ap^2 \sin p(x - ct)$$

that is, $\left(\frac{\partial^2 \phi}{\partial t^2}\right)_x = c^2 \left(\frac{\partial^2 \phi}{\partial x^2}\right)_t$ which is equation [2.10].

The corresponding wave in the negative direction $\phi = a \sin p(x + ct)$ is clearly also a solution. What is the significance of a and of p? a is clearly the maximum value of ϕ—the *amplitude*. Consider now the form of the wave at $t = 0$; then $\phi = a \sin px$. This is a periodic function and ϕ will have the same sequence of values every time px increases by 2π. The distance along the wave between two such cycles is the *wavelength* λ, and hence $p\lambda = 2\pi$ or $p = \frac{2\pi}{\lambda}$. Similarly, if we consider a point $x = 0$ on the wave ϕ will vary with time according to the expression $\phi = a \sin(-pct)$. The sequence of ϕ-values will repeat at intervals equal to the *period* τ of the wave and hence $pc\tau = 2\pi$, $pc = \frac{2\pi}{\tau}$. Thus equation [2.11] may be written symmetrically

$$\phi = a \sin 2\pi\left(\frac{x}{\lambda} - \frac{t}{\tau}\right)$$ [2.12]

or in a more convenient form using $\kappa = \frac{1}{\lambda}$ (the *wave number*) and $v = \frac{1}{\tau}$ (the *frequency*)

$$\phi = a \sin 2\pi(\kappa x - vt).$$ [2.13]

This is perhaps the most useful form and it is important to remember that we have so far shown it to be a solution of the wave equation if a, κ and v are constants and independent of x and t. We shall see later that solutions under other conditions are possible but these need not concern us here.

   This section began as an attempt to treat vibrating systems in terms of waves, but so far the treatment has dealt only with continuous or progressive waves in an unbounded medium. As soon as the medium becomes bounded in any way reflexions of the wave occur and a different condition will develop. Suppose that waves are set up along a linear system (e.g. a string or pipe) which has two boundaries at which the wave is perfectly reflected so that it travels continuously back and forth in between. If it so happens that after two reflexions the wave is in phase with the original wave a steady state will arise. This will clearly depend on a special relationship between the constants of the wave and the boundary conditions. Let the wave in one direction be $\phi_1 = a \sin [2\pi(\kappa x - vt) + \alpha]$ where α is simply a phase term defining the state of vibration when x and t are zero and introduced to make [2.13] more general. The wave in the other direction will then be

$$\phi_2 = a \sin [2\pi(\kappa x + vt) + \beta],$$

where β is another phase constant to take into account possible phase changes at the boundaries. If the steady state is achieved these will be the only two waves to be considered and hence the net ϕ-value will be given by

$$\phi = \phi_1 + \phi_2 = a \sin [2\pi(\kappa x - vt) + \alpha] + a \sin [2\pi(\kappa x + vt) + \beta], \qquad [2.14]$$

since ϕ_1 and ϕ_2 are both solutions of [2.10] which is linear.

$$\phi = 2a \sin \left[2\pi\kappa x + \frac{\alpha + \beta}{2} \right] \cos \left[2\pi vt + \frac{\alpha - \beta}{2} \right]. \qquad [2.15]$$

   This solution of the wave equation is clearly quite different from that typified by [2.13]; it is no longer progressive. This is apparent if we notice that it is possible to find one or more values of x which will make $\left[2\pi\kappa x + \dfrac{\alpha + \beta}{2} \right]$ zero, and hence ϕ zero, for *all* values of t. In other words, nodes or points of no displacement exist—as we found experimentally for strings and plates. Equation [2.15] represents a stationary solution or stationary state. The conditions under which these occur clearly depend on the boundary conditions and will be discussed separately for different systems in the next four sections.

*2.7 Transverse vibration of strings

   In order to investigate the behaviour of a vibrating string we must first find out if, and under what conditions, such a vibration satisfies the wave equation. Then various boundary and starting conditions can be inserted in order to see what limitations exist on the possible solutions.

   We shall assume that ϕ is now the displacement of a particle of the string from its rest position, that this displacement occurs always in the same plane for the whole string and that it is in a direction perpendicular to the string—i.e. there is no longitudinal component. We shall also assume that the tension is great enough to permit the effects of gravity and of air resistance to be ignored.

   Consider a small element of length δx of a string of mass per unit length ρ under tension T (Fig. 2.10). The net vertical force acting on the element is the difference in the vertical components of the tension. At the point x the vertical component is $T \sin \theta$ which, if the displacement and angles are small, $= T \tan \theta = T \dfrac{\partial \phi}{\partial x}$. At the other end it will similarly be $T \sin \psi$. Since no assumption is being made about the form of the curve a direct relationship between ψ and θ cannot be found. It can be assumed however that there

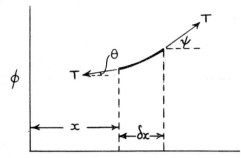

Figure 2.10 Basic diagram for determining the velocity of waves on a string.

is *some* relationship, and further that whatever its form, if the interval δx is small enough, it can be assumed linear; in other words $\psi = \theta + \dfrac{\partial \theta}{\partial x} \delta x$, that is (since the angles are small)

$$T \sin \psi = T\psi = T\left[\theta + \frac{\partial \theta}{\partial x} \delta x\right] = T\left[\frac{\partial \phi}{\partial x} + \frac{\partial^2 \phi}{\partial x^2} \delta x\right].$$

The net force on the element is thus

$$T \frac{\partial^2 \phi}{\partial x^2} \delta x.$$

Then, equating this force to the product of mass and acceleration, we find

$$T \frac{\partial^2 \phi}{\partial x^2} \delta x = \rho \delta x . \frac{\partial^2 \phi}{\partial t^2}$$

$$\frac{\partial^2 \phi}{\partial t^2} = \frac{T}{\rho} \frac{\partial^2 \phi}{\partial x^2}. \qquad [2.16]$$

Whence comparing this with equation [2.10] we see that the wave equation is obeyed and that c, the velocity of waves on the string, is $\sqrt{\dfrac{T}{\rho}}$.

Now suppose a string of length l is clamped rigidly at each end, and consider the resulting boundary conditions to be applied to equation [2.15]. If the string is rigidly fixed at each end then clearly $\phi = 0$ when $x = 0$ and $\phi = 0$ when $x = l$ for all values of t. If $\phi = 0$ when $x = 0$ for all values of t then $\dfrac{\alpha + \beta}{2} = 0$ and hence $\dfrac{\alpha - \beta}{2} = \alpha$.

Equation [2.15] then becomes

$$\phi = 2a \sin [2\pi\kappa x] \cos [2\pi vt + \alpha]. \qquad [2.17]$$

If $\phi = 0$ when $x = l$ for all values of t, $2\pi\kappa l = n\pi$ where n is any integer

$$\kappa = \frac{n}{2l} \quad \text{or} \quad \lambda = \frac{2l}{n}$$

and equation [2.17] becomes

$$\phi = 2a \sin \frac{n\pi x}{l} \cos \left[2\pi vt + \alpha \right]$$

and, since the velocity is constant and equal to c and $v = \kappa c$

$$\phi = 2a \sin \frac{n\pi x}{l} \cos \left[\frac{n\pi ct}{l} + \alpha \right]. \qquad [2.18]$$

(It must be remembered that ϕ here corresponds to the lateral displacement of a point on the string.) Stationary solutions can thus only exist for specific values of λ or v arrived at by allowing n to take different integral values. These are, of course, the modes already discussed in section 2.5. In Fig. 2.7, (a) represents the fundamental mode $n = 1$ in which $\lambda = 2l/n = 2l$; (b) represents the second mode $n = 2$ in which $\lambda = 2l/n = l$ and so on. The frequencies of the successive modes are given by $v = \kappa c = \dfrac{cn}{2l}$ and, since the velocity $c = \sqrt{\dfrac{T}{\rho}}$ is constant for a given string, are clearly in the ratios $1:2:3:4:5$ etc.

*2.8 Longitudinal vibration of air in cylindrical pipes and of solid rods

As in section 2.7, the first step will be to show that the passage of waves along a pipe satisfies the wave equation. The pipe will be assumed to have rigid walls, to have a diameter small compared with the wavelength so that the wave fronts in the pipe may be treated as planes perpendicular to the length of the pipe, and to have a diameter large enough for viscosity effects to be ignored; these conditions hold reasonably well in the majority of practical cases. The motion of all particles is assumed to be parallel to the length of the pipe.

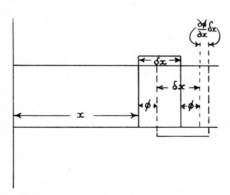

Figure 2.11 Basic diagram for determining the velocity of waves in a pipe.

Let x define the equilibrium position of a particle and ϕ will now represent longitudinal displacement from this equilibrium position measured in the same direction as x. Consider Fig. 2.11; if a layer originally at x is displaced to $x + \phi$, an adjacent layer originally at $x + \delta x$ will be displaced to $x + \delta x + \phi + \dfrac{\partial \phi}{\partial x} \delta x$ (cf. the tension argument in section 2.7). Thus the original thickness of the slab defined by these layers is $(x + \delta x) - \lceil x = \delta x$ and the new thickness is $x + \delta x + \phi + \dfrac{\partial \phi}{\partial x} \delta x - (x + \phi) = \left(1 + \dfrac{\partial \phi}{\partial x}\right) \delta x$. The volume of the

slab has thus increased by a factor $\left(1 + \dfrac{\partial \phi}{\partial x}\right)$. Suppose K is the bulk modulus for the gas,

then the increment of pressure P required to produce this change in volume is clearly given

$$\text{by } K = -\frac{P}{\dfrac{\partial \phi}{\partial x}}$$

$$P = - K \frac{\partial \phi}{\partial x} \tag{2.19}$$

(the negative sign occurs because an increase in pressure causes a decrease in volume).

The mass of the displaced element is $\rho_0 \delta x A$ (A is the area of cross-section) and the force causing motion arises from the differences in pressure acting on the two faces of the element. The pressure on the left-hand face is P and on the right-hand face $P + \dfrac{\partial P}{\partial x} \delta x$ (assuming δx is small enough for there to be an effectively linear relationship between P and x). The net force is thus $- A \dfrac{\partial P}{\partial x} x$; the negative sign arises because if $\dfrac{\partial P}{\partial x}$ is positive the pressure increases from left to right and the net force will be from right to left.

Thus the equation of motion, force = mass × acceleration, becomes

$$- A \frac{\partial P}{\partial x} \delta x = A \rho_0 \delta x \frac{\partial^2 \phi}{\partial t^2}$$

but from [2.19] $\dfrac{\partial P}{\partial x} = - K \dfrac{\partial^2 \phi}{\partial x^2}$, assuming that K remains constant,

hence

$$K \frac{\partial^2 \phi}{\partial x^2} = \rho_0 \frac{\partial^2 \phi}{\partial t^2},$$

$$\frac{\partial^2 \phi}{\partial t^2} = \frac{K \partial^2 \phi}{\rho_0 \partial x^2} \tag{2.20}$$

which is again the wave equation [2.10] with $c = \sqrt{\dfrac{K}{\rho_0}}$. In practice it turns out that the

appropriate value of K is that of the adiabatic elasticity (γP) over the range of audible sounds.

We may now proceed to consider possible stationary solutions for vibrations of air in pipes subject to the assumptions and conditions already specified.

Consider a pipe of length l, open at both ends. The boundary conditions are thus that there is no pressure differential possible when $x = 0$ or when $x = l$. Now $P = - K \dfrac{\partial \phi}{\partial x}$

(equation [2.19]) and hence the boundary conditions are $\dfrac{\partial \phi}{\partial x} = 0$ when $x = 0$ and $x = l$

for all values of t.

P.M.S.—3

Equation [2.15] is again the basic solution—ϕ now represents longitudinal displacement—and hence

$$\frac{\partial \phi}{\partial x} = 4\pi a\kappa \cos\left[2\pi\kappa x + \frac{\alpha + \beta}{2}\right] \cos\left[2\pi vt + \frac{\alpha - \beta}{2}\right] \qquad [2.21]$$

and if $\dfrac{\partial \phi}{\partial x} = 0$ when $x = 0$ for all values of t

$$\frac{\alpha + \beta}{2} = \frac{\pi}{2} \quad \text{whence} \quad \frac{\alpha - \beta}{2} = \alpha - \frac{\pi}{2}$$

$$\frac{\partial \phi}{\partial x} = -4\pi a\kappa \sin\left[2\pi\kappa x\right] \sin\left[2\pi vt + \alpha\right].$$

Now if $\dfrac{\partial \phi}{\partial x}$ also $= 0$ when $x = l$ for all values of t

$$2\pi\kappa l = n\pi$$

$$\kappa = \frac{n}{2l}, \qquad \lambda = \frac{2l}{n} \quad \text{and} \quad v = \frac{nc}{2l}$$

and the same sequence of modes exists as for the stretched string fixed at both ends. Equation [2.15] then becomes on substituting for κ, v, α and β

$$\phi = 2a \cos\frac{n\pi x}{l} \sin\left[\frac{n\pi ct}{l} + \alpha\right] \qquad [2.22]$$

(cf. equation [2.18] but remember that ϕ now represents longitudinal displacement).

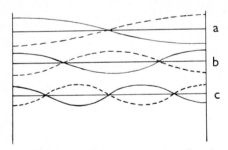

a

b

c

Figure 2.12 The first three modes of a pipe open at both ends.

Although the sequence of frequencies and wavelengths of the stationary state or modes is identical with that for the string, it can be seen that the displacement pattern is reversed (cosine instead of sine). For example, in the mode $n = 1$ the node is in the middle and the antinodes at each end (see Fig. 2.12 and compare Fig. 2.7).

It is obvious that a pipe closed at both ends would give precisely the same series of modes but their displacement patterns would conform to those of the string. This condition is of little practical importance; the pipe with one end open and one closed is however extremely important, and occurs in many instruments.

Suppose x to be measured from the closed end. The boundary conditions are then $\phi = 0$ when $x = 0$ and $\dfrac{\partial \phi}{\partial x} = 0$ when $x = l$. The basic equation is again [2.15], and if the first boundary condition is inserted it becomes:

$$\phi = 2a \sin 2\pi\kappa x \cos[2\pi vt + \alpha]$$

as for equation [2.17] for the string. Thus $\dfrac{\partial \phi}{\partial x} = 4\pi a\kappa \cos 2\pi\kappa x \cos [2\pi\nu t + \alpha]$ which must be zero for all values of t if $x = l$, that is

$$2\pi\kappa l = (2n - 1)\frac{\pi}{2}$$

$$\kappa = \frac{2n - 1}{4l}$$

$$\lambda = \frac{4l}{2n - 1}$$

$$\nu = \kappa c = (2n - 1)\frac{c}{4l}.$$

The frequencies of the modes are thus in the ratio $1:3:5:7$ etc. as n takes successive values 1, 2, 3, 4, etc. and equation [2.15] becomes

$$\phi = 2a \sin \frac{(2n - 1)\pi x}{2l} \cos \left[\frac{(2n - 1)ct}{2} + \alpha \right]. \qquad [2.23]$$

The displacement patterns (Fig. 2.13) are, of course, a mixture of the two cases discussed earlier with a node at one end and an antinode at the other.

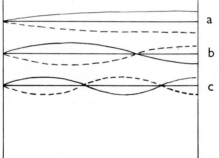

The longitudinal vibration of a solid cylindrical rod is closely analogous to the vibrations of the air in a cylindrical pipe. The modulus of elasticity required turns out in practice to be very close to Young's modulus. The modes are exactly similar to those of a pipe. Thus for an unconstrained rod the sequence follows that for a pipe open at both ends—that is, the frequencies are in the ratios $1:2:3:4:5$ etc. For a rod clamped at its mid-point there must clearly be a node at the middle, and detailed analysis confirms that modes having an antinode at the centre are impossible; the frequency ratios are thus $1:3:5:7$ etc. (See Figs. 2.12(a and c).)

Figure 2.13   The first three modes of a pipe open at one end and closed at the other.

*2.9 Vibrations in two-dimensional membranes and plates

A parallel procedure to that used for strings may be employed for two-dimensional membranes. Suppose that a plane membrane is stretched uniformly. The tension can best be described by analogy with the surface tension of a soap film. If a line is drawn in the surface of the membrane in any direction, then the force exerted by the portion of the membrane on one side of the line on that on the other side is T per unit length, and it acts in a direction normal to the line and in the surface. We may specify position on the membrane in terms of orthogonal coordinates x, y and the quantity ϕ will now represent displacement normal to the surface. Consider a small rectangular element of the surface with sides parallel to x and y

and of lengths δx and δy respectively. The net forces acting on this element are then (see Fig. 2.14) $T\delta x$ parallel with y and $T\delta y$ parallel with x. In section 2.7 it was shown that the net tension on a small element of curved string is $T\dfrac{\partial^2\phi}{\partial x^2}x$; by the same argument it may be shown that the net vertical component of the tension for the element of membrane is

$$T\delta x.\frac{\partial^2\phi}{\partial y^2}y + T\delta y\frac{\partial^2\phi}{\partial x^2}\delta x = T\left[\frac{\partial^2\phi}{\partial x^2} + \frac{\partial^2\phi}{\partial y^2}\right]\delta x\delta y.$$

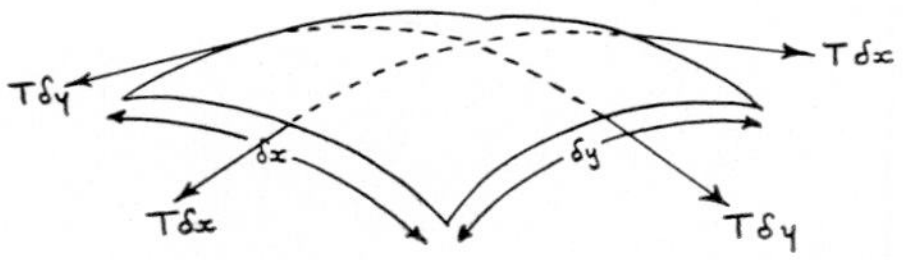

Figure 2.14 Basic diagram for studying the vibration of a membrane.

The mass of the element is $\rho\delta x\delta y$ if the mass per unit area is ρ and thus the equation of motion (cf. equation [2.16]) is

$$T\left[\frac{\partial^2\phi}{\partial x^2} + \frac{\partial^2\phi}{\partial y^2}\right]\delta x\delta y = \rho\delta x\delta y\frac{\partial^2\phi}{\partial t^2}$$

$$\frac{T}{\rho}.\left[\frac{\partial^2\phi}{\partial x^2} + \frac{\partial^2\phi}{\partial y^2}\right] = \frac{\partial^2\phi}{dt^2}. \qquad [2.24]$$

This is clearly a two-dimensional version of the wave equation with the velocity $c = \sqrt{\dfrac{T}{\rho}}$.

Now let us consider possible solutions of this equation. Equation [2.11] was the form of solution which we found appropriate in one dimension; the corresponding two-dimensional equation which should obviously be tried is

$$\phi = a \sin[px + qy - rct]. \qquad [2.25]$$

Under what conditions, if any, is this a solution of 2.24?

$$\frac{\partial\phi}{\partial t} = -arc\cos[px + qy - rct]$$

$$\frac{\partial\phi}{\partial y} = aq\cos[px + qy - rct]$$

$$\frac{\partial^2\phi}{\partial t^2} = -ar^2c^2\sin[px + qy - rct].$$

$$\frac{\partial\phi}{\partial x} = ap\cos[px + qy - rct]$$

$$\frac{\partial^2\phi}{\partial y^2} = -aq^2\sin[px + qy - rct].$$

$$\frac{\partial^2\phi}{\partial x^2} = -ap^2\sin[px + qy - rct].$$

Thus $c^2[-ap^2\sin\{px + qy - rct\} - aq^2\sin\{px + qy - rct\}]$
$$= -ar^2c^2\sin[px + qy - rct]$$
$$p^2 + q^2 = r^2.$$

In other words, [2.25] is a solution of [2.24] if $p^2 + q^2 = r^2$. A moment's consideration will show that a particular pair of values of p and q represents a "line" wave across the membrane (the equivalent of a plane wave in three dimensions). This will be reflected at boundaries in much the same way as we found for one-dimensional waves. If we make the same kind of assumptions as for strings the net displacement for a stationary state will be

$$\phi_1 + \phi_2 = a \sin [px + qy - rct + \alpha] + a \sin [px + qy + rct + \beta]$$

$$= 2a \sin \left[px + qy + \frac{\alpha + \beta}{2} \right] \cos \left[rct + \frac{\alpha - \beta}{2} \right],$$

α and β being the arbitrary phase constants again. Now suppose we are concerned with a rectangular membrane of length X in the x direction and Y in the y direction and rigidly clamped all round the edges, then $\phi = 0$ when $x = 0$, $y = 0$ and $x = X$, $y = Y$. If $\phi = 0$ when both $x = 0$ and $y = 0$, i.e. at the origin, then $\dfrac{\alpha + \beta}{2} = 0$ as for the string and $\dfrac{\alpha - \beta}{2} = \alpha$. The equation then becomes

$$\phi = 2a \sin [px + qy] \cos [rct + \alpha].$$

At the point $x = X$, $y = 0$, $\phi = 0$ and hence

$$pX = m\pi \quad \text{or} \quad p = \frac{m\pi}{X}.$$

Similarly at $x = 0$, $y = Y$, $\phi = 0$ and hence

$$q = \frac{n\pi}{Y},$$

thus

$$\phi = 2a \sin \left[\frac{m\pi x}{X} + \frac{n\pi y}{Y} \right] \cos [rct + \alpha] \qquad [2.26]$$

(cf. equations [2.18] and [2.22] and remember that ϕ now corresponds to normal displacement of a point on the membrane).

But we showed earlier that $r^2 = p^2 + q^2$, thus $r^2 = \dfrac{m^2\pi^2}{X^2} + \dfrac{n^2\pi^2}{Y^2}$. Now equation [2.26]

shows that at a given point x,y, conditions repeat themselves exactly every time t increases by an amount which makes rct increase by 2π,

i.e.

$$rc\tau = 2\pi \quad \text{or} \quad \frac{rc}{v} = 2\pi$$

$$v = \frac{rc}{2\pi}.$$

Thus the frequency of the stationary modes will be

$$v = \frac{rc}{2\pi} = \frac{c}{2\pi} \sqrt{\frac{m^2\pi^2}{X^2} + \frac{n^2\pi^2}{Y^2}}$$

$$v = \frac{c}{2} \sqrt{\frac{m^2}{X^2} + \frac{n^2}{Y^2}}. \qquad [2.27]$$

It is thus clear that even for a square plate the modes will have frequencies in the ratio $1:\sqrt{2}:2:\sqrt{5}$, etc. If the plate is rectangular the modes will have even more complicated frequency ratios. (Note also that if we let Y become very small the plate becomes a string, and then [2.27] reduces to the result already found for a string, i.e. $v = \dfrac{cm}{2X}$.)*

Many simplifying assumptions have been made—for example, only solutions for "line waves" were included, but the analysis gives some idea of the increase in complexity that occurs on moving to two dimensions. For thick plates—such as the Chladni plate—of course the problem is more complicated still as it is necessary to consider the elasticity, bending moment, and so on. The analysis for transverse vibrations of rods or for thick plates will not be attempted.

*2.10 Vibration of air in conical pipes

Conical pipes occur in many musical instruments and, in order to investigate possible stationary states in such systems, waves in three dimensions must be introduced. A conical pipe may be considered to be a figure of rotation about its axis and the waves involved are spherical, having the axis of the tube as wave normal.

The logical extension of the wave equation into three dimensions (cf. equations [2.10] and [2.24]) is

$$\frac{\partial^2 \phi}{\partial t^2} = c^2 \left[\frac{\partial^2 \phi}{\partial x^2} + \frac{\partial^2 \phi}{\partial y^2} + \frac{\partial^2 \phi}{\partial z^2} \right].$$ [2.28]

Since the wave is now spreading out in three dimensions, longitudinal displacement is clearly not the appropriate variable; a scalar quantity is desirable, and one of the most useful is that usually known as the "condensation". It is defined as the increase in density above the rest density of the medium, expressed as a fraction of the rest density, that is condensation $s = \dfrac{\rho - \rho_0}{\rho_0}$. It may seem rather surprising that the quantity ϕ may be interpreted in so many different ways in the wave equation. If any demonstration of the validity of such interchange is needed consider again the derivation of equation [2.20], section 2.8, for longitudinal displacement of air in pipes. The volume of the displaced slab of air was found to have increased its volume by a factor $\left(1 + \dfrac{\partial \phi}{\partial x}\right)$, and, since continuity of mass must be preserved under the conditions stated, it follows that the density must have decreased in the corresponding ratio, that is

$$\frac{\rho_0}{\rho} = 1 + \frac{\partial \phi}{\partial x}$$

or, approximately, if $\dfrac{\partial \phi}{\partial x}$ is small,

$$\frac{\rho}{\rho_0} = 1 - \frac{\partial \phi}{\partial x}, \quad \frac{\rho - \rho_0}{\rho_0} = -\frac{\partial \phi}{\partial x}, \quad s = -\frac{\partial \phi}{\partial x}.$$

* It is also worth noting that a comparable formula, $v = \dfrac{c}{2}\sqrt{\dfrac{m^2}{X^2} + \dfrac{n^2}{Y^2} + \dfrac{l^2}{Z^2}}$, for modes of vibration in a room can be developed.

Thus
$$\frac{\partial^2 s}{\partial t^2} = -\frac{\partial^2}{\partial t^2}\left(\frac{\partial \phi}{\partial x}\right) \quad \text{and} \quad \frac{\partial^2 s}{\partial x^2} = -\frac{\partial^3 y}{\partial x^3}.$$

Now consider equation [2.20],
$$\frac{\partial^2 \phi}{\partial t^2} = \frac{K}{\rho_0}\frac{\partial^2 \phi}{\partial x^2}$$

or on differentiation $w.r.t.x$
$$\frac{\partial}{\partial x}\frac{\partial^2 \phi}{\partial t^2} = \frac{K}{\rho_0}\frac{\partial^3 \phi}{\partial x^3} \quad \text{or} \quad \frac{\partial^2 s}{\partial t^2} = \frac{K}{\rho_0}\frac{\partial^2 s}{\partial x^2},$$

in other words, the substitution of displacement for condensation leaves the differential equation unchanged. We shall assume that this principle holds in three dimensions and for our present purpose let ϕ in equation [2.28] represent s the condensation.

For a conical pipe spherical wave fronts are involved and this leads to a simplification since clearly variations occur only along radii. Equation [2.28] should thus be capable of expression in terms of t, ϕ and r the radius vector. Now $r^2 = x^2 + y^2 + z^2$ whence, if y and z are kept constant

$$2r\frac{\partial r}{\partial x} = 2x \quad \text{or} \quad \frac{\partial r}{\partial x} = \frac{x}{r}$$

$$\frac{\partial \phi}{\partial x} = \frac{\partial \phi}{\partial r}\frac{\partial r}{\partial x} = \frac{x}{r}\frac{\partial \phi}{\partial r}$$

$$\frac{\partial^2 \phi}{\partial x^2} = \frac{x}{r}\frac{\partial^2 \phi}{\partial r^2}\frac{\partial r}{\partial x} - \frac{x}{r^2}\frac{\partial \phi}{\partial r}\frac{\partial r}{\partial x} + \frac{1}{r}\frac{\partial \phi}{\partial r}$$

$$= \frac{x^2}{r^2}\frac{\partial^2 \phi}{\partial r^2} - \frac{x^2}{r^3}\frac{\partial \phi}{\partial r} + \frac{1}{r}\frac{\partial \phi}{\partial r}$$

$$= \frac{x^2}{r^2}\frac{\partial^2 \phi}{\partial r^2} + \frac{y^2 + z^2}{r^3}\frac{\partial \phi}{\partial r}.$$

Similar expressions may be found for $\dfrac{\partial^2 \phi}{\partial y^2}$ and $\dfrac{\partial^2 \phi}{\partial z^2}$ and, as a result, equation [2.28] may be replaced by

$$\frac{\partial^2 \phi}{\partial t^2} = c^2\left[\frac{(x^2 + y^2 + z^2)}{r^2}\frac{\partial^2 \phi}{\partial r^2} + \frac{(y^2 + z^2) + (z^2 + x^2) + (x^2 + y^2)}{r^3}\frac{\partial \phi}{\partial r}\right]$$

$$\frac{\partial^2 \phi}{\partial t^2} = c^2\left[\frac{\partial^2 \phi}{\partial r^2} + \frac{2}{r}\frac{\partial \phi}{\partial r}\right]. \tag{2.29}$$

This can be written in an even more useful form by noting that $\dfrac{\partial^2}{\partial t^2}(r\phi) = \dfrac{r\partial^2 \phi}{\partial t^2}$ (r constant) and $\dfrac{\partial^2}{\partial r^2}(r\phi) = \left[\dfrac{r\partial^2 \phi}{\partial r^2} + \dfrac{2\partial \phi}{\partial r}\right]$ (t constant).

Thus equation [2.29] becomes
$$\frac{\partial^2}{\partial t^2}(r\phi) = c^2\frac{\partial^2}{\partial r^2}(r\phi). \tag{2.30}$$

This is obviously closely related to the one-dimensional form of the wave equation [2.10] and therefore probably has a solution like that given in [2.13],

$$r\phi = a \sin 2\pi(\kappa r - vt)$$

and similarly a stationary form may be expected as in equation [2.15]

$$r\phi = 2a \sin\left[2\pi\kappa r + \frac{\alpha + \beta}{2}\right] \cos\left[2\pi vt + \frac{\alpha - \beta}{2}\right] \qquad [2.31]$$

(remember that ϕ now represents the *condensation*).

Now we may put in appropriate boundary conditions for a conical pipe (see Fig. 2.15).

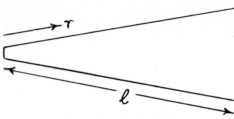

Figure 2.15   Conical pipe.

At the vertex of the cone $r = 0$ and hence $r\phi = 0$ (unless the condensation is infinite—a case which may clearly be ignored). It therefore does not matter whether this end is open or closed. In either case $r\phi = 0$ when $r = 0$ for all t and hence $\dfrac{\alpha + \beta}{2} = 0$ and $\dfrac{\alpha - \beta}{2} = \alpha$ as for the stretched string. Thus

$$r\phi = 2a \sin[2\pi\kappa r] \cos[2\pi vt + \alpha]. \quad [2.32]$$

If the other end is open, then the condensation must be zero—the density outside the end is likely to be very close to the rest density—and hence

$$0 = 2a \sin 2\pi\kappa l \cos[2\pi vt + \alpha] \text{ for all values of } t$$

(*l* is here the length measured along the *sloping side* of the pipe), thus

$$2\pi\kappa l = n\pi, \qquad \kappa = \frac{n}{2l}.$$

Thus $v = \kappa c = \dfrac{nc}{2l}$ and the frequencies of the modes are in the ratio 1:2:3:4—as for a cylindrical pipe open at both ends—and the important result emerges that a conical pipe open at the wide end has the same series of modes as a cylindrical pipe open at *both* ends regardless of whether the narrow end is closed or open. The equation is

$$r\phi = 2a \sin\frac{n\pi r}{l} \cos\left[\frac{n\pi ct}{l} + \alpha\right]. \qquad [2.33]$$

For a cylindrical pipe with the wide end closed the vertex condition is the same as for the last example, but at the wide end the condensation ϕ is likely to be a *maximum*. In other words $\dfrac{\partial\phi}{\partial r}$ will be zero for all values of t. Now from equation [2.32]

$$\phi = \frac{2a}{r} \sin[2\pi\kappa r] \cos[2\pi vt + \alpha]$$

$$\frac{\partial\phi}{\partial r} = 2a \cos[2\pi vt + \alpha]\left[\frac{2\pi\kappa \cos 2\pi\kappa r}{r} - \frac{\sin 2\pi\kappa r}{r^2}\right].$$

And this must be zero for all t when $r = l$,

i.e.
$$2\pi\kappa \cos 2\pi\kappa l = \frac{\sin 2\pi\kappa l}{l}$$

$$\tan 2\pi\kappa l = 2\pi\kappa l. \qquad\qquad [2.34]$$

The roots of this equation are best considered graphically (see Fig. 2.16). Here the two equations $y = 2\pi\kappa l$ and $y = \tan 2\pi\kappa l$ are plotted together, and it can be seen that intersections occur at points for which $2\pi\kappa l$ is rather less than $\dfrac{(2n + 1)\pi}{z}$ and becomes nearer to this exact value as n increases. The lowest mode therefore has

$$2\pi\kappa l < \frac{3\pi}{2}, \qquad \kappa < \frac{3}{4l}, \qquad v < \frac{3c}{4l}$$

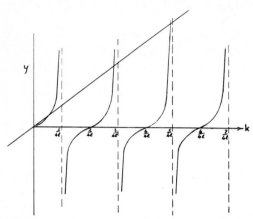

Figure 2.16 Graphical solution of the equation giving the modes for a conical pipe closed at both ends.

which is less than 1·5 times the frequency of the corresponding open pipe. The frequencies of the modes do not form an exact harmonic series but the higher modes approach the series 5:7:9:11, etc.

2.11 Tones derived from rotation

There are a number of obvious ways of deriving musical sounds from rotating systems. The simplest, which has already been mentioned, is the Savart wheel, a purely mechanical device consisting of a toothed wheel which strikes a piece of card or a sheet of hard plastic material as it rotates. The sound produced is extremely harsh and contains a great deal of noise in addition to a small proportion of musical sound. It is far removed from a pure tone and is not likely to find a place as a musical instrument. The same basic principle is used in the klaxon motor horn, the sound being amplified by a thin diaphragm attached to the stud which is struck by the teeth of a rotating cogwheel. The siren too has already been mentioned; its tone is rather more musical than that of the Savart wheel, but there is still considerable noise and the musical component is certainly not a pure tone. Its principal use is as a device for establishing a note of a given pitch for comparison purposes; the frequency can easily be determined by counting the holes and timing the revolutions. In its simplest

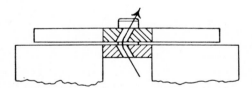

Figure 2.17 Section through Cagniard de la Tour's improved siren.

form there is one jet of air which is interrupted by the holes in a rotating wheel. In the modification developed by Cagniard de la Tour there are as many jets, arranged in the face of a cylindrical wind-chest, as there are holes in the wheel. The holes in both the wind-chest and in the disc are made oblique in opposite directions so that the escaping air drives the wheel (see Fig. 2.17). The sound produced by this modified form is considerably louder than that of the simple type. The wave forms of notes produced by a Savart wheel and by a Cagniard de la Tour siren are shown in Figs. 2.18(a) and (b). More recently the siren has been developed as a generator of controlled wave forms of very high intensity. Allen & Watters (1959), for example, have described a form in which the holes in the rotor become slots and the holes in the stator take on a complex outline. An equation relating the variation of uncovered port area with the pressure set up in the throat was derived, and hence the port shape necessary to give sinusoidal (or any other) wave forms could be determined. Extremely high-intensity pure tones can be produced with harmonics at a level less than 1 per cent. of the fundamental.

The remaining methods have all been used in electronic organs, and some of their more detailed characteristics will be considered in Chapter 11. Electromagnetic generation is the basis of the Hammond (1935) organ. The principle is to rotate a disc of soft iron or mu-metal, with teeth on its periphery, close to a magnet round which a coil has been wrapped. The fluctuations in the magnetic field caused by the movement of the teeth near the pole of the magnet induce currents in the coil which may then be amplified. It is relatively simple to demonstrate the principle of such a tone generator in the laboratory, but the problem of producing a pure tone in this way—by suitable shaping of the teeth and/or the pole piece—is a difficult one. Electrostatic generation is the basis of the Compton (Bourn, 1949) electrone organ. A rotating disc carrying metallic segments rotates near to a fixed plate bearing representations of wave forms, and periodic variations in capacity occur as the plate rotates. The variable capacitor so formed is charged by means of fixed potential sources through

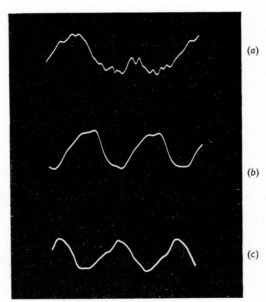

(a)

(b)

(c)

Figure 2.18 Oscillograph traces of the wave forms given by: (a) A Savart wheel. (b) A Cagniard de la Tour siren. (c) The crude photoelectric generator described in the text.

a resistance. As the capacity varies, so the charging current will vary, and with it the potential drop across the resistance; it may then be used as the grid control of a triode valve, and hence to produce variation in output current. Again it is relatively simple to demonstrate, but equally difficult to produce, a pure wave form. The third method involves the use of a photoelectric cell (e.g. Schouten, 1940a); it consists of a transparent disc rotating between a lamp and a photocell. Wave shapes or variations in transparency are painted on the disc and hence as its rotates the current fluctuates, again giving rise to a periodically-varying current, which can be amplified and fed to a loudspeaker. The form of output depends principally on the shape reproduced on the disc and to a certain extent on the geometry of the lamp and cell. A very simple demonstration model has been suggested to me by V. H. Attree which incorporates a transistorised amplifier and which will drive a miniature loudspeaker quite satisfactorily. No attempt is made to produce any given wave form; it merely produces periodic pulses, and the result is recognisable as a musical sound (Fig. 2.18(c) shows the actual waveform). The circuit is shown in Fig. 2.19. In the version used for demonstration a series of holes has been drilled in an aluminium disc in concentric rings; the number in each ring is made proportional to the frequency required to produce the notes of a musical scale, and hence by moving the cell and lamp, which are mounted together on a forked arm one on either side of the disc, primitive tunes can be played.

2.12 Tones derived from electrical oscillation

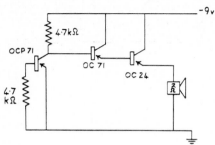

Figure 2.19 Circuit of a simple transistor amplifier for a photoelectric generator

The possibility of using electrical oscillations as a source of musical sound probably derives from Duddell's singing arc (1900), in which a tuned circuit of a coil and a capacitor were shunted across an arc and, by varying the constants, the natural frequency could be changed. The noise of the arc itself became a musical note whose pitch was determined by the constants of the electrical circuit. Since that time there have been numerous attempts to make use of oscillating circuits using valves, thyratrons, transistors, and other electronic devices. It is a field in which amateurs as well as professionals have contributed and many instruments have been built. The use of a separate oscillator for each note can prove costly, but as soon as variable frequency circuits are introduced there are severe problems unless the instrument is used purely for solo playing. It will suffice now to know that electrical oscillations provide valuable sources of variable pure tones in the laboratory, and also that many wave forms other than that of a pure sine wave may be produced by suitable modifications to the circuit.

It is also useful to note the close analogy which exists between electrical and mechanical oscillations. This analogue has been helpful in two directions. The study of mechanical vibrating systems had begun before that of electric circuits, and hence early electric circuit analysts turned to the parallel mechanical system for guidance. More recently, however, electrical circuit theory has made such rapid advances that electrical analogues are frequently used to assist the understanding of mechanical systems.

The obvious starting point for a brief summary of the relationship is resistance; in an electrical circuit the presence of resistance entails a conversion of energy into heat, and the same applies in mechanics or acoustics. In ordinary metallic conductors the resistance R is related to the electromotive force E and to the current I by Ohm's law

$$R = \frac{E}{I}.$$

In a mechanical system the driving force F is clearly analogous to the e.m.f. and the resulting velocity v to the current, and we find

$$R = \frac{F}{v}.$$

In mechanical systems mass is the measure of the inertia of the system, i.e. of its reluctance to commence oscillation; the parallel is inductance, which tends to oppose the build-up of an alternating current. Electrically, $E = L\dfrac{dI}{dt}$ where L is the inductance, and the corresponding mechanical expression is $F = M\dfrac{dv}{dt}$ — the familiar equation of force = mass × acceleration.

In section 2.4 it was pointed out that the essential requirements of a mechanical vibrating system were restoring forces—usually elastic—which tend to return the system to its former state undisturbed, and inertia which tends to delay the return and subsequently to carry the system beyond the neutral point to maintain the oscillation. In an electrical circuit it is the capacitance which provides this effect, and we find $E = \dfrac{q}{C}$, where q is the quantity of charge involved when an e.m.f. E is applied to a system of capacitance C. Now the current in an electrical circuit is $\dfrac{dq}{dt}$ and so, since we use current as the analogue of velocity, charge is the analogue of distance moved, and we should find in a mechanical system $F = \dfrac{d}{C'}$, where C' is the mechanical analogue of capacitance; its meaning can be made clear if we consider the compression of a spring. The required force is proportional to the distance moved by the free end and the constant of proportionality is the stiffness of the spring; this must be the reciprocal of the analogous electrical quantity C and hence it is usual to introduce a mechanical term—compliance—to represent the reciprocal of stiffness. C'—the compliance—is thus the mechanical analogue of capacitance.

Full discussions of the remarkable extent to which this parallel development can be taken are given in the literature, e.g. Davies (1934), Olson (1943); it will suffice at this point to note that the parallel to equation [2.3] in electrical terms is $-\dfrac{q}{C} = L\dfrac{d^2q}{dt^2}$ or $\dfrac{q}{C} = -L\dfrac{dI}{dt}$, and this is the equation governing the electrical oscillations in a resistanceless circuit.

2.13 Summary

The first step in the investigation is now complete; a survey of the various ways in which a simple musical tone can be produced and varied in pitch has been made. In particular, since vibrators play such an important role in most instruments, we have studied the mechanism by which the frequency of a vibrator remains constant and whereby the existence of different modes for a given vibrator is possible. It does not, however, require a particularly well-trained ear to arrive at the conclusion that there is a world of difference between the simple tone—produced for example by a string vibrating in its fundamental mode—and a single note of the same pitch played on a conventional orchestral instrument. The pure tone can be described as "thin" or "characterless", whereas the note of a well-played orchestral instrument is often described as "rich" or "brilliant". The next step in the investigation is thus to search for a scientific explanation of this difference and of the differences in tonal quality between one instrument and another. The next chapter is concerned with the beginning of this investigation.

CHAPTER 3

The Origin of Differences in Tonal Quality

3.1 The examination of wave forms

The investigation started with the examination of wave forms to determine the essence of a musical sound. Now, having studied the production of simple tones, we should again examine their wave forms in comparison with those produced by conventional instruments. In Fig. 3.1 are shown the traces of the note A (for the frequency 440 c.p.s.) first as a pure tone and then, successively, on a tuning fork, a violin and an oboe. Although the patterns differ considerably one common factor is clear; the basic pattern repeats with reasonable precision at the same rate. We therefore have to ask ourselves, "What is the origin of the changes of shape of the repetition unit?". Fig. 3.1(d) is very different from 3.1(a), and it is not difficult to imagine that 3.1(d) contains, in addition to the fundamental tone, other vibrations of a higher frequency which give rise to the "kinks". How could such higher-frequency vibrations arise? One possible source could be the simultaneous vibration of the system in one or more of its higher-frequency modes.

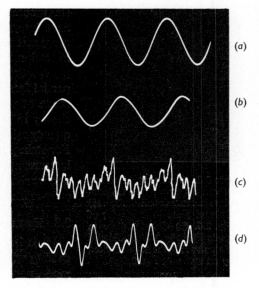

Figure 3.1 Oscillograph traces of notes of the same pitch (440 c.p.s.): (a) Pure tone. (b) Tuning-fork. (c) Violin. (d) Oboe.

3.2 The possibility of vibration in several modes at once

The Chladni plate provides an important clue. In the section on modes of vibration (2.5) the method of making the plate vibrate in a given mode was described. Figs. 3.2(a), (b) and (c) show the trace of three such distinct modes, but in 3.2(d) the trace obtained when the plate is struck with a hammer is given. It is clear that trace (d) contains elements of the other three; the plate may be vibrating in several modes at once. It seems at least plausible, therefore, that a possible source of the quality of tone in a conventional musical instrument is that it is vibrating in several modes simultaneously and that this too is the source of the kinks in the curve.

Before proceeding further it will be well to consider precisely what we mean by "addition" in this context. As far as Fig. 3.2 is concerned the composite curve could be made up of the sums of the ordinates of various components at corresponding values of t. Is the addition of waves as simple as this in practice? Fortunately it does turn out to be so under a large variety of circumstances. This fact is a particular manifestation of the much more general principle of superposition, which simply states that when two or more waves pass through a given point they have no effect on each other whatsoever; each has its own effect at the point

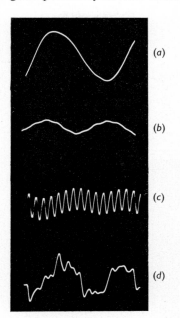

considered, and the net result to an outside observer is merely the algebraic sum of the two. This principle can be observed if one studies the behaviour of waves on the surface of water; if two stones are thrown into a pond the expanding circles of ripples pass through each other and then proceed completely unaffected. It is unfortunate in many ways that the term "interference" was introduced to describe the interaction of two or more sets of waves. The interference fringes that are observed when two waves pass through the same region are merely the manifestation to an outside observer of the instantaneous algebraic sum of the two; there is no permanent interference and the waves pass on unchanged. The more mathematical aspects of this principle will be discussed in section 3.6.

We shall now return to consider the effect of adding the partial frequencies of a system vibrating in more than one mode at once. The overtones of the Chladni plate were shown in the last chapter to have rather complicated frequency relationships; the same is true for a bell (Lehr, 1952). For strings and pipes which form the source of tone in most instruments, however, the relationships are much simpler, and we shall therefore consider only the addition of harmonically-related modes.†

Figure 3.2 Oscillograph traces of various sounds: (a) Chladni plate in mode (a) of Fig. 2.6. (b) Chladni plate in mode (b) of Fig. 2.6. (c) Chladni plate in mode (c) of Fig. 2.6. (d) Chladni plate struck at the point marked by an arrow in Fig. 2.6(d).

3.3 Harmonics of strings and pipes

It is important to be clear about the nomenclature in dealing with modes of vibration. The terms that occur are mode, partial, overtone and harmonic. The terms mode and partial are almost synonymous and may be applied to any vibration no matter how complex; mode tends to be used if a single vibration is being considered, and partial when the reference is to one component of a mixture. The designation of a particular mode of vibration or of a particular partial vibration by a number, or a sequence of numbers, is a matter for convention, though usually the vibration of lowest frequency will be designated the fundamental or first mode or first partial. The term overtone may be applied to any of the modes except the fundamental, and there is no other restriction on the use of this term. Harmonic, however, is usually reserved for modes or partials whose frequencies bear simple ratios to

† It is important to realise that in the theoretical section many assumptions were made which are not necessarily valid in practice, and in fact even for strings and pipes the modes are not exactly harmonically related. We shall consider the effect of such deviations in Chapter 7.

one another defined by a harmonic series, i.e. their frequencies are in the ratio 1:2:3, etc. The numbering of *harmonics* is always that of the corresponding value of "*n*" in the harmonic series; thus the fundamental mode is always the first harmonic. For a system having modes with frequencies in the ratio 1:3:5, etc., the mode of frequency 3 could thus be referred to as the second mode or partial, as the first overtone, but as the third harmonic; the second harmonic would here be said to have zero amplitude.

Let us now consider the sequence of partials of strings and of pipes which (as shown in sections 2.7 2.10) are usually almost harmonic. The exceptions are conical pipes nearly closed at the wide end which sometimes find a place in organs and whose partials are

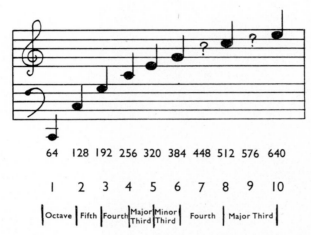

| 64 | 128 | 192 | 256 | 320 | 384 | 448 | 512 | 576 | 640 |

| 1 | 2 | 3 | 4 | 5 | 6 | 7 | 8 | 9 | 10 |

| Octave | Fifth | Fourth | Major Third | Minor Third | | Fourth | | Major Third |

Figure 3.3 Notes, frequencies (Scientific Pitch), and intervals corresponding to the first ten harmonics.

not harmonic. The sequence for a string clamped between two well-defined supports is the complete series 1, 2, 3, 4, etc. The corresponding notes and intervals are given in Fig. 3.3 up to the tenth harmonic. The seventh and ninth harmonics do not fit into the normal scale accepted by western ears (see Chapter 8). The sequence for a cylindrical pipe open at both ends, or for a conical pipe open at the wide end and either closed or open at the narrow end, is the same as for the string. The sequence for a cylindrical pipe closed at one end, however, is different, even harmonics being of zero amplitude and the series is 1, 3, 5, 7, etc. Thus, if the idea of vibration in several modes at once is tenable, it should be possible to imitate the wave shape and the tone of a musical instrument by suitable mixtures of pure tones in the frequency ratios 1:2:3, etc.

3.4 The addition of harmonics

The simplest way to investigate the effect of mixing pure tones is to use an electronic source. An oscillator or signal generator producing a pure sinusoidal output is the most suitable. If two or three such sources are available then it is quite adequate to use a simple resistance network to add their output voltages and to feed the resultant to a loudspeaker of suitable impedance and/or a cathode-ray oscillograph. If only one source is available the effects may be demonstrated quite satisfactorily by using a tape recorder as an intermediate source.

Let us consider first of all the addition of two notes with frequency ratio 1:2. If the note of lower frequency is sounded continuously and its octave introduced intermittently one is conscious of a change in quality rather than of the addition of a second note. Fig. 3.4 shows the effect on the oscillograph trace. It is clear that the desired results—a change in quality and a kink in the curve—have been achieved.

An excellent method of demonstrating the addition of harmonics has been developed by

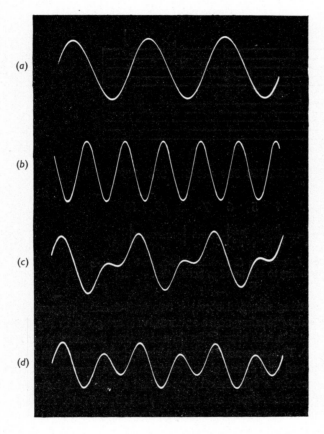

(a)

(b)

(c)

(d)

Figure 3.4 Oscillograph traces of various sounds: (a) Pure tone (b) Pure tone of twice the frequency of (a). (c) Mixture of (a) and (b) roughly in the proportions 2:1. (d) Mixture of (a) and (b) roughly in the proportions 1:2.

Mr. F. Merry, of Leigh County Secondary School. It consists of a set of vertical wires—rather like a vertical abacus—on which slide lengths of drinking straws cut to correspond to the ordinates of a sine curve. Figure 3.5 shows a model, based on Mr. Merry's ideas, for addition of components in the ratio 1:3:5. In (a) the lower set of straws represents the fundamental; coloured wooden beads have been added above and below each straw to emphasise the outlines and to give a firm support for the straws. The upper straws represent the third harmonic and are held in place by a slotted metal strip. In (b) the strip has been removed and the addition of the two components can be seen. The drinking-straw model

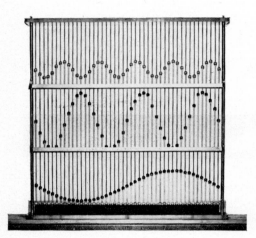

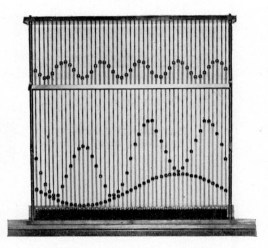

Figure 3.5 (*a*) Photograph of model before summation.

Figure 3.5 (*b*) Photograph of model showing summation of first and third harmonics.

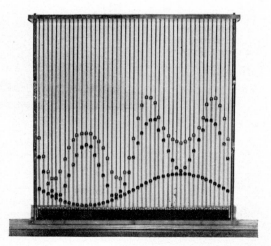

Figure 3.5 (*c*) Summation of first, third and fifth harmonics.

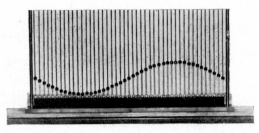

Figure 3.6 (*a*) Representation of the fundamental.

Figure 3.6 (*b*) Aluminium plate representing second harmonic.

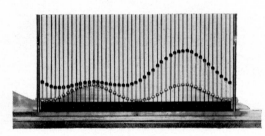

Figure 3.6 (c) Summation of fundamental and second harmonic.

Figure 3.6 (*d*) Summation of fundamental and second harmonic with different phase relationship.

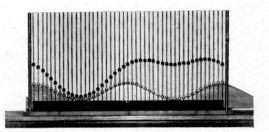

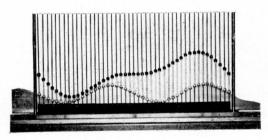

Figure 3.6 (*e*) Summation of fundamental and second harmonic with a third phase relationship.

may, of course, be extended to a number of harmonics; in (c) the addition of 1, 3 and 5 is shown.

3.5   The effect of phase differences in addition

An alternative way of using the wave model is illustrated in Fig. 3.6(a), (b) and (c). The fundamental is again represented by the lower set of straws, but the second component to be added is represented by an aluminium plate which has been cut to the correct profile; in the figure it represents the second harmonic. This plate can slide along behind, and in contact with, the wires so that the lower beads ride up on the plate and the addition is performed. This method of operation immediately draws attention to the problem of relative phase. If

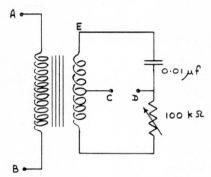

Figure 3.7   Circuit diagram for phase-shift network (input AB, output CD).

the plate is moved into different positions the wave profile of the sum is clearly quite different (Fig. 3.6 (d) and (e)). Up to now we have ignored this possibility and have tacitly assumed that all harmonics have a common starting condition—say $x = 0$ when $t = 0$—and henceforth remain in step. Is this necessarily true, and what would be the effect on the ear if the relative phase of the harmonics changed?

This question can also be answered with signal generators. The relative phase can be

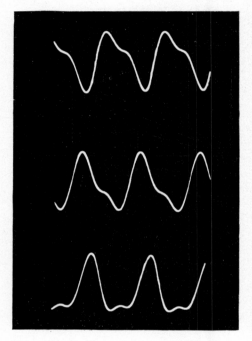

Figure 3.8   Oscillograph traces showing summations of first and second harmonics with three different phase relationships.

adjusted—using a cathode-ray oscillograph to monitor the composite shape—either by making minute frequency changes in one oscillator for a fraction of a second, thus allowing one component to gain on the other, or by using a phase-shift network. (A convenient circuit is shown in Fig. 3.7.) The result is very striking and of great importance; there is no effect on the ear whatsoever. All the sounds represented by the traces of Fig. 3.8—each of which consists of the sum of two pure tones in the frequency ratio 1:2 with constant amplitude but different phase differences—appear to the ear to be absolutely identical. The demonstration is more striking if the audience sees the change in resultant shape actually occurring on the oscillograph screen, and can hear the sound at the same time. It is thus clear that the ear is insensitive to phase, but it must be stressed at this stage that we have only demonstrated this fact for continuous tones in a harmonic relationship; reconsideration of this experimental result may be necessary when at a later stage we consider intermittent or otherwise varying tones and tones whose frequencies are close together (section 9.4.5).

*3.6 Mathematical aspects of the summation of waves

In an earlier section the principle of superposition was mentioned, and it will be useful now to consider briefly the parallel mathematical ideas. In section 2.10 the general wave equation was introduced in its three-dimensional form:—

$$c^2 \left[\frac{\partial^2 \phi}{\partial x^2} + \frac{\partial^2 \phi}{\partial y^2} + \frac{\partial^2 \phi}{\partial z^2} \right] = \frac{\partial^2 \phi}{\partial t^2} \qquad [3.1]$$

where ϕ is the quantity—displacement, pressure, etc.—in which the form of the wave is being expressed. Although this is a second-order differential equation it is linear, that is no

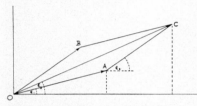

Figure 3.9 Vector addition.

powers higher than one of ϕ or of any of its derivatives occur. For such an equation it was stated that if $\phi = f_1(t)$ is a solution and $\phi = f_2(t)$ is also a solution then $\phi = f_1(t) + f_2(t)$ is also a solution. This is the mathematical statement of the principle of superposition. We shall discuss in Chapters 8 and 9 what happens if the system being studied is not governed by a linear differential equation.

If the two oscillations being added have the same angular frequency but have a general phase relationship their resultant may be found by vector addition. Suppose, for example, that the two oscillations to be added are

$$\phi_1 = a \cos (\omega t - \varepsilon_1) \quad \text{and} \quad \phi_2 = b \cos (\omega t - \varepsilon_2)$$

then their sum is $a \cos \omega t \cos \varepsilon_1 + a \sin \omega t \sin \varepsilon_1 + b \cos \omega t \cos \varepsilon_2 + b \sin \omega t \sin \varepsilon_2$

$$= \cos \omega t [a \cos \varepsilon_1 + b \cos \varepsilon_2] + \sin \omega t [a \sin \varepsilon_1 + b \sin \varepsilon_2]$$

$$= A \cos [\omega t - \varepsilon_3]$$

where $\qquad\qquad\qquad\qquad A \cos \varepsilon_3 = a \cos \varepsilon_1 + b \cos \varepsilon_2$

and $\qquad\qquad\qquad\qquad A \sin \varepsilon_3 = a \sin \varepsilon_1 + b \sin \varepsilon_2.$

In Fig. 3.9 OA is of length a in direction ε_1 and OB (or AC) is of length b in direction ε_2. OC clearly represents A and angle XOC represents ε_3. Suppose now that $\varepsilon_1 = 0$ and $\varepsilon_2 = 90°$

$$\phi_1 + \phi_2 = a \cos \omega t + b \sin \omega t \qquad [3.2]$$

and the sum can also be written $A \cos (\omega t - \varepsilon)$

where $\qquad\qquad\qquad\qquad A \cos \varepsilon = a \Big\}$

and $\qquad\qquad\qquad\qquad A \sin \varepsilon = b \Big\}. \qquad\qquad [3.3]$

Clearly $\qquad\qquad\qquad\qquad \tan \varepsilon = \frac{b}{a} \quad \text{and} \quad A = a^2 + b^2.$

Thus a wave of arbitrary phase $A \cos(\omega t - \varepsilon)$ can be represented as the sum of a sine and cosine wave both *in phase* (equation [3.2]) with amplitudes given by equations [3.3] This is an extremely useful substitution which we shall use later, and the principle of superposition makes it clear that the two alternative representations are exactly equivalent.

*3.7 The distribution of amplitude among the harmonics

The idea of simultaneous vibration in several modes has now been introduced, and it is necessary to consider what actually happens when a string is plucked or a rod struck. What determines the proportions of the various harmonics present in the resultant tone? The method of analysis follows the same general lines whatever the problem, but we shall here consider only the simplest case—that of a string drawn to one side at a certain point and then released.

In section 2.7 we considered the transverse vibration of a string clamped at both ends and found that a series of specific modes could exist, specified by equation [2.18]

$$\phi = 2a \sin \frac{n\pi x}{l} \cos \left[\frac{n\pi ct}{l} + \alpha \right]$$

where $2a$ is the amplitude, l the length of the string, c the velocity of sound, x the position, measured along the string, of a particle whose displacement at time t is ϕ, n is the integer defining the mode and α is a phase constant. Let us now make the assumption that the composite motion of a plucked string after release can be regarded as the sum of an infinite number of modes of this type in various proportions, that is

$$\phi = \sum_{n=1}^{n=\infty} 2a_n \sin \frac{n\pi x}{l} \cos \left[\frac{n\pi ct}{l} + \alpha_n \right] \qquad [3.4]$$

a_n and α_n being the amplitudes and phases respectively of the various components. Suppose now that equation [3.4] represents the motion of a string initiated by drawing a point distant pl from one end (p is a fraction) a distance h to one side (Fig. 3.10).

It is convenient to re-write equation [3.4] in the form

$$\phi = \sum_{n=1}^{n=\infty} \sin \frac{n\pi x}{l} \left[A_n \cos \frac{n\pi ct}{l} + B_n \sin \frac{n\pi ct}{l} \right] \qquad [3.5]$$

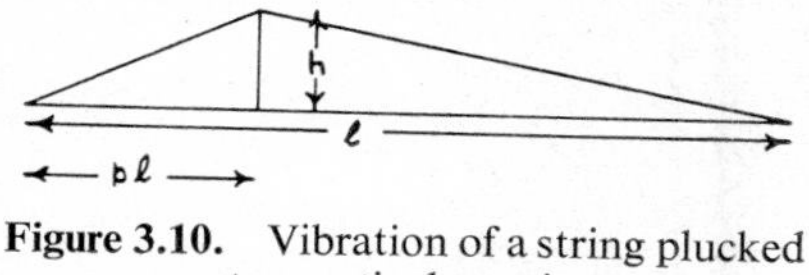

Figure 3.10. Vibration of a string plucked at a particular point.

using the result of equations [3.2] and [3.3] and substituting $A_n = 2a_n \cos \alpha$ and $B_n = 2a_n \sin \alpha$ and noting that A_n and B_n are total amplitudes of sinusoidal or cosinusoidal modes, that is, they are each double the amplitude of the individual forward and reverse progressive components making up the stationary wave. It remains to find values of A_n and B_n which arise when the cord is plucked in the way defined. Let us consider the initial boundary conditions, that is let $t = 0$.

$$\phi = \sum_{n=1}^{n=\infty} A_n \sin \frac{n\pi x}{l} \qquad [3.6]$$

and this must correspond to the profile shown in Fig. 3.10. The velocity of the string when $t = 0$ is everywhere zero and thus

$$\frac{\partial \phi}{\partial t} = \sum_{n=1}^{n=\infty} \sin \frac{n\pi x}{l} \left[\frac{-A_n n\pi c}{l} \sin \frac{n\pi ct}{l} + \frac{B_n n\pi c}{l} \cos \frac{n\pi ct}{l} \right]$$

$$= \sum_{n=1}^{n=\infty} \frac{B_n n\pi c}{l} \sin \frac{n\pi x}{l} \quad \text{when} \quad t = 0$$

and if this is zero for all values of x, B must be zero. The coefficients A_n may be obtained by using the mathematical device of multiplying both sides of equation [3.6] by $\sin \frac{\pi m x}{l} dx$ and integrating from 0 to l; m is another integer. This is a useful procedure because

$$\int_0^l \sin \frac{\pi n x}{l} \sin \frac{\pi m x}{l} \delta x$$

is zero for all integral values of n and m unless $n = m$ in which case the value of the integral is $\frac{1}{2}l$. Thus

$$\int_0^l \phi \sin \frac{m\pi x}{l} dx = \int_0^l \sum_{n=1}^{n=\infty} A_n \sin \frac{n\pi x}{l} \sin \frac{m\pi x}{l} dx$$

and since for any particular value of m there is now only one term in the summation which is non-zero, namely that for which $n = m$, we may write

$$A_n \frac{l}{2} = \int_0^l \phi \sin \frac{n\pi x}{l} dx$$

$$A_n = \frac{2}{l} \int_0^l \phi \sin \frac{n\pi x}{l} dx. \qquad [3.7]$$

Now for the example under consideration the integration must be divided into two portions. From 0 to pl the equation for ϕ when $t = 0$ is $\phi = \frac{h}{pl}x$, and from pl to l the equation is $\phi = \frac{h(l - x)}{(1 - p)l}$. Thus

$$A_n = \frac{2}{l} \left[\int_0^{pl} \frac{h}{pl} x \sin \frac{n\pi x}{l} dx + \int_{pl}^l \frac{h(l - x)}{l(1 - p)} \sin \frac{n\pi x}{l} dx \right]$$

which on integration by parts yields

$$A_n = \frac{2h \sin n\pi p}{n^2 \pi^2 p(1 - p)}. \qquad [3.8]$$

Several facts emerge at once: (*a*) the amplitude of all components is proportional to h, the initial displacement; (*b*) if np is integral the amplitude of the nth harmonic is zero—that is, any mode which would normally have a node at the point of plucking is absent; (*c*) in order to give the maximum possible amplitude in a given mode the point of plucking must be such that $np = \dfrac{2m + 1}{2}$, that is at a point of maximum amplitude for that particular mode so that $\sin n\pi p = 1$.

There will be $\dfrac{1}{p}$ possible ways of choosing a point to satisfy condition (c) and of these the one giving maximum amplitude is that for which $p(1 - p)$ is a minimum. Let $q = p(1 - p)$ then $\dfrac{dq}{dp} = 1 - 2p$ which $= 0$ if $p = \frac{1}{2}$. Thus in order to select the point giving maximum amplitude we choose p as near as possible to $\frac{1}{2}$, that is the string must be plucked at the antinode nearest to the centre of the string. The elimination of certain modes by selection of a suitable point of plucking is used by piano-manufacturers to eliminate the undesirable seventh and ninth harmonics which do not lie in the normally accepted scale (see also section 6.3 and 10.6).

The derivation of the values of A_n and B_n is a special case of the procedure known as Fourier analysis which will be discussed in more physical terms in the next chapter.

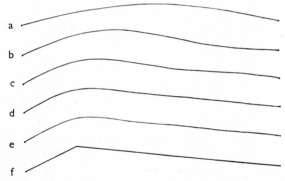

Figure 3.11   (a)–(e) Syntheses of 1, 2, 3, 4 and 6 terms representing the components of the plucked string shown in (f).

To illustrate the result of the analysis leading up to equation [3.8] a numerical example will be given. We shall consider a string 1 m. in length ($l = 100$ cm.) plucked 10 cm. to one side ($h = 10$ cm.) at a point 20 cm. from one end ($p = \frac{1}{5}$). On substituting these values into equation 3.8 the following values are obtained for the amplitudes of the first six harmonics

$$A_1 = 7{\cdot}5 \text{ cm.}$$
$$A_2 = 3{\cdot}03 \text{ cm.}$$
$$A_3 = 1{\cdot}32 \text{ cm.}$$
$$A_4 = 0{\cdot}47 \text{ cm.}$$
$$A_5 = 0$$
$$A_6 = -0{\cdot}2 \text{ cm.}$$

It will be seen that the fifth harmonic is absent in accordance with condition (b) above— np is integral. Figure 3.11 shows the effect of successively adding these terms. Figure 3.11(a) is A_1 alone, b is $A_1 + A_2$, and so on; Fig. 3.11(e) is the sum of the first six harmonics, and f is the actual initial condition of the string. As terms are successively added the sum approaches more closely to the initial shape.

After release the subsequent motion is as shown in Figure 3.12; this figure was derived by considering the original wave shape (ACDB in Fig. 3.12(a)) to be made up of two identical component waves (APQB). These are assumed to move at the same velocity in opposite directions, and their sum is taken at successive intervals of time. The thick lines in Fig. 3.12(b), (c) and (b) show three such resultants, the components in each case being shown as thin lines. The interesting feature is that much of the string remains stationary for large

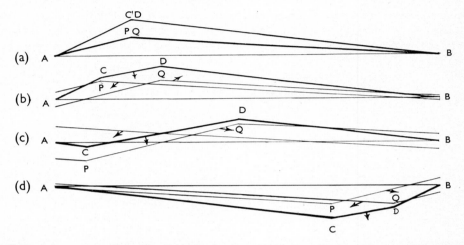

Figure 3.12   Subsequent motion of the plucked string shown in Fig. 3.11(f) after release (thick line) derived as the sum of two identical component waves moving in opposite directions (thin line).

parts of the cycle; portions AC and DB in each of the examples shown are practically stationary, and part CD moves parallel to itself.

3.8   The experimental result of adding harmonics

We have seen that it is possible to alter the quality of a musical tone by adding harmonics and that the addition alters the shape of the wave trace in more or less the way required to match real instruments. It is possible in fact to achieve a remarkably good match remembering, of course, that there is one "free" variable—the relative phase—which can be altered without affecting the tone. Figure 3.13(a) shows the trace of a synthetic oboe tone made up of only three components with the frequency ratios $1:2:3$, and Fig. 3.13(b) shows the trace of the real oboe which was being matched; the correspondence is quite good. The sound, however, is quite easily distinguished. If a single note of long duration is played there is a reasonable comparison, but with short notes the two can easily be identified. It is clear, therefore, that we have not yet completely achieved the aim of finding the source of quality differences, though it is clear that harmonic mixture—vibration in several modes at once—

plays an important part. Before pursuing the further factors influencing quality in Chapter 5 it is important to look at the process of harmonic addition the other way round. In this chapter we have considered mainly the problem of mixing harmonics to give a certain tone—

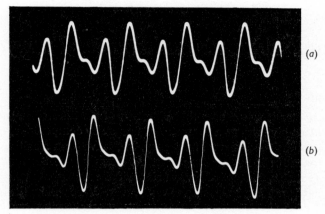

Figure 3.13 (*a*) Oscillograph trace of a mixture of three pure wave forms with frequencies in the ratio 1:2:3 roughly matching that produced by an oboe. (*b*) Wave trace of sound produced by a real oboe sounding the same note as for (*a*).

harmonic synthesis. In section 3.7, however, we saw how for one special case—the vibrating string—it is possible to determine the harmonic components from the initial wave shape, that is to analyse a complex wave into its harmonic components. This procedure is of such importance that the whole of the next chapter will be devoted to it.

CHAPTER 4

Harmonic Analysis and Fourier Transformation

4.1 Introduction

In the last chapter it was shown that vibrators of the kind often used in conventional musical instruments give rise to a sequence of frequency components, each of which is an integral multiple of the fundamental frequency. The wave form resulting from this addition is a repetitive function; it repeats exactly at the frequency of the fundamental. Suppose, however, that we take a mixture of several sinusoidal components which do not appear to have any specific harmonic relationship to each other. What will be the result? A moment's thought will show that it is always possible to find a fundamental frequency of which the given components are harmonics. For example, if we take the frequencies of 68, 119, 204 and 289 c.p.s. these are all multiples of 17 and so can be regarded as the fourth, seventh, twelfth and seventeenth harmonics of a fundamental of frequency 17. Although the fundamental itself has zero amplitude, the combined wave form would repeat exactly 17 times per second. If a prime number is included in the sequence it may be represented as a harmonic of a fundamental frequency 1 cycle per second, and correspondingly if non-integral frequencies are included a fractional fundamental is required. Thus any collection of frequencies can be made to fit into a harmonic series though the fundamental may not be present at all. Figure 4.1, for example, shows the sum of three wave forms with frequencies 6, 12 and 15 c.p.s. which can be regarded as the second, fourth and fifth harmonics of a fundamental of frequency 3 c.p.s., and it may be clearly seen that the combined wave form repeats exactly three times in one second even though there is no 3 c.p.s.-component actually present. It is not surprising, therefore, to find that any repetitive wave form can be represented as the sum of an infinite sequence of harmonics, the amplitude and phase of which are both permitted variables, and that the fundamental is determined by the rate of repetition. It is much more surprising to find that there is only one characteristic phase and amplitude for each

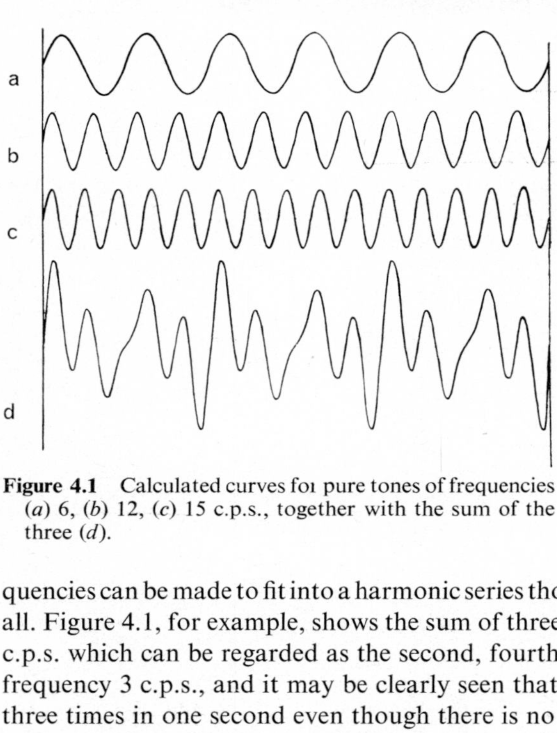

Figure 4.1 Calculated curves for pure tones of frequencies (a) 6, (b) 12, (c) 15 c.p.s., together with the sum of the three (d).

harmonic which will enable the whole series to add up to the given function; it is also extremely difficult to give a rigorous mathematical proof of this fact. The problem, of course, is to find the specific amplitudes and relative phases required to produce the given wave form.

It was pointed out in section 3.6 that a sine (or cosine) wave of arbitrary phase may always be represented as the sum of a sine and cosine term of zero phase, with amplitudes depending on the phase of the initial wave. It follows then that a complicated periodic wave shape can be represented by the sum of sine and cosine terms all in phase but with specific amplitudes which are to be determined; in section 3.7 this determination was carried out for one example. It is important to notice that up to this point we have talked about analysing wave shapes; this is because in practice wave shapes have certain properties—for example, absence of discontinuity—which facilitate an equivalent representation as the sum of sine and cosine terms. It turns out that the representation is of much wider validity and—subject to certain provisos about continuity which are nearly always fulfilled in physical problems—it applies to any periodic function. The series of terms making up the composite wave form is called a Fourier series, and the process of determining the magnitude of the components is called Fourier analysis. The basic ideas were introduced by a number of workers, but were first formalised by Fourier (1822) during the course of his work on heat flow. The analytical process may be carried out in many different ways. We shall commence with the more physical methods, and leave the more mathematical ideas until later in the chapter.

4.2 Simple harmonic analysis

Given adequate patience and practice it is possible for many people to train themselves to concentrate their attention on the separate harmonics present in a complex sound, and hence to perform "instant" Fourier analysis. This exercise is often complicated by special circumstances and is at best only qualitative. The simplest physical aid to analysis capable of reasonably precise use involves the phenomenon of resonance (see Chapter 5). Helmholtz (1877) introduced the valuable technique using a series of tuned resonators to assist the ear in identifying harmonics. They are usually spheres of metal or glass which have a fairly wide neck, and opposite to the neck a narrow tube which can fit into the ear. (A simple way of manufacturing a demonstration resonator is to seal a narrow glass tube to the base of a round-bottomed flask.) Each resonator has a characteristic frequency, and if this is present as a partial in the sound being analysed it is considerably amplified by the resonator when placed in one ear (the other ear must be closed by means of a plug). It is often possible after identifying particular harmonic components by means of such a resonator to hear them directly without its use. Until the advent of electrical methods of analysis the Helmholtz resonator was much the most satisfactory device available to assist the ear. Analysis is also possible by means of a series of tuned reeds which can be seen to vibrate in sympathy if a component of the correct resonant frequency is present; they are, however, rather less sensitive than the Helmholtz resonator.

Crude but effective demonstration of harmonic analysis can be performed using the resonance of piano strings. For example, if the C above middle C is depressed and held down (without striking the note—the depression is merely to release the damper) and then middle C is struck and damped immediately, the second harmonic will resonate with the undamped string and the component will be heard to "sing out" from the fundamental sound. Higher harmonics can also be demonstrated in this way.

4.3 Electronic analysis

A full discussion of the available methods of electronic analysis would be out of place in this book, but a brief description of the characteristics of two or three techniques will be given. Further details and useful comparisons are given by Olson (1957) and Beranek (1960). The simplest electronic analyser is an electrical analogue of the Helmholtz resonator; it consists merely of a filter network which will transmit only frequencies in a very narrow range. Such filters can be made extremely selective, but of course a separate filter is required for each frequency to be measured. It would obviously be more convenient if the analyser could be made tunable. An example of such a tuneable system is the heterodyne analyser, in which the incoming signal is mixed with the output of a tuneable oscillator which can be adjusted until the sum or difference (see section 8.4) of its frequency and that of some one of the components in the experimental signal is exactly equal to that of a highly-selective tuned amplifier. The disadvantage of this system is that to operate satisfactorily it needs an experimental signal which persists unchanged for a long period. There are two useful ways of dealing with less stable signals. One is to use broader-band filters with a fixed percentage band width; filters with a band width of one octave, half-octave, or one-third octave are readily available. If the fundamental then varies within the range of one particular filter the harmonics will remain (because of the constant percentage) within the range of the corresponding higher filters. The disadvantage of broad-band filters alone is that their resolution is naturally low and they are insensitive to changes within the band width. A single pure tone of extremely narrow band width might easily be missed in relation to a much weaker background of noise with a broad spectrum. An alternative system which has been described for example by Olson (1957) involves the pre-recording of the signal. It may either be recorded completely on tape or a short section of signal may be recorded on a tape loop or magnetic drum. If the complete signal is recorded a small section of the tape is passed over one quadrant of a rotating drum carrying four play-back heads at 90° intervals. The short section of signal in contact with the quadrant of the drum is thus converted into a repetitive signal by the rotation of the heads and can be analysed. The tape loop or recording on a magnetic drum similarly convert a short section into a continuous repetitive signal.

As with most instruments care is needed in interpreting and comparing the result obtained by means of the various techniques. Beranek (1960) gives some striking comparative results for the analysis of the same signal by several different instruments which underline the need for a clear understanding of the behaviour of a particular system in interpreting its results.

Special analysers have been developed for work on speech sounds in which it is desirable to study the time variation of the harmonic content. The technique—usually described as visible speech—involves recording sound in a continuous loop and playing back through successive different filters. The result is presented as a two-dimensional figure with time as the horizontal axis, frequency as the vertical axis and the blackness of line indicating the intensity. A series of articles in the *Journal of the Acoustical Society of America* discuss different aspects of the technique following an introduction by Potter (1946).

4.4 Optical analysis

In the last two sections we have been concerned with the direct physical problem of analysing a sound into its equivalent harmonic components. A less direct, but sometimes more informative, approach is to record the precise wave form of the sound by means of a cathode-ray oscillograph and then to perform the analysis by mathematical or other means. There are many forms of mechanical and electromechanical Fourier analysers—the Kelvin tide predictor is a typical example—but they do not fall within the direct scope of this book. We shall, however, consider an optical method of analysing wave forms, not because of it special advantages as a method of computation but because it forms an excellent way of introducing some of the more complicated developments with which it is intended to deal later in the chapter.

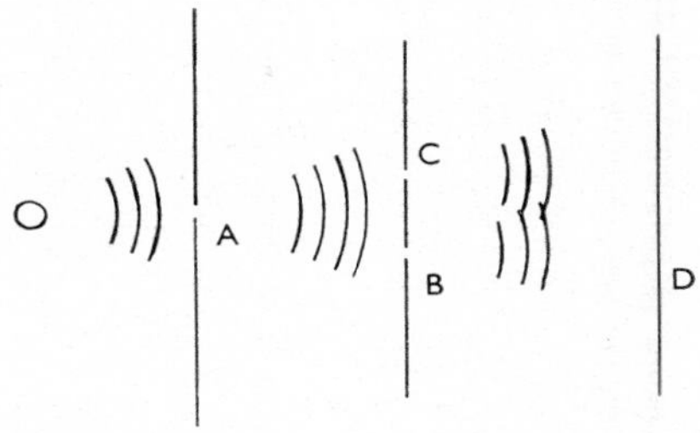

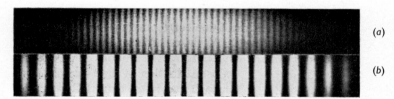

Figure 4.2 Diagram of apparatus for Young's fringes.

A convenient starting point for the discussion is the well-known Young's fringe experiment in optics; the experimental arrangement is shown in Fig. 4.2. Monochromatic light falls on a single narrow slit A which then acts as a source to provide coherent (i.e. effectively in-phase) illumination of the two slits B and C. On a screen placed at D interference fringes—bands of light varying sinusoidally in intensity—are observed. Figure 4.3 is a photograph of such fringes. In preparing (*a*) the slits B and C were wider apart than in preparing (*b*); the inverse relationahip between the separation of the slits and the separation of the fringes can clearly be seen. A useful demonstration of the origin of these fringes can be performed with a piece of thick white string on which black bands have been painted—the bands are intended as crude representations of the peaks and troughs of a sinusoidal wave. The ends of the string are tied to a bar at points representing the positions of the slits B and C. By moving

(*a*)

(*b*)

Figure 4.3 Young's fringes: (*a*) Slits wide apart. (*b*) Slits closer together.

a peg placed in the loop in a direction parallel to the bar to represent the screen position the variation in phase difference between the "waves" from the two sources can be seen (see Fig. 4.4). If now the fixing points are moved closer together along the bar it can be shown that larger movements of the loop have to be made between points at which the waves are in and out of phase; the corresponding fringes are thus further apart.

It is well known that in any optical system if the light paths are reversed the light will follow the same route back through the system. Thus it follows that if we can produce a sinusoidal distribution of light in the plane D, the various waves from it should eventually add up at B and C to form two narrow bands of light corresponding to the two slits. In theory one could go back and forth between these two light distributions indefinitely. They are equivalent representations of the same information and given one—e.g. the wavelength of the sinusoidal bands—one can always deduce the other, e.g. the separation of the slits.

Suppose now that there are four slits, two close together (B and C) and two at a greater distance apart (E and F), both symmetrically placed with respect to the arbitrary centre of the system (Fig. 4.5). Each pair alone gives rise to a sinusoidal distribution at D, and since the principle of superposition holds for light waves (see section 3.2) the combined

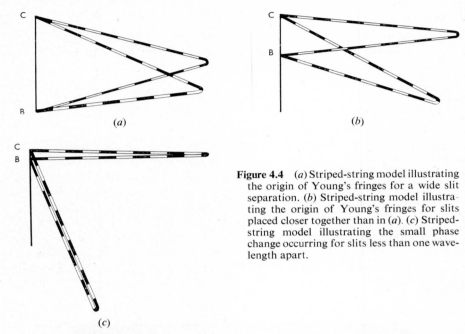

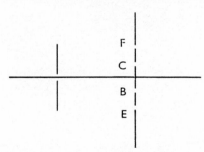

Figure 4.4   (a) Striped-string model illustrating the origin of Young's fringes for a wide slit separation. (b) Striped-string model illustrating the origin of Young's fringes for slits placed closer together than in (a). (c) Striped-string model illustrating the small phase change occurring for slits less than one wavelength apart.

result on the screen should be a distribution corresponding to the algebraic sum of the two sine waves. Figure 4.6 shows the result. Again, considering the reversal of light paths we see that we have a method of Fourier analysis. If a representation of the function to be analysed

Figure 4.5   Young's fringe arrangement with four slits.

as a distribution of light and shade is placed in the plane D then in the plane BC we should have lines of light corresponding to each sinusoidal component of the function. In order to realise this experimentally some refinements are required. It is convenient to prepare the function as a transparency distribution and to illuminate it with parallel light. The resulting complementary function may then be observed in the back focal plane of a second lens; the arrangement is that used in optics for observing Fraunhofer diffraction patterns. Full details of the apparatus with which the photographs illustrating this section were prepared are given by Taylor & Hughes (1953) and by Taylor & Lipson (1964). Other versions of the optical method of analysis have been described by Schouten (1938), who used variable-area sound-film recordings as diffraction gratings and by Brown (1939) who used variable-density sound-film recordings in a similar way.

In order to represent the distribution the negative portions of the sinusoidal function must be represented with a phase-change of π. Various methods by which this can be done have been described by Taylor & Lipson but are not within the scope of this book. A simple

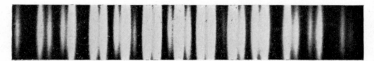

Figure 4.6 Young's fringes with four slits.

method is to replace the function by $(1 + \sin\theta)$ which is everywhere positive; the result is exactly the same as for $\sin\theta$ except for the addition of a peak at the centre corresponding to

a "zero" harmonic. In this study we are concerned only with one-dimensional distributions; the second dimension of the mask is of no real interest and can in fact be used to represent the amplitude. Figure 4.7 shows some analyses prepared merely by cutting out the shape of a function, thus using the y-coordinate as amplitude. It should be noted that only the central line of the resulting patterns (perpendicular to y) is significant.

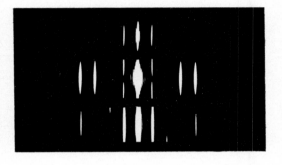

4.5 Fourier transformation

The process of Fourier analysis has now been introduced as a means of transforming information, given in terms of a complicated waveform drawn on an amplitude-time diagram into a series of harmonics, which could be shown as an amplitude-frequency diagram; both are equivalent representations of the same information. It has also been seen that the same process relates a transparency-distance distribution with an intensity-distance distribution in the corresponding diffraction pattern. In the first example time and frequency are inversely related. In the second the wider the separation of the slits in the Young's fringe experiment the closer together are the peaks

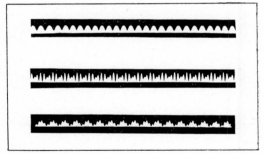

Figure 4.7 Optical analyses using "cut out" wave forms. The upper example is a single pure tone; the middle example is the sum of two components of frequencies three and four times that of the first pure tone; the lower example is the sum of the original pure tone and another of four times the frequency. The masks are shown in the same order in the lower half of the photograph.

in the corresponding sine curve, in other words the two "distances" are inversely related. The practice has therefore arisen of referring to the two distributions as existing in different "spaces" in which dimensions are reciprocally related. Thus in the first example Fourier analysis enables one to transform information from time space into frequency space; in the second the transformation is from object space to diffraction space. In general the spaces are referred to as real and reciprocal. Figure 4.8 shows three examples of transformations of periodic objects. It does not matter whether *a, b, c* or *d, e, f* are regarded as real or

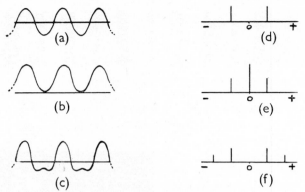

Figure 4.8   Three examples of Fourier mates.

reciprocal space, or whether *a, b* and *c* represent sound waves, tidal wave forms, or transparency distributions.

It will be noted that in the optical examples each "frequency" component occurs twice, once on either side of the centre, and in the diagrams of Fig. 4.8 we have represented this

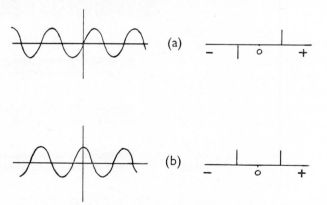

Figure 4.9   (*a*) Representation of a sine wave in real space and in reciprocal space.
(*b*) Representation of a cosine wave in real space and in reciprocal space.

by the use of negative values of the position-coordinate in *d, e,* and *f*. This raises the question of the meaning of a negative frequency if the same convention is to be used throughout. The problem also exists in time space, since if we deal with a truly infinite wave train it can only be represented as extending indefinitely in both directions from an arbitrary zero, i.e. it involves negative time. The concept of negative time—implying continued existence before the arbitrary starting time of the experiment—is not too difficult to accept. Negative frequency may, however, be a little more difficult. Let us consider an infinite sine wave with the arbitrary zero of time chosen at a point for which the amplitude is zero (Fig. 4.9). If we proceed in the positive-time direction from zero the amplitude first rises; if, on the other hand, we proceed in the direction of negative time the amplitude first falls. The phase in fact is 180° different. In order to represent this different sequence we need to be able to specify frequency measured both positively and negatively; thus the full designation for the sine curve is as shown in Fig. 4.9(a), and the corresponding relationship for a cosine curve is shown in Fig. 4.9(b). Here the sequence is the same in both directions from zero time, and so the positive and negative frequency components are identical. Jennison (1961) uses an analogue based on the rotation of a.c. generators; if two generators have the same frequency they may be used in parallel to produce an electricity supply, but it is essential that they are rotating in the same direction—i.e. that they have frequencies of the same sign. If this is not arranged serious consequences will ensue when they are connected together.

Many functions to be analysed may be complex and hence a complete representation of the result ought to include phase information. This can be done either by using two diagrams—one to give the amplitude of each component and the other the phases—or, more usually, by using the principle, already mentioned several times, that a wave of arbitrary phase can always be represented as the sum of in-phase cosine and sine waves of amplitudes determined by the phase of the original wave. Thus the two necessary diagrams will give the amplitudes of the cosine and sine components separately (if the original wave of arbitrary phase is represented as a complex quantity the cosine and sine components clearly represent the real and imaginary parts respectively). Both representations for several different wave forms are shown in Fig. 4.10. In Fig. 4.10(a) the wave is a pure sinusoid with a phase of 60° relative to that of a cosine wave. In Fig. 4.10(b) the wave is a sinusoid of smaller amplitude and a phase of − 90°. In Fig. 4.10(c) the wave form is the sum of the two forms used in (a) and (b). Finally, in Fig. 4.10(d) the wave has the same form as that of Fig. 4.10(c) but is referred to a different origin. It will be noted that the amplitude diagram is the same for both Fig. 4.10(c) and (d). In many acoustic examples the phase is regarded as unimportant, and hence the analysis is often presented as amplitude alone. The vital point to be stressed at this stage is that the wave form (e.g. Fig. 4.8(c)) and the frequency spectrum (e.g. Fig. 4.8(f)) are equivalent ways of expressing the same function.

From time to time there have been arguments about whether harmonics have real existence and whether a sound consists of a complex vibration or of a sum of simpler components. This sort of discussion is quite meaningless as long as we are dealing with linear systems and with continuous tones of effectively infinite duration. As far as this book is concerned we shall assume that the linearity condition is fulfilled for the purposes of all chapters up to and including chapter 7; after that we shall have to consider the effects of non-linearities, and until then we shall regard the wave form and frequency spectrum as completely equivalent representations. They are special examples of what are called Fourier mates. The second condition regarding infinite duration is very rarely fulfilled in practice, and we shall now begin to consider the implications of the restrictions usually imposed in reality.

In section 4.1 it was pointed out that any group of pure tones may be regarded as harmonics of a common fundamental; the more complex the relationship between the frequencies of the components and the larger the number in the group the lower would be the required frequency of the fundamental. If the frequencies were all integral then the fundamental for a large group might have to have a frequency of 1 c.p.s.; if non-integral fre-

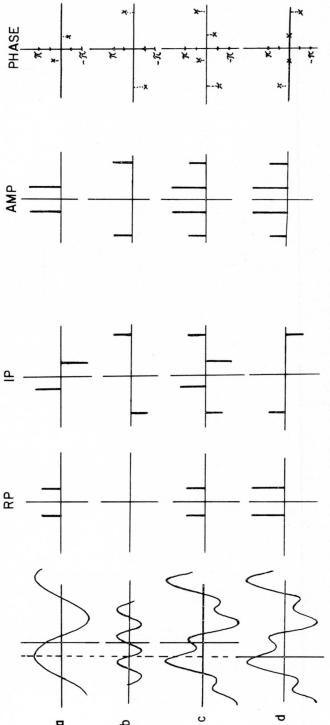

Figure 4.10 Representation of complex waves (*a*), (*b*), (*c*), and (*d*) in real space, the real part in reciprocal space, the imaginary part in reciprocal space, amplitude in reciprocal space, and the phase in reciprocal space.

quencies were involved the fundamental would have to be less than unity in frequency. The word "fundamental" in this paragraph has been used to mean the *effective* fundamental, and it must be remembered that it may not in fact be present as an actual component. It does, however, represent the repetition rate of the whole curve being analysed (see, for example, Fig. 4.1). Suppose now that we try to analyse a curve which repeats only after a long period of time, that is its fundamental frequency approaches zero and hence the separation of the harmonics which may be present also approaches zero. In the limit when the curve is completely non-periodic the separation of the harmonics becomes zero and in fact the spectrum is a continuous function. A simple example from optics is the diffraction pattern of a single slit shown in Fig. 4.11(a); there is only one slit and it is thus a completely non-repetitive function and its diffraction pattern can be seen to be a continuous function. The

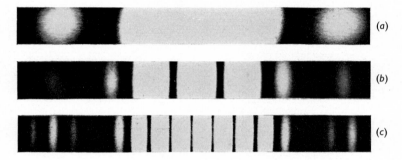

Figure 4.11   (a) Optical-diffraction pattern for a single slit. (b) Optical-diffraction pattern for two slits of the same width as that in (a). (c) Optical-diffraction pattern of two slits of the same width as (a) but wider apart than in (b).

line drawings of Fig. 4.12(a) represent the functions concerned in real and reciprocal space. In acoustics this would correspond to a single pulse, and it can be seen that its frequency spectrum includes a wide range of frequencies in a continuous distribution, not as separate harmonics. The process which began as Fourier analysis, whereby a continuous curve in one space could be represented by a discrete set of terms in the other space, has now become the relationship between two continuous functions; it is now known as Fourier transformation. The two curves are known as Fourier transforms or Fourier mates of each other, and the process connecting them is one of integration rather than of summation (see section 4.8 for mathematical treatment).

4.6 The convolution principle

In the last section we considered the extension of Fourier analysis to a non-periodic function and hence to determine the spectrum of a function of short duration. Let us now consider what happens if we build up this function of short duration into a periodic one by successive repetition. Again the optical illustration provides the best introduction. In Fig. 4.11(b) is shown the effect of placing two slits side by side and in Fig. 4.12(b) is the corresponding line drawing. It can be seen that the pattern is multiplied by a sinusoidal "fringe" function. Figs. 4.11(b) and (c) and 4.12(b) and (c) show that the spacing of the slits and of the peaks of the sine curve is reciprocal. If now the pattern is made completely repetitive the peaks of the sine curve become sharpened (compare the sharpness of Fabry-Perôt multiple-reflection interference-fringes with those of a Michelson interferometer with one reflection). We now have repetition in one space and have returned to a discrete series of terms in the other; the important point to notice is that the amplitude of the discrete harmonic components is still controlled by the amplitude of the pattern of the single slit. The process of repetition in one space can be seen to give rise to "sampling" at specific points in the other space. This is an example of the important property known as convolution (an alternative name is "folding"). The repeated slit pattern may be said to be the convolution of the single slit with a multipoint function indicating the positions at which it

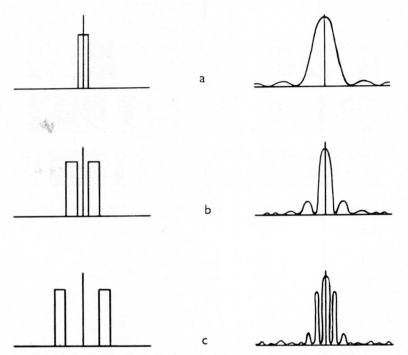

Figure 4.12   Line drawings representing the functions in real and reciprocal space roughly corresponding to the diffraction patterns of Fig. 4.11, but for broader slits.

should be placed (the process has been likened to card-dealing in which one card, or a group of cards, is given successively to each participant). The result in the other space turns out to be the product of the transforms of the two functions taken separately; in the example already given it is the product of the transform of the single slit and the transform of the point function, which, in fact, is an infinite series of harmonics of equal intensity.

The reciprocal process also exists. In Fig. 4.13 the first diffraction pattern is that of an effectively infinite series of very narrow slits—the point function referred to in the last paragraph. The second shows the result of multiplying this infinitely repetitive function by a rectangular function of a limited duration which allows only five of the slits to take part. The result can be seen to be a spreading of each harmonic into a continuous region; it is the convolution of the original transform with the diffraction pattern of the rectangular pulse or slit. Although the convolution principle is not as well known by name as it should be it is really quite a familiar process. In an optical instrument, such as a microscope for example, a restriction in the aperture corresponds to multiplication of the scattering or diffraction pattern of the object by some limiting function; the resulting image—which is the Fourier transform of this diffraction pattern—is thus the convolution of a perfect image, with the Fourier transform of the aperture. If the aperture is of infinite extent its transform is a single point and the image is perfect. If, on the other hand, the aperture is not infinite then the image is bound to be blurred and the blurring will increase as the size of the aperture is reduced. In acoustics the principle is of extreme importance because every time a sound

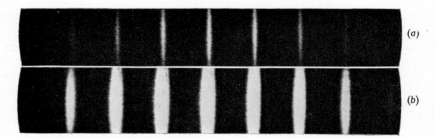

(a)

(b)

Figure 4.13 (a) Optical-diffraction pattern for a large number of very narrow slits. (b) Optical-diffraction pattern for five only of the slits in the grating used for (a).

wave passes through a filter, tube, electronic circuit, or almost any other piece of equipment, it becomes "multiplied" by the characteristic response of the system, and the resulting change in harmonic content can be deduced immediately by the convolution principle. Frequent use will be made of this idea in later sections.

4.7 Further basic properties of Fourier transforms

Although the convolution-multiplication principle expresses one of the most important of the properties of Fourier transforms there are other corresponding operations in real and reciprocal space with which it is useful to be familiar. If the function in one space is translated a given distance the amplitude of the function in the other space remains unchanged; only the phase is affected. Thus in an optical example, if the mask representing the object to be transformed is translated in a plane perpendicular to the incident parallel beam of light the Fraunhofer diffraction pattern in the back focal plane of the observing lens remains unchanged in position and appearance; the eye, of course, is insensitive to phase. In acoustics this property is so obvious that a translation of a wave in time space, i.e. a change in the arbitrary zero, is usually termed a phase change.

If two functions are added in one space then their transforms add vectorially in the other space. It is important to notice that in the addition process the relative phases are significant; the functions in real space must be referred to a common origin before the vectorial addition is performed. Clearly two sine waves of the same frequency added in-phase will result in a sine wave of twice the amplitude; two sine waves with 180° phase difference will give zero resultant.

The reciprocal relationship of dimensions has already been discussed, but for completeness it should be included in the present list of properties. If the scale of a function in one space is multiplied by a factor p then the scale of its corresponding function in the reciprocal space will be multiplied by a factor $1/p$.

*4.8 Elementary mathematical treatment of Fourier transformation

It will be convenient to introduce the mathematics of Fourier transformation by means of the optical analogue already mentioned. In the earlier sections we began by studying periodic functions and later generalised the discussion to include non-periodic functions; in the mathematical treatment we shall deal first with general non-periodic functions and treat periodic functions as a particular case. Let us consider the scattering or diffraction of light (or other radiation) by a distribution of matter along a line normal to the direction of the incident parallel monochromatic beam of radiation. An arbitrary origin is chosen on the line at A (Fig. 4.14) and we suppose that the scattering amplitude from a small element surrounding A is taken as unity and that the amplitude scattered from a small element of length δx at the point B distant x from A is $\rho(x)\delta x$. Let us further suppose that all elements scatter in phase with the incident beam (or with a constant phase shift). In order to find

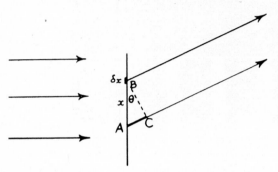

Figure 4.14   Diagram for one-dimensional scattering.

the total amplitude scattered in a particular direction it is necessary to find the relative phase differences between the contributions which arise because of the differing path lengths. In a direction making an angle θ with the incident direction the path difference between the two scattered beams is AC (Fig. 4.14) which equals $x \sin \theta$. The phase difference is thus $\dfrac{2\pi x \sin \theta}{\lambda}$, and hence the complex representation of the vector scattering from the element δx at B relative (in both phase and amplitude) to the unit vector from A will be

$$\rho(x) \exp\left\{\frac{2\pi i x \sin \theta}{\lambda}\right\} \delta x. \qquad [4.1]$$

Thus the total scattered in the direction θ from the whole line distribution will be

$$\int_{-\infty}^{\infty} \rho(x) \exp\left\{\frac{2\pi i x \sin \theta}{\lambda}\right\} dx. \qquad [4.2]$$

It is convenient to eliminate the wavelength dependence in the general expression and also to use a linear rather than an angular specification of the direction of observation in the scattering pattern. A point distant p from the axis of a screen at right-angles to the incident direction at a distance D from the object, where D is assumed to be large compared with p, would correspond to $\sin \theta = \dfrac{p}{D}$; it is then convenient to substitute $s = \dfrac{p}{D\lambda}$ so that $s = \dfrac{\sin \theta}{\lambda}$.

The total scattering is then expressed as a function of s which we shall call $G(s)$ and from equation [4.2] it can be seen that

$$G(s) = \int_{-\infty}^{\infty} \rho(x) \exp\{2\pi ixs\}\, dx. \qquad [4.3]$$

This is a much more symmetrical expression than 4.2 and relates a function $\rho(x)$ in object or real space with a function $G(s)$ in diffraction or reciprocal space. The relationship between s and the actual distance p clearly depends only on the wavelength and on the constant D which is a characteristic of the apparatus. Equation [4.3] is thus general and applies to any apparatus and wavelength.

The reciprocal relationship between the object and its diffraction pattern discussed in section 4.4 suggests that there should be symmetrical mathematical properties. In order to explore this possibility we may follow a procedure similar to that used by Wilson (1949) in a three-dimensional application to X-ray diffraction. Let us suppose that a function $F(x)$ exists which is related to $G(s)$ by an expression corresponding to [4.3],

$$F(x) = \int_{-\infty}^{\infty} G(s) \exp\{2\pi ixs\}\, ds. \qquad [4.4]$$

Thus

$$F(x) = \int_{-\infty}^{\infty} \left[\int_{-\infty}^{\infty} \rho(t) \exp\{2\pi its\}\, dt\right] \exp\{2\pi ixs\}\, ds,$$ where t is a dummy variable in

x-space. If the order of integration is then changed—a procedure which would require careful justification from a strict mathematical standpoint—we may write

$$F(x) = \int_{-\infty}^{\infty} \left[\int_{-\infty}^{\infty} \exp\{2\pi i(t + x)s\}\, ds\right] \rho(t)\, dt. \qquad [4.5]$$

The integral in the inner bracket needs careful consideration. If $t = -x$ it becomes infinite since $\exp\{0\} = 1$. If, on the other hand, $t \neq -x$ the exponential function oscillates symmetrically about an average value 0 and hence its integral is 0. We therefore need to consider the existence of $F(x)$ as other than 0 only when $t = -x$. Let us now consider the function $\int_{-\infty}^{\infty} \exp\{2\pi i(t + x)s\}\, ds$ as a function of t in order to perform the other integration. We have already seen that it is zero everywhere except at $x = -t$ and there it is infinite. It is useful, however, to consider first its integral between finite limits. Consider, for example, $\int_{-n}^{n} \exp\{2\pi i(t + x)s\}\, ds$ where n is an integer, that is

$$\left\{\frac{1}{2\pi(t + x)}[\sin 2\pi(t + x)s - i\cos 2\pi(t + x)s]\right\}_{-n}^{n} = \frac{2\sin 2\pi(t + x)n}{2\pi(t + x)}.$$

We are interested in the integration of this quantity with respect to t. If we make the substitution $(t + x) = y$ and $2\pi n = m$ it becomes $\dfrac{2n}{m}\int_{-\infty}^{\infty} \dfrac{\sin(my)}{y}\, dy = \dfrac{4n}{m}\int_{0}^{\infty} \dfrac{\sin(my)}{y}\, dy.$ Now

this integral is a standard form and has the value $\dfrac{\pi}{2}$ for all values of m greater than 1, and

hence the whole expression equals $\dfrac{4n}{m}\cdot\dfrac{\pi}{2} = 1$. Thus the area under the curve is unity for all

n greater than $\dfrac{1}{2\pi}$ and is still unity when n approaches infinity. The curve then becomes infinitely high at the single point $x = -t$, and 0 everywhere else but maintains its area of unity. It is in fact a unit peak function or Dirac function to which reference will later be made. If we go back to equation [4.5], $F(x)$ is only other than zero when $x = -t$ and then is equal to $\rho(t) \times 1 = \rho(-x)$. Thus the function we are looking for, obtained by finding the diffraction pattern of the diffraction pattern, is the original object again but inverted. In order to maintain the complete symmetry it is usual to include the negative sign in the exponential term in one of the transformations and hence we write

$$G(s) = \int_{-\infty}^{\infty} \rho(x) \exp\{2\pi i x s\}\, dx \qquad\qquad [4.6]$$

$$\rho(x) = \int_{-\infty}^{\infty} G(s) \exp\{-2\pi i x s\}\, ds. \qquad\qquad [4.7]$$

It does not matter in which of the two expressions the negative sign occurs as long as consistency is maintained. We shall use the positive exponent for transformation in the direction real to reciprocal space, as in equation [4.6]. Functions [4.6] and [4.7] are called Fourier mates of each other. $G(s)$ is said to be the Fourier transform of $\rho(x)$, and $\rho(x)$ may be described as the inverse Fourier transform of $G(s)$; they correspond to the functions discussed at the end of section 4.5.

*4.9 Mathematical treatment of some Fourier-transform properties

Let us first consider what happens if a function in real space is translated through a fixed distance. Let us suppose that the function $\rho(x)$ whose transform is given by equation [4.6] is translated by a distance a along the x-axis. We may then write

$$G(s) = \int_{-\infty}^{\infty} \rho(x) \exp\{2\pi i(x + a)s\}\, dx$$

$$= \left[\int_{-\infty}^{\infty} \rho(x) \exp\{2\pi i x s\}\, dx\right] \exp\{2\pi i a s\}$$

$$= \exp\{2\pi i a s\}\,.\,G(s). \qquad\qquad [4.8]$$

Now the modulus of $\exp\{2\pi i a s\}$ is always unity, and hence there is no change in amplitude, only in phase.

Suppose now that two such identical distributions $\rho(x)$ are added with a separation of a. It is first necessary to reduce them to a common origin and we will suppose that this is midway between them. We may then write

$$G_{a/2} = \exp\left\{2\pi i \frac{as}{2}\right\} G(s)$$

$$G_{-a/2} = \exp\left\{-2\pi i \frac{as}{2}\right\} G(s)$$

and hence the sum of the two is

$$G(s)\left[\exp\left\{2\pi i \frac{as}{2}\right\} + \exp\left\{-2\pi i \frac{as}{2}\right\}\right] = 2G(s) \cos 2\pi \frac{as}{2}. \qquad\qquad [4.9]$$

Thus the sum is the product of the original transform and a cosinusoidal fringe function of amplitude 2.

Let us now apply this to the example quoted in section 4.7 of the addition of two sine waves first in phase and then with a translation equivalent to half a period. $G(s)$ is clearly a function which is non-zero at only two points, $s = v$ and $s = -v$, where v is the frequency of the wave. If both waves are in phase $a = 0$, $\cos 2\pi \dfrac{as}{2}$ is unity, and the result of the addition

is merely to double the amplitude of the spectrum of either. If, on the other hand, the separation corresponds to $180°$ phase difference $a = \dfrac{\tau}{2} = \dfrac{1}{2v}$ but G only exists when $s = \pm v$, and hence the sum equals $2G(s) \cos \pi a v = 0$.

We should now consider the mathematics of convolution. Let us suppose that we have two functions $\rho(x)$ and $\sigma(x)$ in real space and that their Fourier transforms are $G_\rho(s)$ and $G_\sigma(s)$. We wish to find the result in real space which corresponds to the multiplication of these two transforms in reciprocal space. The Fourier transform of the product is

$$\int_{-\infty}^{\infty} G_\rho G_\sigma(s) \exp\{-2\pi ixs\}\, ds$$

but

$$G_\rho(s) = \int_{-\infty}^{\infty} \rho(t) \exp\{2\pi its\}\, dt$$

where t is a dummy variable in x space. We may thus write for the Fourier transform of the product

$$\int_{-\infty}^{\infty} G_\sigma(s)\left[\int_{-\infty}^{\infty} \rho(t) \exp\{2\pi its\}\, dt \exp\{-2\pi ixs\}\right] ds$$

which, on changing the order of integration, yields

$$\int_{-\infty}^{\infty} \rho(t)\left[\int_{-\infty}^{\infty} G_\sigma(s) \exp\{-2\pi i(x-t)s\} ds\right] dt$$

$$= \int_{-\infty}^{\infty} \rho(t)\sigma(x-t)\, dt, \qquad\qquad [4.10]$$

This must therefore be the operation in real space which corresponds to multiplication in reciprocal space and which was introduced earlier as "convolution".

Various symbols have been used to represent it, e.g. $_{\rho\sigma}(x)$, $\rho(x)*\sigma(x)$, etc. We shall use the second of these symbols. The physical significance has been discussed by many authors, e.g. Ewald (1940), Jennison (1960), Lipson & Taylor (1958). Perhaps the easiest way of understanding it is to make use of a simple piece of demonstration equipment, the principle of which has been suggested by various authors in different connections, e.g. Robertson (1943), MacLachlan (1957). Consider three screens P, Q and R (Fig. 4.15) placed at equal distances apart and parallel to each other, and suppose that the first is preceded by a diffusing screen D and a light source S. Suppose further that P and Q are photographically-produced transparencies with density varying in the t-direction to represent one-dimensional functions and that R is a white screen. Let the transparency at a point A on P distant t from the arbitrary axis be $\rho(t)$ and the amount of light transmitted by a small element δt will thus be proportional to $\rho(t)\delta t$. Suppose that the transparency of screen Q represents a function

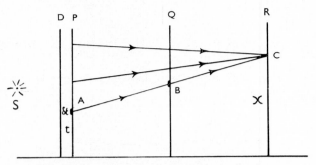

Figure 4.15   Device for experimental convolution.

ϕt and consider the illumination at a point C on R distant x from the axis, and consider a ray travelling from A to C. It will intersect screen Q at B, a distance

$$t + \frac{x - t}{2} = \frac{x + t}{2}$$

from the axis. Thus the transparency at that point will be $\phi\left(\dfrac{x + t}{2}\right)$. The illumination at C due to that particular ray will thus be $\rho(t)\phi\left(\dfrac{x + t}{2}\right)\delta t$ and the total illumination at C from the whole screen P will therefore be $\displaystyle\int_{-\infty}^{\infty} \rho(t)\phi\left(\frac{x + t}{2}\right) dt$. Suppose now that $\phi(t)$ is in fact a half-scale representation of the function $\sigma(t)$ whose convolution with $\rho(t)$ we set out to find, and further let us suppose it to be in-verted, i.e. $\phi\left(-\dfrac{t}{2}\right) = \sigma(t)$, thus the illumination at any point x on the screen is

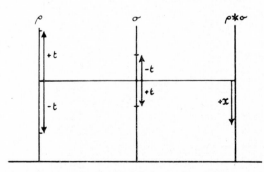

Figure 4.16   Modified apparatus for convolution demonstration.

$\displaystyle\int_{-\infty}^{\infty} \rho(t)\sigma(x - t)\ dt$. If we then reverse the axis of x on the screen R it becomes $\displaystyle\int_{-\infty}^{\infty} \rho t \sigma(x - t)\ dt$ which is the convolu-tion as defined by equation [4.10].

We can therefore produce the convolu-tion of two functions by preparing a full-scale representation of one of them and a half-scale inverted representation of the other, and measuring the positive value of x on the final screen in the same direction as that for the middle one (see Fig. 4.16). Let us use this model to consider one or two simple convolu-tions. Suppose that $\rho(t)$ is a function which is zero everywhere except at two points X and Y

(Fig. 4.17). Let $\sigma(t)$ be a set of several points M, N, O, etc.; the convolution of the two can be seen to be the first function placed at each point of the second (compare the card-dealing analogy used earlier). In Fig. 4.18 a slightly more complex example of the same kind is demonstrated.

The model permits the extension to two dimensions quite easily and examples are shown in Fig. 4.19. Suppose that the first of the two functions is a pattern of some kind and the second is a single point function. The model (Fig. 4.19) is in effect a pinhole camera, and if the pinhole is truly a point the image is merely the inversion of the original—that is, the convolution of the original with a point (this, of course,

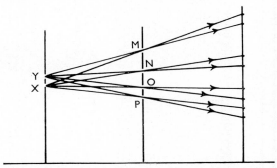

Figure 4.17 Diagrammatic result of the convolution of two simple functions.

ignores diffraction effects). If, on the other hand, the pinhole is enlarged the image will become blurred and we see again that this is the convolution of the original image with the large hole—each point on the image is replaced by a disc corresponding to the size of the large hole

Finally, let us consider the use of the convolution principle in relating the transforms of non-periodic and periodic functions. Suppose that a function $\rho(x)$ is continuous over a relatively small range of x and is then zero in each direction to infinity (a single square pulse would be a typical example). We wish to investigate the effect on its spectrum, or Fourier

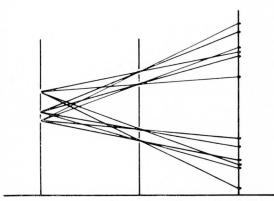

Figure 4.18 Diagrammatic result of the convolution of two slightly more complicated functions.

transform, of repeating the function at regular intervals indefinitely (making, in the example given, a continuous train of equally-spaced pulses). The repetitive function can be regarded as the convolution of the single unit with a point function indicating the periodicity. The point function itself may lead to difficulties unless it is carefully defined, as it is necessary for it to be of infinitesimal width and yet to have a finite content when integrated. The type of function which we met earlier in this section is useful here. If we take, for example, a Gaussian curve chosen to have a total area under the curve of unity, and

then allow its width to shrink and its maximum height to increase until, in the limit, it has infinite height and zero width but still an area of unity, it would serve our purpose. Such a function is sometimes called a peak function of content unity, often written Z_a^1 or more generally Z_a^m, where a is the value of x at which the function is infinite (it is assumed zero everywhere else), and m is the integrated value at this point. Multiple peak functions can also be useful; for example $Z_{a_n}^1$ would be a function which is zero everywhere, except at the sequence of points

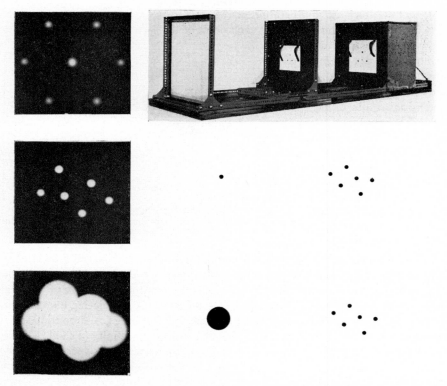

Figure 4.19   Apparatus for preparing convolutions optically. The photograph on the left at the top is the result derived from the masks shown in position in the apparatus; the second and third rows illustrate results from two pairs of screens. The final convolution is on the left in each.

$a_1, a_2 \ldots a_n$ at each of which it is infinite, but with an integrated value of 1. This function could be used to produce the repetitive function which we require; in fact the repetitive function could be written $\rho(x)*Z_{a_n}^1(x)$. Let us first check that this does give the required repetitive function. The convolution written out in full is

$$\rho(x)*Z_{a_n}^1(x) = \int_{-\infty}^{\infty} Z_{a_n}^1(t)\rho(x-t)\,dt, \qquad [4.11]$$

but by the definition of $Z_{a_n}^1$ it is zero unless $t = a_n$, thus equation [4.11] becomes

$$\int_{-\infty}^{\infty} Z_{a_n}^1(a_n)\rho(x-a_n)\,dt.$$

At any particular point x at which the convolution is being calculated $(x - a_n)$ takes a series of definite values, and hence we may write $\rho(x)*Z_{a_n}^1(x) = \sum \rho(x - a_n)\int_{-\infty}^{\infty} Z_{a_n}^1(a_n)\,dt$. Now by the definition of $Z_{a_n}^1$ the integration equals unity and hence the convolution equals

$\sum \rho(x - a_n)$ which is merely the function $\rho(x)$ placed at each of the points $x = a_1, a_2 \ldots a_n$ as required.

The transform of the convolution is the product of the individual transforms and hence we need to know the transform of the peak function; it is $G_Z(s) = \int_{-\infty}^{\infty} Z_{a_n}^1 \exp\{2\pi i x s\}\, dx$ and again since Z is only non-zero when $x = a_n$, and there has the integrated value 1, it becomes $\sum_n \exp\{2\pi i a_n s\}$. Thus the total transform is $G_\rho(s) x \sum_n \exp\{2\pi i a_n s\}$. Now the exponential part of this oscillates continuously as a_n and s change. At any particular value of s the average value is zero if n is very large indeed unless it so happens that $a_1 s, a_2 s$, etc., are all exactly integral. If, as we said at the beginning of the discussion, the points a_n are regularly spaced with the separation d, we may write $a_n = nd$ and hence nds must be integral, or since n is already integral ds must be integral. Thus the final transform is zero everywhere except at points such that $ds = m$, i.e. $s = \dfrac{m}{d}$. Thus we have a series of point functions whose separation is inversely proportional to d but whose amplitude is proportional to $G_\rho(s)$. This of course, is exactly where the discussion started and we now have again the Fourier series of harmonic terms of fundamental $\dfrac{1}{d}$. The important point which emerges, and which has already been stressed, is that the amplitude of the orders of diffraction (or of the harmonics) is related to the function representing the repeated unit. The spectrum or transform of the repetitive function can thus be regarded as samples at regular intervals of the transform of the single unit.

4.10 Some consequences of the convolution concept

One of the immediate consequences of applying the convolution-Fourier-transform method of thinking to problems connected with sound waves is that it draws one's attention immediately to the fact that, unless a sinusoidal wave train is infinite in duration, its frequency cannot be precisely defined. A wave train of finite length is obviously the *product* of an infinite train and a function which is zero everywhere except between the limits defining the length. Thus the transform of the limited train is the *convolution* of the transform of the infinite train (which is a peak function defining the frequency—see Fig. 4.7) and the transform of the defining function (which is of the general form shown in Figs. 4.11(a) and 4.12(a)). Thus the limited train has a spectrum which spreads over a range of frequencies and the shorter the train, the wider the frequency spread.

This can be a useful approach to many problems in physics. For example, it is one aspect of the uncertainty principle. The frequency of the wave may only be precisely defined if it is of infinite duration and hence its location in time is indeterminate. If its location in time is made more precise—i.e. the wave train is reduced to negligible length—then its transform spreads out through all frequency space and hence its frequency is indeterminate. The same arguments apply to other variables, and one can see a close formal connection between the concepts of Heisenberg's uncertainty principle and the physically-demonstrable convolution ideas which may be very helpful to less-mathematically-minded students.

The same approach is useful in understanding some aspects of the difference between wave and group velocity. Though not strictly within the terms of reference of this book an outline of the derivation is given to show how usefully the approach via sound and Fourier transformation can be. Suppose that the velocity of pure sine waves in a certain medium is dependent on their frequency. It follows that, for an infinite train of pure sinusoidal waves—which according to the last paragraph has a perfectly definite frequency—there is a precise velocity—the wave velocity. On the other hand, if the wave train is limited in extent, or subject to some other modulating function, its frequency spectrum will inevitably spread and hence it will acquire a *velocity* spectrum too; that is different components will travel at different speeds. Thus, on arrival at a point some distance away, a phase distribution will exist. If the relationship between frequency and velocity is linear over the region in question, the phase across the distributed spectrum will change linearly and the straight line representing the phase will rotate uniformly with distance travelled. What effect does this have when the wave is re-synthesised from its spectrum? In section 4.7 we saw that a phase change without amplitude change in one space is related to translation in the other space. Thus in addition to the movement of the wave by vt in a time t (where v is the average wave velocity) the group will have moved in relation to the wave. In the time t the wave will thus

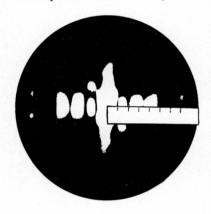

Figure 4.20 Optical transform of the mask shown inset; it represents one repeat unit of the sum of two components of frequency ratio 3:4. The scale superimposed shows the positions at which the optical transform should be sampled to obtain the harmonic analysis; clearly only harmonics three and four are present.

undergo a phase change of $\dfrac{2\pi}{\lambda}vt$, and if the velocity is related to κ, the wave number, the phase change within the group itself will clearly be $\dfrac{2\pi}{\lambda}\dfrac{dv}{d\kappa}\kappa . t = -2\pi\lambda\dfrac{dv}{d\lambda}\kappa . t$.

Now in section 4.9 we saw that a translation of a in one space corresponds to a phase shift of $2\pi as$ in the other and hence, in the expression for the group phase shift, if s is represented by κ, a is represented by $-\lambda\dfrac{dv}{d\lambda}t$. Thus the total distance moved by the group is $vt - \lambda\dfrac{dv}{d\lambda}t$. The velocity of the modulation or group is thus $v - \lambda\dfrac{dv}{d\lambda}$, the familiar expression for the group velocity.

Finally, a practical application will be given. In the optical analyses shown in Fig. 4.7 repeated wave forms were used. Each could be regarded as a convolution of a repeated peak function with the shape of one repeat unit, and as shown in section 4.6 the combined transform is really the sample, at regular intervals, of the transform of one repeat unit. The process of analysis can thus be simplified and only one repeat unit used to prepare the mask. Figure 4.20 shows an example; it is for two waves with frequencies in the ratio 3:4 and corresponds to the centre example of Fig. 4.7.

4.11 Summary

We have now seen how complicated repetitive (and hence musical in the sense defined in Chapter 1) sounds can be analysed into Fourier components in order to study in more detail their origin. We also saw in Chapter 3 that mixtures of harmonics can be produced artificially to match the wave traces of conventional instruments while sounding continuous notes. In the discussion of Fourier transformation the idea of analysing non-repetitive functions was introduced, and the lack of match in quality between artificially-synthesised sounds and the instruments being imitated for sounds of shorter duration suggests that non-repetitive components might be responsible for the further differences in quality. It is also apparent that the sort of sound generators which have been considered so far—with the possible exception of flat plates—tend to give rather weak sounds and that some steps need to be taken to amplify the sound produced. We shall see in the next chapter that there is a strong link between the provision of amplification and the existence of non-periodic or transient components.

CHAPTER 5

Amplification, Matching and Coupled Systems

5.1 The need for amplification

Most simple sources of sound, excluding plates, produce very weak tones which are not very useful from a musical standpoint. A tuning-fork held in the hand, a wire stretched between two clamps on a solid rod with no sound box, or a plain narrow-bore pipe with mouthpiece or side-hole for generating tones of a flute type, all produce very quiet sounds (if a scrap violin is available a very useful demonstration device can be made by replacing the body by a solid length of wood, say 2 in. × 2 in. in cross-section). Clearly some form of amplification is needed in order to create useful instruments. In order to see how this may be done we must first examine the reasons for the weakness of the sound.

Crudely stated the reason for the relative weakness of sound is that the sources do not create a large enough disturbance in the air. The ear responds to the amplitude of vibration in ways which we shall discuss in detail in Chapter 9, but it is clear that it needs relatively large amplitude disturbances associated with relatively small pressure changes. This follows from a consideration of the nature of the first detecting element—the tympanum, or drum (see section 9.4.2). In a tuning-fork, however, the surface area available for coupling the vibrations of the fork to the air is small although the forces involved, and hence the pressure variations which can in principle be produced, are large. What is required is the equivalent of a lever system to change the high-force-low-amplitude movement into low-force-high-amplitude movement. Analogies with electrical circuits can be helpful and there is a close parallel between pressure and e.m.f., and also between current and particle velocity. A large amplitude at fixed frequency necessarily means a large velocity and so the motion available has a high ratio of force-to-velocity, and this is analogous to a high e.m.f.-to-current ratio, in other words, it is analogous to a high-impedance generator. Transmission in the air involves a much lower force-to-velocity ratio and is analogous to a low-impedance transmission. In electrical terms, therefore, it is a matching transformer or amplifier that is required. We shall consider first the practical ways in which the problem is solved in real instruments and later investigate the theoretical basis of the methods used.

5.2 Impedance matching

The tuning-fork is perhaps the most familiar example of the use of a coupled system for amplification; as soon as the vibrating fork is allowed to touch a solid board the sound produced is considerably increased in loudness. The necessary corollary—from the point of view of energy conservation—is that the sound dies away much more rapidly. The coupled system of fork and board has become an effective sound radiator. What happens, of course, is that the transverse vibrations of the prongs produce longitudinal movement of the stem as a whole (Fig. 5.1(*a*). This movement is coupled to the board which in turn vibrates and is able to create a much larger disturbance by virtue of its area. The interaction between the large board and the air clearly produces a reaction on the fork equivalent to heavy damping and hence the sound diminishes more rapidly. This example corresponds to the use of a lever to change the ratio of force to particle velocity. Other examples of the same method exist; for example the sounding board of a piano behaves in this way. In the brass instruments the large flare also acts as a matching system although the mechanism is rather different. In simple terms, the relatively high-pressure variations in the narrow tube become much lower in pressure when "spread out" by the horn. In this instrument, however, it is much more difficult to distinguish the two components of the coupled system: the matching unit has become an integral part of the primary vibrating unit. The consideration of air in pipes illustrates an important way of thinking about the problem of matching. In a narrow cylindrical pipe with no flare the discontinuity at the end is so great that most of the energy of a wave travelling along the pipe is reflected back and only a small proportion emerges. The flare improves the match between the pipe and the outer air, and hence less is reflected from the discontinuity and more emerges. If one produced a theoretically-perfect match in which there could be no reflection there would, of course, be no primary sound because the existence of a note of definite pitch depends on the reflection to set up standing waves in the pipe. The amount of "feedback" required to maintain the oscillation is thus controlled by the end conditions, and in fact one of the effects of the various mutes used by players of brass instruments to alter the tone is to change the matching conditions in a way which is frequency-dependent; different frequency components are thus emphasised or diminished and the tonal quality in addition to the loudness is affected. This view in terms of reflection of waves at discontinuities corresponds to that used by electrical engineers in studying the propagation of electrical waves along transmission lines, where again careful matching between sections is necessary to ensure maximum transmission and minimum reflection, and also where the existence of discontinuities gives rise to standing waves.

Figure 5.1 (*a*) Vibration of a tuning-fork.

Neither the sounding board nor the flare is specifically effective at some one frequency, and—just as in the electrical analogue—it is often easier and more efficient to use a tuned matching system which acts at only one frequency, although this obviously imposes restrictions if one is designing an instrument on which it is desired to play tunes. We shall, however, consider this limited technique first.

5.3 Resonance amplification

The phenomenon of resonance may be used effectively for amplification. Returning again to the example of the tuning fork, the replacement of the board by an open-ended wooden box of dimensions such that the natural frequency of vibration of the air in the box in one of its modes corresponds roughly to that of the fork results in very efficient sound radiation (see Fig. 5.1(*b*)). The vibrations of the side wall set up by the fork cause air alternately to enter and leave from the open end, and if this rate corresponds to a natural mode of vibration of the air quite large amplitudes can be built up. Less rigid coupling can be used if resonance is involved, for example as in the well-known school experiment. A tuning fork is held over the open end of a tube whose lower end is immersed in a tank of water to enable the effective length to be adjusted (Fig. 5.1(c)); when the resonant length is found a loud sound is produced even though the coupling is very light.

The use of tuned resonators as amplifiers is not very common in modern musical instruments. It occurs in the xylophone, marimba, and other similar instruments in which the sound produced by striking a wooden or metal plate of specific dimensions is amplified by a

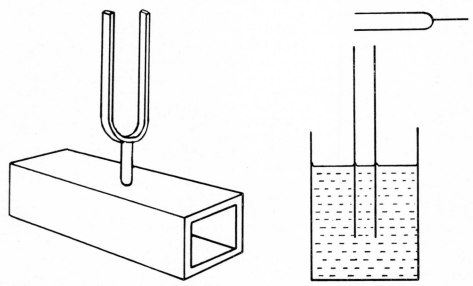

Figure 5.1 (b)Vibration of a tuning-fork on a resonant box.   **Figure 5.1** (c) Resonance experiment.

long tube suspended beneath it and adjusted to be of resonant length. The purpose here is not so much to amplify the whole sound as to amplify that part of the rather harsh, noisy sound of the initial note which is musically desirable. The quality is changed considerably by the amplification process (see section 7.2). At various times in the past, however, instruments have been built which involve the use of resonant vibrators, particularly strings. Examples are the viola d'amore and its larger relation the baryton which differ from the viols chiefly by the addition of so-called sympathetic strings. The curious tromba marina which had only one playing string but large numbers of sympathetic strings inside the sounding box is another example. Further discussion of actual instruments will be found in Chapter 10, and a theoretical discussion of the resonance process is given in section 5.9.

5.4 Broad-band amplification

Of much greater importance in musical instruments is the possibility of constructing a resonant amplifier which will respond over a very broad band. Although this would seem in principle to be difficult there are many examples of its achievement. The members of the string family of musical instruments almost all use a development of the tuned box, discussed in the last section, modified in order to respond over a wider band. There are two distinct ways of approaching the problem. A study of the equations of section 5.9 can show that narrowness of the response curve of a resonant system depends on the damping; a heavily-damped system will respond less strongly than a lightly-damped one, but it will cover a wider range of frequencies. A classical demonstration of this phenomenon was suggested by Barton (1918) and his experiment has been described by Alexander Wood (1940). A series of pendula of different lengths in which the bobs are light paper cones is suspended on lengths of cotton which in turn are fixed to a horizontal string; also attached to the string is a pendulum of intermediate length with a heavy bob. When the heavy pendulum is set swinging the oscillation is communicated to the others by the horizontal string, and the resulting various oscillations can be observed. If the effective damping is modified by loading the cones with metal rings, the relationship between the sharpness of the resonance and the damping may be demonstrated.

The other approach is to study the effect of combining several resonators to cover different regions of the frequency spectrum. The response of two resonators coupled together is not the sum of the two taken separately; there is a mutual reaction of one on the other, and it is possible to produce systems using this principle which have a reasonable response over a fairly wide range. It is necessary also to bear in mind that a complex system may have a more numerous set of modes of vibration than a simple one, and if these can be brought sufficiently close together the net result will be broad-band amplification. The violin family probably uses all three of these approaches. The choice of thin wood as a material is probably governed at least partly by the need for fairly high damping to broaden the responses; the complex shape not only of the air cavity but of the wood itself (it is non-uniform in thickness over the back and front) probably ensures a multiplicity of modes and constitutes in effect several resonators coupled together (see section 10.2). Two interesting examples of broad-band amplification depending on damping have appeared in the new instruments invented and played by the group known as Structures Sonores, Lasry-Baschet (Baschet, 1963). One is the use of plastic air cushions as resonators, which probably owe their relatively wide coverage to the heavy damping by the soft plastic material. The other is the use of large tubes to amplify the sounds produced in metal rods in which the broad band is achieved by heavy damping in the coupling arrangement (see section 11.3).

5.5 The starting transient

We have seen that the problem of increasing the loudness of the sound produced by a primitive vibrator involves its coupling with another system which may or may not be sharply resonant but will certainly have some natural frequencies of its own. The consequent interaction between the two systems must therefore be studied. Up to now we have really considered only the steady state; we must now consider what happens during the period of establishment of this steady state. We shall take first of all a particular example, that of the guitar; its essential components are the strings which are the primary sources, and the body which is the broad-band amplifier. When a string is plucked and released it will immediately vibrate in a certain mixture of modes, and at this precise moment there will be no vibration of the body or of the air in the body. The vibrations of the string are then impressed on the body via a bridge, and there will clearly be a period during which energy is transferred and the body is gradually brought into the state of vibration. In the intervening period there may be complex interactions between the two systems which will take some

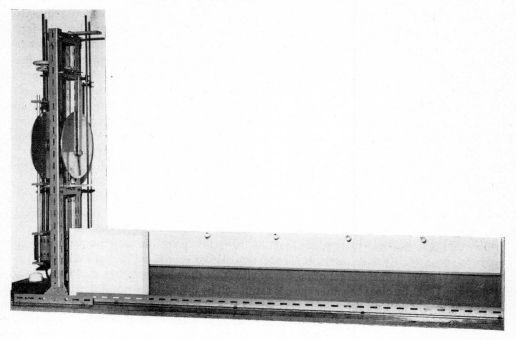

Figure 5.2 Water-wave analogue of reed and pipe. The apparatus is shown
above and five successive stages in the initiation of a wave are also
shown, on the right.

time to resolve, and these may result in considerable complications of the wave form.
Expressed in rather crude terms the result could be described as an argument between the
two components, which is finally settled when the steady state is reached. The final result
will depend on many variables but the most important are the tightness of the coupling and
the stability of the two separate systems. For example, if the driving member is very massive
and stable and the coupling between it and the driven (much lighter) system is fairly tight
the "argument" is likely to be settled very quickly and the combination will settle down at
the frequency of the driving system. On the other hand, if the systems are rather similar and
the coupling is light the argument may persist for a considerable length of time.

Most instruments fall between these two extremes though perhaps in general they are
slightly nearer to the first type than to the second. A demonstration experiment illustrating
the first of the two extremes can be performed by using the standing waves on the surface of
water set in motion by a wooden plunger. A long tank (say about 2 m. long, 30 cm. deep and
5 cm. in width from front to back) is half-filled with coloured water. A plunger operated by
a motor-driven crank creates waves of a given frequency at one end, and by altering the
effective length of the tank standing wave patterns corresponding roughly to those produced
in a pipe may be set up (Fig. 5.2). When the water in the tank is at rest the oscillations
of the plunger are commenced and quite distinct waves are seen to travel to the end of the
tank and to return. After a few double transits the standing wave is established. If during
this early stage attention is concentrated on the water surface at the end remote from the

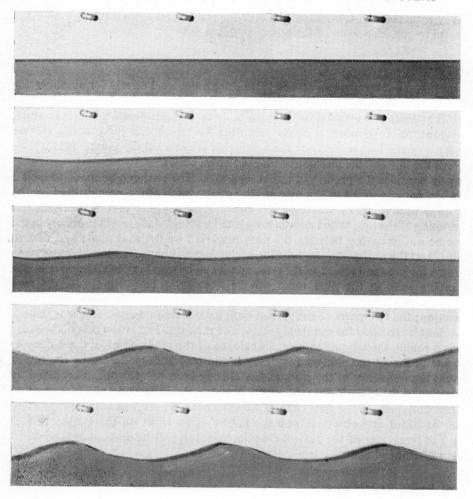

plunger distinct variations in the character of the motion can be observed; it is usually too slow at first and then quite suddenly begins to vibrate at the final frequency.

The other extreme—two similar, lightly coupled systems—can be illustrated by means of two pendula of more or less equal lengths and with heavy bobs, both suspended from a horizontal stretched string to give some measure of coupling. If one is set moving and the system is left to itself the other will slowly take up the oscillation until it is oscillating violently and the first is reduced to rest; the reverse process then occurs and the energy is passed back and forth from one pendulum to the other for a considerable time. The sum of the two oscillations thus has quite a complicated form. The wave form generated in the intermediate period between the initiation of the oscillation and the steady state—the argument already mentioned—is usually known as the starting transient; it will be considered mathematically in section 5.8.

Coupled systems in musical instruments occur for reasons other than amplification and it will be useful to consider some of the others at this point.

5.6 Coupled systems

One of the commonest instances of a coupled system not used merely for amplification is the reed. For example, in the oboe the primary tone is generated by the reed which is held in the lips of the player and coupled to the main body of the instrument, which is a conical pipe (for demonstration purposes a cheap substitute for an oboe is the practice chanter used by students of the bagpipes; if the wind chamber is removed the double reed can be placed between the lips and the instrument played like an oboe).

Let us again consider the process of initiating a note. The reed can be made to emit a loud noise when not connected to the pipe at all, and the pitch of the note emitted can be varied over quite wide limits by altering the pressure of air supplied and the position and degree of clamping of the lips. When a given note is to be sounded there will probably in the first instance be a discrepancy between the note produced by the reed alone and that to which the pipe is set (by the opening and closing of the various holes). The initial disturbance will travel down the pipe and return to the reed, and it can be seen that, in addition to building up a standing wave in the pipe, there will be a complex interaction with the reed itself. The reaction resembles even more closely the "argument" used as a descriptive term in the last section; the two parts of the system each have a characteristic frequency and a compromise must be reached for the steady state. The tank demonstration described in the last section is a rough, though not complete, analogue of the reed and pipe; the difference is that in the tank model the plunger frequency is constant and unaffected by the return waves, whereas the frequency of the reed, as has already been pointed out, is modified by the reflected wave in the pipe. It does, however, illustrate the basic concept of the starting transient reasonably well. In the next chapter we shall consider ways in which the starting transient can be heard and observed, and the nature of its effect on the quality of real instruments. The remainder of the present chapter, however, will be devoted to theoretical considerations of damped and coupled systems.

*5.7 Damped simple periodic motion

In section 2.4 we found that the differential equation governing the motion of a body solely under the influence of restoring forces proportional to the displacement from a fixed point was (equation [2.3])

$$- kx = m \frac{d^2x}{dt^2},$$

where k is the force per unit displacement, x the instantaneous displacement, t the time, and m the mass, and we went on to study its interpretation. The natural angular frequency of such a motion is $\omega = \sqrt{\dfrac{k}{m}}$. Suppose now that there are damping forces operating in addition to the existing forces. Most frictional or viscous resistance is proportional to the velocity of the object being damped; we shall therefore suppose that a damping force of $2f$ per unit velocity exists (the 2 merely saves arithmetic later). Equation [2.3] may then be re-written

$$m \frac{d^2x}{dt^2} + 2f \frac{dx}{dt} + kx = 0. \qquad [5.1]$$

This will represent damped or decaying oscillations of some kind, and so to begin with we shall try an exponential solution such as $x = A \exp(\alpha t)$ where A and α are constants which will depend on the problem. It is clear that $\frac{dx}{dt} = A\alpha \exp \alpha t$ and $\frac{d^2x}{dt^2} = A\alpha^2 \exp\{\alpha t\}$, and hence on substituting back into equation [5.1] we obtain

$$mA\alpha^2 \exp\{\alpha t\} + 2fA\alpha \exp\{\alpha t\} + kA \exp\{\alpha t\} = 0,$$

i.e.
$$m\alpha^2 + 2f\alpha + k = 0,$$

and this is clearly the condition under which our proposed solution is valid. In other words, $x = A \exp\{\alpha t\}$ is a solution of equation [5.1] if

$$\alpha = \frac{-2f \pm \sqrt{4f^2 - 4mk}}{2m} = -\frac{f}{m} \pm \sqrt{\frac{f^2}{m^2} - \frac{k}{m}}. \qquad [5.2]$$

If both sign alternatives are solutions then their sum is also a solution since the equation is linear. As it is a second-order equation two arbitrary constants are required, and hence the complete solution obtained by substituting from [5.2] into the trial solution is

$$x = \exp\left\{-\frac{f}{m}t\right\}\left[A_1 \exp\left\{\sqrt{\frac{f^2}{m^2} - \frac{k}{m}}t\right\} + A_2 \exp\left\{-\sqrt{\frac{f^2}{m^2} - \frac{k}{m}}t\right\}\right]. \qquad [5.3]$$

If $\frac{f^2}{m^2} \geq \frac{k}{m}$ the exponents are real, and hence the displacement x merely decreases exponentially with time.

We are not concerned with either of these cases, although it is interesting to note that when $\frac{f^2}{m^2} = \frac{k}{m}$ the displaced vibrator returns to its rest position in the shortest possible time and just does not overshoot. If $\frac{f^2}{m^2} < \frac{k}{m}$ it overshoots and the motion becomes oscillatory. We shall consider the consequences of this condition in more detail. Let us substitute $\theta = \sqrt{\frac{k}{m} - \frac{f^2}{m^2}}$ (note change in order under the square-root sign) and hence equation [5.3] becomes

$$x = \exp\left\{-\frac{f}{m}t\right\}[A_1 \exp\{i\theta t\} + A_2 \exp\{-i\theta t\}], \qquad [5.4]$$

or

$$x = \exp\left\{-\frac{f}{m}t\right\}(A_1 + A_2)\cos\theta t + i\exp\left\{-\frac{f}{m}t\right\}(A_1 - A_2)\sin\theta t.$$

The displacement x is now complex and both its real and its imaginary parts must separately be solutions of the original equation, i.e.

$$x_1 = \exp\left\{-\frac{f}{m}t\right\}(A_1 + A_2)\cos\theta t$$

$$x_2 = \exp\left\{-\frac{f}{m}t\right\}(A_1 - A_2)\sin\theta t.$$

Since the equation is linear $x_1 + x_2$ is also a solution, and hence

$$x = \exp\left\{-\frac{f}{m}t\right\}(C\cos\theta t + D\sin\theta t)$$

where

$$C = A_1 + A_2 \quad\text{and}\quad D = A_1 - A_2$$

or

$$x = \exp\left\{-\frac{f}{m}t\right\}a\cos(\theta t - \varepsilon), \qquad [5.5]$$

where $a = \sqrt{C^2 + D^2}$, $a\cos\varepsilon = C$ and $a\sin\varepsilon = D$; a and ε are determined by the initial

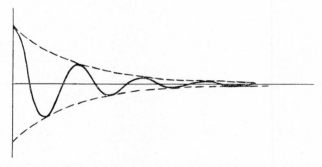

Figure 5.3 Exponentially-damped motion showing the two envelope curves dotted.

conditions and may be found by substitution. The resulting motion is clearly oscillatory with a period

$$\frac{2\pi}{\theta} = \frac{2\pi}{\sqrt{\dfrac{k}{m} - \dfrac{f^2}{m^2}}}.$$

Note that this is longer than the undamped period which is merely $\dfrac{2\pi}{\sqrt{\dfrac{k}{m}}}$ and that it becomes

longer as the damping increases. The amplitude, however, is decreasing because of the negative exponent, and in fact the oscillation occurs between two enveloping curves

$$x = a\exp\left\{-\frac{f}{m}t\right\} \quad\text{and}\quad x = -a\exp\left\{-\frac{f}{m}t\right\} \text{ (see Fig. 5.3).}$$

*5.8 Forced vibration

We must now consider what happens if we introduce into the damped system just described an external periodic force tending to make it oscillate at some period not necessarily equal to its own natural period (this is, of course, a simplified model of a typical coupled system in a musical instrument such as a reed and a pipe; the simplification arises because we have to assume that the imposed periodic force is unaffected by the response of the system to which it is applied). Let us suppose that the maximum value of the force is F and that its angular frequency is n; it may thus be represented by $F \sin (nt)$ and the equation of motion now becomes

$$m \frac{d^2x}{dt^2} + 2f \frac{dx}{dt} + kx = F \sin (nt).$$ [5.6]

It seems fairly clear that if the force is maintained for a long time at a completely stable frequency the system is ultimately bound to fall into step and to vibrate with the frequency $\frac{n}{2\pi}$. Let us therefore postulate a solution $x = A \sin (nt - \delta)$ where A is the final amplitude and δ is the angle by which the displacement lags behind the periodic force causing the motion—we clearly have no right to assume that it will be in phase. Then

$$\frac{dx}{dt} = An \cos (nt - \delta)$$

$$\frac{d^2x}{dt^2} = - An^2 \sin (nt - \delta)$$

which on substitution into equation [5.6] gives

$$- mAn^2 \sin (nt - \delta) + 2fAn \cos (nt - \delta) + kA \sin (nt - \delta) = F \sin (nt)$$

$$\cos (nt)[mAn^2 \sin \delta + 2fAn \cos \delta - kA \sin \delta]$$
$$+ \sin (nt)[2fAn \sin \delta - mAn^2 \cos \delta + kA \cos \delta - F] = 0.$$

Now if this is to be satisfied for all values of t, *both* the bracketed quantities must be zero, and hence

$$(mn^2 - k) \sin \delta + 2fn \cos \delta = 0,$$ [5.7]

and $$2fn \sin \delta - (mn^2 - k) \cos \delta = \frac{F}{A}.$$ [5.8]

Thus, from [5.7],

$$\tan \delta = \frac{2fn}{k - mn^2}$$

which gives

$$\sin \delta = \frac{2fn}{\sqrt{4f^2n^2 + (k - mn^2)^2}}$$

and $$\cos \delta = \frac{k - mn^2}{\sqrt{4f^2n^2 + (k - mn^2)^2}}$$

which on substitution into [5.8] gives

$$\frac{F}{A} = \frac{4f^2n^2}{\sqrt{4f^2n^2 + (k - mn^2)^2}} + \frac{(k - mn^2)^2}{\sqrt{4f^2n^2 + (k - mn^2)^2}}$$

$$A = \frac{F}{\sqrt{4f^2n^2 + (k - mn^2)^2}}$$

$$= \frac{F \sin \delta}{2fn}$$

so our postulated solution is satisfied if

$$A = \frac{F \sin \delta}{2fn} \quad \text{and if} \quad \delta = \tan^{-1} \frac{2fn}{k - mn^2},$$

i.e. the solution is

$$x = \frac{F \sin \delta}{2fn} \sin (nt - \delta). \qquad\qquad [5.9]$$

From equation [5.9] the solution can be seen to contain no *arbitrary* constants; the original equation is a second-order one and hence its general solution ought to contain two such constants. This is therefore a particular solution or a particular integral. The theory of differential equations tells us that the complete solution will be the sum of this solution and a complementary function which is the solution of an auxiliary equation. It is found by making the inhomogeneous term in the original equation—i.e. the one which does not contain x or its derivatives—equal to zero. The auxiliary equation is thus [5.1], the solution to which we have already found (equation [5.5]). The general solution of equation [5.6] should thus be the sum of [5.5] and [5.9]; this can be checked by substitution, and since it now contains two arbitrary constants it is a complete solution

$$x = \exp \left\{ -\frac{f}{m}t \right\} a \cos (\theta t - \varepsilon) + \frac{F \sin \delta}{2fn} \sin (nt - \delta). \qquad\qquad [5.10]$$

The arbitrary constants are a and ε and these will be determined by the starting conditions (see section 5.11).

The exponential term clearly decreases with time and when t becomes infinite it disappears altogether and we are left with the second term only; this is a vibration of the same frequency as the imposed force. There is no trace of the natural frequency θ of the system although the phase lag δ depends on the constants of the slave system k, f and m. It is difficult from an equation in this form to visualise how important or otherwise the first or transient term is. Later in the section we shall examine a concrete example in which the constants of a particular system are introduced, and this will help to make the significance of the various terms clearer. First, however, we must examine the condition under which the amplitude becomes a maximum as the frequency of the impressed forces changes—the condition known as amplitude resonance.

*5.9 Amplitude or displacement resonance

In the following discussion it will be assumed that we are only concerned with the ultimate steady state and that any transient terms have died away. Earlier in the chapter it was shown that the amplitude of the composite motion of a system undergoing forced vibration is given by

$$A = \frac{F}{\sqrt{4f^2n^2 + (k - mn^2)^2}}.$$ [5.11]

This clearly has a maximum value when $4f^2n^2 + (k - mn^2)^2$ has a minimum value, which will occur when $\dfrac{d}{dn}\{4f^2n^2 + (k - mn^2)^2\} = 0$, i.e. when $8f^2n - 4mn(k - mn^2) = 0$. It is convenient now to reintroduce the natural undamped angular frequency of the system $\omega = \sqrt{\dfrac{k}{m}}$ and we may therefore write $8f^2n - 4m^2n(\omega^2 - n^2) = 0$, or $n^2 = \omega^2 - \dfrac{2f^2}{m^2}$. The amplitude is thus a maximum when the period of the force is

$$\frac{2\pi}{n} = \frac{2\pi}{\sqrt{\omega^2 - \dfrac{2f^2}{m^2}}}.$$ [5.12]

It is important to notice that this gives a period which is not only longer than the free undamped period but also longer than the damped period for unforced vibrations $\left(\text{which is } \dfrac{2\pi}{\sqrt{\omega^2 - \dfrac{f^2}{m^2}}}\right)$. We shall now consider the magnitude of the amplitude under resonance conditions. Equation [5.11] can be re-written

$$A = \frac{F}{\sqrt{4f^2n^2 + m^2(\omega^2 - n^2)^2}}$$

which at resonance becomes

$$\frac{F}{\sqrt{4f^2n^2 + m^2\left(\omega^2 - \omega^2 + \dfrac{2f^2}{m^2}\right)}} = \frac{F}{\sqrt{4f^2n^2 + 2f^2}}.$$

It should be noted that if $f = 0$ then the amplitude is infinite and of course the frequency is the same as that of the undamped vibration.

When the slave system is moving with maximum amplitude it will obviously be moving with a relatively high velocity, but it is important to consider whether in fact the condition for maximum velocity coincides with the condition for a maximum amplitude. We shall see in the next section that it does not in fact occur under precisely the same conditions.

*5.10 Velocity resonance

Again, we shall only be concerned with the conditions after the steady state is reached, in other words when the motion is governed by the equation

$$x = \frac{F \sin \delta}{2fn} \sin (nt - \delta).$$

The particle velocity $\frac{dx}{dt}$ is thus

$$\frac{F \sin \delta}{2f} \cos (nt - \delta).$$

This will have a maximum or minimum value when $\frac{d^2x}{dt^2} = 0$ which is clearly only so if $\sin (nt - \delta) = 0$, in which case x is also zero. This corresponds to a maximum value and we have the obvious result that the velocity reaches a maximum each time the particle passes through its undisplaced position. At this position $\cos (nt - \delta)$ is unity and so the actual velocity at this point is

$$\frac{F \sin \delta}{2f} = \frac{Fn}{\sqrt{4f^2n^2 + (k - mn^2)^2}}.$$

This represents the maximum velocity in a given cycle and will itself have a maximum value as n changes when k is equal to mn^2, i.e. if $n = \sqrt{\frac{k}{m}}$, in other words when the forcing frequency is equal to the natural frequency of the undamped system. Substitution of this value for n in the expression for the amplitude (equation [5.11]) shows that even if the damping is zero the amplitude does not reach infinity under conditions of velocity resonance.

*5.11 Practical examples

We shall now proceed to calculate the behaviour of a simple experimental system under various conditions in order to assess the relative importance of the terms involved. The simplest and most direct application of the mathematical treatment used so far is that to a mass suspended on a spring, with damping provided by allowing the mass to move in a liquid. Experimentally the damping may be varied over a wide range by using mixtures of glycerine and water in various proportions. It is not difficult in this way to simulate critical damping and the oscillatory and overdamped states on either side of the critical condition. We shall consider first a particular undamped system; we shall then consider the modification of its behaviour by three different degrees of damping (all less than critical as it is only the oscillatory solution that is of real interest in music), and finally we shall study its behaviour when periodic forces of various frequencies are imposed on it.

The system to be considered consists of a mass m of 20 gm. suspended at the lower end of a light, long spring whose characteristics are such that an extension of 1 cm. necessitates a force of 2,880 dynes (i.e. $k = 2,880$ dynes cm.$^{-1}$). The natural angular frequency of the system in the undamped condition is thus

$$\omega = \sqrt{\frac{k}{m}} = 12 \text{ radians sec.}^{-1}.$$

Thus if the mass is displaced 5 cm. from its mean position and released from rest the subsequent motion will be given by

$$x = 5 \cos (12t). \tag{5.13}$$

A graph of this function is shown in Fig. 5.4 (thin lines).

Now let us suppose that three different damping conditions, A, B, C, are imposed; in A the resistive force per unit velocity is 20 dynes sec. cm.$^{-1}$, in B 80 dynes sec. cm.$^{-1}$ and in C 200 dynes sec. cm.$^{-1}$, i.e.

$$2f_A = 20$$

$$2f_B = 80$$

$$2f_C = 200.$$

Hence the angular frequencies of the three damped motions are of the form (see section 5.4)

$$\theta_A = \sqrt{\frac{k}{m} - \frac{f_A^2}{m^2}}$$

which on substituting the stated values gives

$$\theta_A = 11 \cdot 99 \text{ radians sec.}^{-1}$$

$$\theta_B = 11 \cdot 85 \text{ radians sec.}^{-1}$$

$$\theta_C = 10 \cdot 90 \text{ radians sec.}^{-1}.$$

Thus the damped motions are (from section 5.5)

$$\left. \begin{array}{l} x_A = a_A \exp \left\{ -\tfrac{1}{2}t \right\} \cos (11 \cdot 99t - \varepsilon_A) \\ x_B = a_B \exp \left\{ -2t \right\} \cos (11 \cdot 85t - \varepsilon_B) \\ x_C = a_C \exp \left\{ -5t \right\} \cos (10 \cdot 90t - \varepsilon_C) \end{array} \right\}. \tag{5.14}$$

Let us now suppose that for all three conditions the motion starts with a displacement of 5 cm. from the mean position as before and that it starts from rest, in other words the starting conditions are

$$x = 5 \quad \text{and} \quad \frac{dx}{dt} = 0 \quad \text{when} \quad t = 0.$$

Thus substituting in equations [5.14] we arrive at

$$\left. \begin{array}{l} 5 = a_A \cos \varepsilon_A \\ 5 = a_B \cos \varepsilon_B \\ 5 = a_C \cos \varepsilon_C \end{array} \right\}. \tag{5.15}$$

Differentiating [5.14] we obtain

$$\frac{dx_A}{dt} = -11 \cdot 99 a_A \exp\{-\tfrac{1}{2}t\} \sin(11 \cdot 99t - \varepsilon_A) - \tfrac{1}{2} a_A \exp\{-\tfrac{1}{2}t\} \cos(11 \cdot 99t - \varepsilon_A)$$

$$\frac{dx_B}{dt} = -11 \cdot 85 a_B \exp\{-2t\} \sin(11 \cdot 85t - \varepsilon_B) - 2a_B \exp\{-2t\} \cos(11 \cdot 85t - \varepsilon_B)$$

and

$$\frac{dx_C}{dt} = -10 \cdot 9 a_C \exp\{-5t\} \sin(10 \cdot 90t - \varepsilon_C) - 5a_C \exp\{-5t\} \cos(10 \cdot 9t - \varepsilon_C)$$

which when $t = 0$ give

$$\left. \begin{array}{l} 11 \cdot 99 a_A \sin \varepsilon_A - \tfrac{1}{2} a_A \cos \varepsilon_A = 0 \\[4pt] 11 \cdot 85 a_B \sin \varepsilon_B - 2a_B \cos \varepsilon_B = 0 \\[4pt] 10 \cdot 90 a_C \sin \varepsilon_C - 5a_C \cos \varepsilon_C = 0 \end{array} \right\} \cdot \qquad\qquad [5.16]$$

Hence

$$\tan \varepsilon_A = \frac{\tfrac{1}{2}}{11 \cdot 99}, \qquad \varepsilon_A = 2° \, 24' \quad \text{or} \quad 182° \, 24' = 0 \cdot 042 \text{ radians or } 3 \cdot 184 \text{ radians}$$

$$\tan \varepsilon_B = \frac{2}{11 \cdot 85}, \qquad \varepsilon_B = 9° \, 34' \quad \text{or} \quad 189° \, 34' = 0 \cdot 167 \text{ radians or } 3 \cdot 309 \text{ radians}$$

and

$$\tan \varepsilon_C = \frac{5}{10 \cdot 9}, \qquad \varepsilon_C = 24° \, 38' \quad \text{or} \quad 204° \, 38' = 0 \cdot 430 \text{ radians or } 3 \cdot 572 \text{ radians.}$$

Thus from equation [5.14]

$$a_A = \frac{5}{\cos \varepsilon_A} = 5 \cdot 005 \quad \text{or} \quad -5 \cdot 005$$

$$a_B = \frac{5}{\cos \varepsilon_B} = 5 \cdot 065 \quad \text{or} \quad -5 \cdot 065$$

and

$$a_C = \frac{5}{\cos \varepsilon_C} = 5 \cdot 5 \quad \text{or} \quad -5 \cdot 5.$$

We must take a consistent pair of values so we shall take the smaller value of ε_A and ε_B and ε_C with the positive value of a_A and a_B and a_C and so the final expressions are

$$\left. \begin{array}{l} x_A = 5 \cdot 005 \exp\{-\tfrac{1}{2}t\} \cos(11 \cdot 99t - 0 \cdot 042) \\[4pt] x_B = 5 \cdot 065 \exp\{-2t\} \cos(11 \cdot 85t - 0 \cdot 167) \\[4pt] x_C = 5 \cdot 500 \exp\{-5t\} \cos(10 \cdot 90t - 0 \cdot 43) \end{array} \right\} \cdot \qquad\qquad [5.17]$$

and

Figure 5.4 shows a plot of these three motions with the original undamped motion super-imposed to facilitate phase comparison.

Let us now consider the application of a periodic force of angular frequency 12 radians sec.$^{-1}$ (i.e. velocity resonance condition) to the system with the three different degrees of damping. We shall also consider the application of periodic forces of frequencies 10 and 14 radians sec.$^{-1}$ to the system under damping conditions A. In all cases the magnitude of the applied force will be 14,400 dynes. The composite equations (obtained by substitution in equation [5.10]) are thus:

$$x_1 = a_1 \exp\left\{-\tfrac{1}{2}t\right\} \cos(11{\cdot}99t - \varepsilon_1) + \frac{14{,}400}{20 \times 12} \sin\delta_1 \sin(12t - \delta_1)$$

$$x_2 = a_2 \exp\left\{-2t\right\} \cos(11{\cdot}85t - \varepsilon_2) + \frac{14{,}400}{80 \times 12} \sin\delta_2 \sin(12t - \delta_2)$$

$$x_3 = a_3 \exp\left\{-5t\right\} \cos(10{\cdot}90t - \varepsilon_3) + \frac{14{,}400}{20 \times 12} \sin\delta_3 \sin(12t - \delta_3)$$

$$x_4 = a_4 \exp\left\{-\tfrac{1}{2}t\right\} \cos(11{\cdot}99t - \varepsilon_4) + \frac{14{,}400}{200 \times 10} \sin\delta_4 \sin(10t - \delta_4)$$

$$x_5 = a_5 \exp\left\{-\tfrac{1}{2}t\right\} \cos(11{\cdot}99t - \varepsilon_5) + \frac{14{,}400}{20 \times 14} \sin\delta_5 \sin(14t - \delta_5).$$

Now $\delta = \tan^{-1}\dfrac{2fn}{k - mn^2}$ and the values of δ obtained by substitution are

$$\delta_1 = 90° = 1{\cdot}5708 \text{ radians}$$
$$\delta_2 = 90° = 1{\cdot}5708 \text{ radians}$$
$$\delta_3 = 90° = 1{\cdot}5708 \text{ radians}$$
$$\delta_4 = 12°\,45' = 0{\cdot}2225 \text{ radians}$$
$$\delta_5 = 164°\,57' = 2{\cdot}8790 \text{ radians}.$$

The complete equations to which boundary conditions $x = 0$ when $t = 0$ and $\dfrac{dx}{dt} = 0$ when $t = 0$ are to be applied are thus:

$$x_1 = a_1 \exp\left\{-\tfrac{1}{2}t\right\} \cos(11.99t - \varepsilon_1) + 60 \sin\left(12t - \frac{\pi}{2}\right)$$

$$x_2 = a_2 \exp\left\{-2t\right\} \cos(11{\cdot}85t - \varepsilon_2) + 15 \sin\left(12t - \frac{\pi}{2}\right)$$

$$x_3 = a_3 \exp\left\{-5t\right\} \cos(10{\cdot}90t - \varepsilon_3) + 6 \sin\left(12t - \frac{\pi}{2}\right)$$

$$x_4 = a_4 \exp\left\{-\tfrac{1}{2}t\right\} \cos(11{\cdot}99t - \varepsilon_4) + 15{\cdot}84 \sin(10t - 0{\cdot}2225)$$

$$x_5 = a_5 \exp\left\{-\tfrac{1}{2}t\right\} \cos(11{\cdot}99t - \varepsilon_5) + 13{\cdot}3 \sin(14t - 2{\cdot}8790).$$

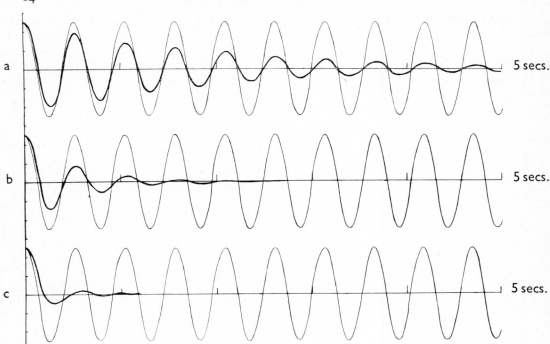

5 secs.

5 secs.

5 secs.

Figure 5.4 Damped motion of the experimental system (bold lines): (*a*) Light damping. (*b*) Moderate damping. (*c*) Heavy damping. In each case the thin line represents the natural undamped motion.

If the boundary conditions are substituted the five pairs of values of a and ε may be found and the resulting equations are:

$$x_1 = 60 \cdot 06 \exp\left\{-\tfrac{1}{2}t\right\} \cos\left(11 \cdot 99t - 0 \cdot 042\right) + 60 \sin\left(12t - \frac{\pi}{2}\right)$$

$$x_2 = 15 \cdot 21 \exp\left\{-2t\right\} \cos\left(11 \cdot 85t - 0 \cdot 167\right) + 15 \sin\left(12t - \frac{\pi}{2}\right)$$

$$x_3 = 6 \cdot 6 \exp\left\{-5t\right\} \cos\left(10 \cdot 90t - 0 \cdot 430\right) + 6 \sin\left(12t - \frac{\pi}{2}\right)$$

$$x_4 = 13 \cdot 0 \exp\left\{-\tfrac{1}{2}t\right\} \cos\left(11 \cdot 99t + 1 \cdot 304\right) + 15 \cdot 84 \sin\left(10t - 0 \cdot 2225\right)$$

$$x_5 = 16 \cdot 0 \exp\left\{-\tfrac{1}{2}t\right\} \cos\left(11 \cdot 99t - 1 \cdot 349\right) + 13 \cdot 3 \sin\left(14t - 2 \cdot 8790\right).$$

Figures 5.5(*a*–*e*) show these curves. In each case a curve representing the driving force has been included to emphasise the amplitude and phase changes which occur during the transient phase. The beats between the transient and the steady state can clearly be seen for x_4 and x_5.

5.12 Summary and results

We have now seen that the coupling together of two vibrating systems, which is necessary for amplification or for modification of timbre, leads to the existence of transients or "argu-

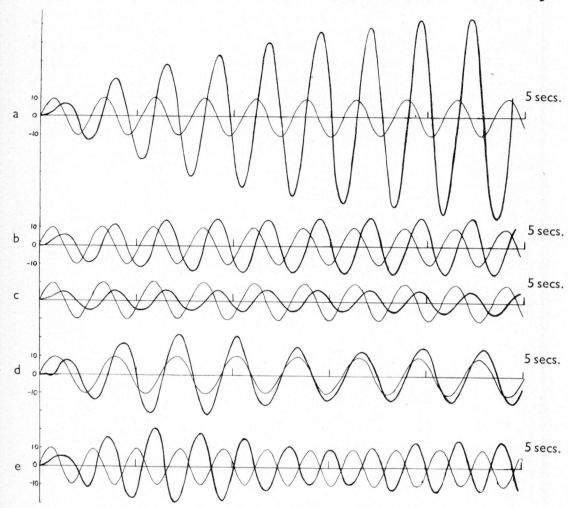

Figure 5.5 Motion of the damped experimental system executing forced vibrations (bold lines): (*a*) Lightly damped with forcing frequency equal to the natural frequency. (*b*) Moderately damped with the forcing frequency equal to the natural frequency. (*c*) Heavily damped with the forcing frequency equal to the natural frequency. (*d*) Lightly damped with the forcing frequency less than the natural frequency in the ratio 5:6. (*e*) Lightly damped with the forcing frequency greater than the natural frequency in the ratio 7:6.

In each case the thin line represents the forcing vibration and it is included to demonstrate the phase relationship during the transient and steady states.

ments" between the two. In the mathematical sections various calculations were performed and the results have been summarised in Figs. 5.4 and 5.5. They represent the form of the vibration curve for a 20 gm. mass suspended at the end of a long light spring vibrating freely, then under three damping conditions, and finally under the influence of different imposed periodic forces. In each diagram the full line represents the complete motion and the thin line represents the periodic imposed force. The "beats" which occur between the transient and steady-state motion in some of the examples can clearly be seen.

Complicated as these curves are they still do not represent the real conditions existing in a musical instrument. We have not taken into account the reaction of the slave system on the master system; almost invariably the imposed periodic vibration will not maintain constant frequency. We have also assumed that the master oscillation comes into being immediately at its full amplitude, whereas in fact it will also build up from zero amplitude and hence have its own non-periodic form during the build-up period. The actual starting conditions existing in a musical instrument are thus extremely complex, and it is clear that it will be necessary to study next the various methods of initiating musical sounds—plucking, bowing, blowing, etc.—since they will obviously have a profound influence on the initial state of the vibrations. We shall also have to investigate the relative importance of the transient terms in actual instruments and to discover whether there is a characteristic, recognisable sound associated with the transients. These problems will be discussed in the next chapter.

CHAPTER 6

Starting Transients and the Initiation of Vibrations

6.1 Introduction

The complicated behaviour of the vibrating system of a musical instrument during the initiation of a sound has already been discussed. The whole of this irregular part of the motion—which includes the true transient terms arising from coupled systems and also the disturbances which arise from the method of excitation—is usually described as the "starting transient". The question now to be discussed is whether the transient has a characteristic musical quality and whether its presence plays a real part in determining the quality of sound developed by a musical instrument; the first section of the chapter is devoted to this problem. We shall then go on to discuss the various methods used to initiate vibrations and their characteristics. The methods will include the bowing, plucking, and striking of strings, edge tones and reeds used to excite vibrations in air columns, and miscellaneous less conventional devices such as electrical and thermal methods. Finally, the extension of the concept of Fourier transformation to assist in analysing starting transients will be discussed, first in general terms and then in a more mathematical form.

6.2 The experimental observation of starting transients

In section 5.6 the oboe was suggested as a typical example of a coupled system; it also provides a useful introduction to the observation of starting transients. If a series of staccato notes is played on an oboe it is possible to hear the transient as a distinct tonal quality lasting only a fraction of a second at the beginning of each note; the effect has been likened to the quacking of a duck. Attention can most easily be focused on an effect if it can be removed so that a comparison can be made with and without the phenomenon being studied, and fortunately the advent of the tape recorder has made this a relatively simple experiment. As each note is about to be sounded the recording level control is turned to zero and then smoothly returned to normal level after a short interval. The experiment can be done during the initial recording. It is simpler, however, if two tape recorders are available, to make a straightforward recording first and then to eliminate the transients during the process of re-recording on to a second tape. The simplification arises because it is then possible to study the precise timing beforehand and also because the elimination of the transient can be repeated until a satisfactory timing is achieved. The resulting tone—which still has the same steady-state harmonic content—sounds significantly different. The effect is reminiscent of a mouth-organ or even, in the higher registers, of a violin. The same sort of experiment can of course be done with other instruments. The piano provides a particularly striking example as here the transient is very violent and relatively short-lived, and further there is no steady state but an immediate exponential decay. The piano sounds more like a mouth-organ when a slow rise is substituted for the normal violent initiation.

A second useful method of observing transients is comparable with the use of slow motion in taking cine films. A tape recorder is again used, but the tape is made to run at a high speed during recordings; when played back at slow speed the pitch of the basic note is of course much reduced, but the transient is extended in time and it is sometimes possible to hear quite distinct beats and other non-uniform effects. A third method of demonstrating the importance of transients in the recognition of instrumental quality—though not of hearing the effects themselves—involves the use of live players. A group of instrumentalists —for example, flute, oboe, clarinet, and violin—is asked to play out of sight of the audience. They all play together a certain chord but almost immediately one member stops playing. Most audiences can identify the instruments which start but it is often much more difficult for them to distinguish which one ceased to play. This suggests that starting transients occurring when the whole group begins to play assist the identification; the change in the steady harmonic content, however, is much more difficult to recognise, and hence must be of less importance in making the identification.

The final method to be described is not only helpful in drawing attention to the importance of transients, but can also produce some rather amusing results. It again involves the use of a tape recorder. In this method the tape is played back in the reverse direction (Meyer and Buchman, 1931; George, 1954). (There are several ways of doing this. With a single-track tape recorder the tape is simply turned over; with dual-track recording it can sometimes be done if provision is made on the machine for "back spacing".) It is clear that any continuous sinusoidal components present will be unaffected by the reversal—that is the harmonic content will remain the same. Any transient effects, however, will obviously occur in abnormal places, and hence will become obvious (George claims that there is also an effect on the steady state—see section 9.4.5.). Again the piano provides the most striking example; the exponential decay of the lightly-damped strings becomes a slow exponential build-up on reversal. The resulting sound resembles that of an organ except for the odd abrupt ending of each note. The identification with organ tone draws attention to the much greater importance of the *beginning* rather than the ending of a note; a true organ note both rises *and* falls exponentially.

6.3 The initiation of vibrations

Having shown that transient effects are distinctly heard and that they play a major part in determining the quality of sound associated with an instrument, we must now look more closely at the influence of the precise method of initiation of the vibrations. There are two groups of methods. The first includes those methods which do not produce a continuous note: the vibration is initiated by a single disturbance of some kind and then decays. The striking and plucking of stretched strings and the striking of percussion instruments are the principal examples. The second group includes all the methods of continuously feeding energy into a vibrating system to maintain a steady note; it includes frictional, electrical, thermal, and pneumatic methods. Some systems, of course, do not fall specifically into one or the other category. For example, in a double reed instrument, such as an oboe, the excitation of the air column is clearly continuous and hence would fall in the second group, but the initiation of the vibration of the reed itself involves some of the processes which would tend to place it nearer the first group. For our present purpose, however, we shall consider the main vibrating system and ignore the hybrid nature of some instruments.

6.4 Impulsive excitation

It has already been mentioned that the principal methods of impulsive excitation are plucking and striking: the main difference between these two methods is that in plucking the system starts from a disturbed position with more or less zero velocity, in other words it starts with all its energy in the form of potential energy. In striking, however, the vibrator is disturbed by a rapidly-moving object which has considerable momentum; hence all parts of the system are not displaced in the same way initially nor does the system move from rest. There is thus potential and kinetic energy in existence at the time of initiation. We shall see that one of the important factors to be taken into consideration in both methods is the shape of the object used to create the deformation. In section 3.7 the subsequent vibration of a string plucked at a single point was discussed and the assumption made that the object used for the displacement had zero dimensions along the length of the string. This is clearly never true in practice, and it is not difficult to see that a distribution along the length of the string would result in the absence of some harmonics; those with nodes within the area of contact would in fact be missing. Thus, in general, the broader the disturbing object the less rich in harmonics will be the resulting sound. We have already seen that the position of the point of plucking along the string influences the harmonic content; it is now clear that the shape of the deformed string before release is of equal importance.

The vibration of a struck string is considerably more complicated. The aim of course is to transfer energy to the string and this should be done ideally in as smooth a way as possible. If the hammer is too hard the string may bounce on the hammer, and this will produce undesirable additional noises. If the hammer is much too soft it may adhere to the string with subsequent undesirable results when the hammer ought to fall clear. Some of these additional noise effects will be discussed in more detail in the next chapter. Helmholtz (1877) made a theoretical study of struck strings in which he assumed that the time of contact between the hammer and the string is negligible. Kauffman (1895) rejected this theory and showed that the time of contact is relatively long compared with the period of vibration of the string. His theory depends on the fact that the portion of the string in contact with the hammer will be considerably displaced before the rest of the string begins to move at all. Hence a wave is generated even before the displaced point has reached its maximum displacement. George & Beckett (1927) have verified the general basis of Kauffman's theory by an exhaustive series of experiments and also conclude that—because of the initial wave already mentioned—it is possible to excite a stronger fundamental by using a massive hammer striking the string close to one end than by striking near the middle. This is in direct opposition to the behaviour of plucked strings, for which we have already shown in Chapter 3 that the maximum fundamental is excited by plucking at the mid-point. It provides an additional reason why the hammers in, for example, a piano are placed nearer to one end of the string (the other reason, it will be remembered, was to minimise the proportion of the undesirable seventh and ninth harmonics).

The same sorts of considerations apply to the striking of two-dimensional plates as, for example, in the glockenspiel, xylophone, tympani, etc. It can be shown that if a plate or membrane is struck at a point at which a node would occur for a particular partial, that partial would be absent from the subsequent vibration. Thus again the broader the striking implement the more higher modes will be absent. For plates this is usually desirable, since the partials are not harmonic, and the pleasantest tone is usually produced by rather broad padded hammers. There is, of course, some noise produced by the actual blow, and this must be taken into account; it will be discussed in the next chapter.

In all instruments which use plucking or striking as a method of excitation it is necessary to pay special attention to the rapid removal of the hammer or other mechanical device to prevent interference with the subsequent free vibration of the string or plate.

6.5 The continuous excitation of vibrations

In order to initiate and to maintain a vibration for a long period it is clearly necessary to pay close attention to the phase of the injected energy. This is particularly true if the energy is to be fed in as a succession of small impulses. It is a familiar fact of everyday life that a child's swing can be made to oscillate with a large amplitude if impulses are applied at precisely the right moment during the cycle; if the timing is incorrect the swing will be brought to rest very quickly. There are two ways of achieving correct timing. One involves the use of existing oscillations in the main vibrator to control the injection of further energy (this corresponds roughly to the control of the valve system in an internal combustion engine); the other involves the use of an injection device which has a natural period of its own and which can be brought into tune with the main vibrator. The injection device itself will probably depend on the first type of control to build up its own vibrations. As usual it is rather difficult to make hard-and-fast divisions and many systems have elements of both types of control. For example, the reed system of a woodwind instrument has a natural period but is also very considerably affected by the action of the pipe. We shall first consider a common example of maintained oscillations in which the timing is controlled by the primary vibrating system—the bowing of stringed instruments.

6.5.1 The bowing of strings and other "stick-slip" techniques

The physics of bowed strings has been investigated by a number of workers including Helmholtz (1877), Raman (1918a), and more recently Keller (1953) and Friedlander (1953). The practicability of bowing depends on the frictional properties of certain materials whereby the resistive force is less when two bodies are in relative motion than when they are stationary. When the bow is placed on the string and drawn to one side the initial effect is the same as that of plucking—the string "sticks" to the bow and is drawn aside until the elastic restoring forces exceed the frictional forces between the bow and the string. These forces, of course, depend partly on the pressure with which the bow is applied. Once the breakdown has occurred the string will begin to return to its normal position, and, because of its relative motion, the resistive forces will be less. The motion will continue until it reaches the point at which the string reverses and begins to move with the bow again. The force will then increase and the two will stick together until once more the maximum deviation is achieved. It is not difficult to see that timing of the "stick-slip" motion is automatically governed by the string and that the maximum deviation is controlled by the pressure of the bow and the frictional properties of the system. It is also clear that the amount of energy fed in will depend on the velocity of the bow, as this in turn determines the portion of the cycle over which sticking occurs. A single performer thus has considerable control over the amplitude both in terms of the pressure and of the velocity of bowing, and these two variables are useful because the pressure also has an effect on the damping. Under very heavy bowing pressure the damping may be increased differentially for different modes with a consequent effect on the tonal quality. Keller deduced that the quality of sound produced depends primarily on the ratio of the bow velocity to bow pressure, and pointed out that this is in agreement with the experience of performers who find it necessary to increase the velocity with a simultaneous decrease in pressure in order to modify the quality.

The position of the bowing point on the string is another variable which affects the quality of tone. A bow consisting of a single hair of infinitesimal width should excite all modes except those having a node at the precise point of bowing. In practice the width of

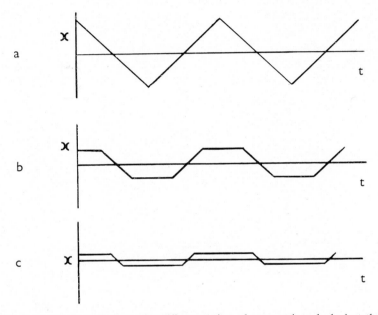

Figure 6.1 Displacement-time diagrams for different points along a string plucked at the mid-point; *a* is the motion of the mid-point, *b* and *c* are for points successively nearer to one end.

the bow eliminates other possible modes and tends to diminish the proportion of higher harmonics as does a broad plucking device. The actual motion of the bowed string, however, is quite different from that of a plucked string. It was shown in section 3.7 that the motion of any given point on a plucked string involved a period at rest, a period with a constant speed in one direction, a further period at rest, and finally a period with constant speed equal and opposite to that in the earlier part of the cycle. The displacement-time diagram for points at several positions on a plucked string is shown in Fig. 6.1. Helmholtz studied the motion of bowed strings under his "vibration microscope" in which the objective was clamped to one prong of a vibrating tuning fork. An illuminated grain of starch fixed to the string was arranged so that the vibration direction was perpendicular to that of the objective, and hence Lissajous' figures are seen. From the resulting figures displacement diagrams were plotted for different points along the string. The corresponding set to those of Fig. 6.1 was found to be like that of Fig. 6.2. Raman confirmed Helmholtz's general observations and they are also in agreement with the later work of Keller and of Friedlander. Thus when the string is bowed at the usual place (1/5th–1/8th from one end) the *mid*-point ascends and descends with equal velocities and behaves very like the mid-point of the plucked string.

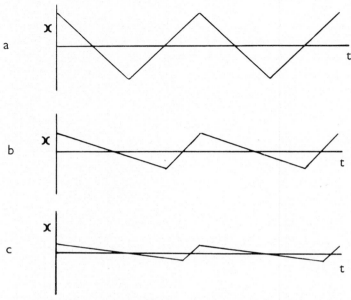

Figure 6.2 Displacement-time diagrams for different points along a string bowed at the usual point (about 1/5th to 1/8th from one end); *a* is the motion of the mid-point, and *b* and *c* are for points successively closer to one end.

Other points, however, ascend and descend at two quite distinct and constant velocities and there is no rest period. At the point of bowing the smaller of the two velocities is equal to that of the bow; the return velocity is higher in the ratio $p:p-1$, where p is an integer and the point of bowing is $1/p$ of the length of the string from one end. Krigar-Menzel and Raps (1893) extended this rule to include bowing at some other point q/p from one end where q and p are both integers and q is not a factor of p. The relative velocities are still in the same ratio as before and are independent of q. Thus, for example, bowing at 1/5th, 2/5th, 3/5th, etc., of the length from one end leads to exactly the same velocity ratio at the point of bowing, namely $1:4$. The actual motion of a bowed string was deduced by Helmholtz and confirmed by the later workers and is as shown by the heavy line in Fig. 6.3. The point P is supposed to move round the two parabolic curves APB and BQA so that the foot of the perpendicular D travels with constant velocity. Fourier analysis

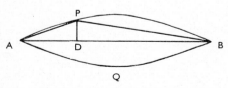

Figure 6.3 Subsequent motion of a bowed string as deduced by Helmholtz.

of this wave shape shows that harmonics are present, but not in the same sort of ratios as those for a plucked string or for those of a struck string.

Nearly all the members of the viol and violin families make use of bows made of horse-hair treated with resin to provide the necessary frictional characteristics. It has already been pointed out that the source of the vibration is the special characteristic of so-called "dry friction" in which the resistive force for bodies in relative motion is less than that for bodies at rest. Both Keller and Friedlander have shown that oscillations always take place. It is not possible to find a bowing speed and pressure which will give a constant deflection of the string as would occur if some kind of lubrication were provided. One rather unusual and now rare member of the string family—the hurdy-gurdy—uses a wooden disc fed with resin which occupies roughly the position of the bridge of a violin and rotates about an axis parallel to the strings. The stick-slip friction between the wooden disc and the strings provides the same kind of motion as that provided by the more conventional bow. The instrument has "drone" strings in permanent contact with the wheel and melody strings which can be brought into contact with the wheel at will. Stick-slip excitation by stroking with a resined cloth was mentioned in an earlier section as a method of producing notes from brass or wooden rods in longitudinal vibration, and there are two further applications in instruments which are worthy of discussion; both make use of glass lubricated with pure (detergent-free) water. The first is the instrument described as "musical glasses". In its simplest form it consists of a collection of drinking glasses filled to a greater or lesser extent with water for tuning purposes and set into vibration by rubbing a moistened finger with a circular motion round the rim. A more sophisticated version of this instrument designed by Benjamin Franklin and popular for a time in the eighteenth century under the name of "harmonica" had glass bowls mounted on a common rotating axis. The lower edges of the bowls dipped into a tank of water and they were graduated in size to provide different notes. It was only necessary to hold the finger on the rim of any particular bowl to excite vibrations. The final application to be discussed is in a very modern instrument—the cristal organ—designed and played by the group already mentioned in section 5.4, Structures Sonores, Lasry-Baschet. In this instrument the primary vibrators are metal plates to which glass rods are attached at right-angles. Lateral vibration of the plates can thus be excited by longitudinal vibration of the glass rods; the longitudinal excitation in turn is produced by stroking the rods with wet fingers. The instruments are described in more detail in section 11.3.

6.5.2 Electrical and thermal excitation and maintenance of vibrations

Two further methods of excitation in which the timing is provided entirely by the main vibrator must be included for completeness, although neither is in use in genuine musical instruments. Both find a place in demonstration experiments in sound, and the electrical method is also occasionally used in providing a steady source of sound for pitch comparisons.

The electrical method applies principally to strings and to tuning-forks. The exciting force is applied by means of an electro-magnet which displaces the vibrator from its rest position when a current is passed through it. For strings an alternative is to pass a current through the string itself and to place it between the poles of a magnet. In either case it is necessary to vary the current in a periodic manner in order to build up and maintain oscillations. The crudest method which can be used satisfactorily with a fork involves a simple interruption of the current. The mechanism is similar to that of an electric bell; a contact with one pole of the fork is so arranged that when the electro-magnet disturbs the pole from its rest position the circuit is broken and the pole returns under elastic forces to make contact again (see Fig. 6.4(*a*)). A more refined method applicable to either strings or forks involves a small pick-up, which may consist of a small coil wrapped on a magnetised core, placed near to the vibrator. Any existing vibration thus generates an oscillatory current

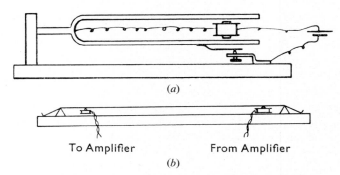

(*a*)

To Amplifier   From Amplifier

(*b*)

Figure 6.4   (*a*) Electrically-maintained tuning-fork. (*b*) Electrically-maintained vibrating wire.

of the same frequency in the pick-up coil, and this can be amplified and fed—via a phase control if necessary—to drive the main electro-magnet (see Fig. 6.4(*b*)). Adjustment of the phase and gain of the amplifier may be necessary to ensure that oscillation is maintained.

The thermal method, which is impractical for musical purposes because of its slowness in response, was first investigated by Rijke (1859). It can most easily be demonstrated with a tube of brass about 2 in. in diameter and 2–3 ft. long. The tube is clamped in a vertical position and a piece of wire gauze is inserted about 6 in. from the lower end (see Fig. 6.5). A bunsen-burner flame held in the lower end of the tube can then be used to heat the gauze for a few seconds. Very soon a powerful and relatively pure tone is emitted and if the bunsen burner is then withdrawn the sound will persist for a considerable time. A similar effect may be produced by inserting the gauze a few inches from the top of the tube and placing a small piece of solid carbon dioxide on it. In both arrangements convection currents are set up and the initiation of the flow also initiates a standing wave in the tube. The subsequent action will be described for the hot-air method; the cold method works in exactly the opposite way. As air passes up through the heated gauze into the tube it expands and its expansion tends to increase the flow up the tube. When the part of the cycle involving expul-

Figure 6.5   sion of air from the tube arrives, air which is already hot passes through the
Rijke's tube.   gauze and no further expansion takes place. There is thus an intermittent force which happens to be in the right relative phase to build up the oscillation. A similar effect can be produced without the gauze if a small-diameter jet of coal gas is allowed to burn in the lower end. These "singing flames" were discovered by Higgens in 1777;

Richardson (1953a) gives a discussion and further references, and shows that standing waves in the gas supply also occur, causing the flame itself to oscillate.

Thermally-induced vibrations have a long transient period which can easily be heard. The amplitude tends to build up exponentially but there are complications because as the air in the pipe heats up so the velocity of sound in the pipe changes; the frequency of the lowest natural mode of vibration thus rises. The initial period thus involves a slow rise in both amplitude and pitch. If the tube is very long and narrow in bore further complications may arise because modes other than the fundamental may be excited and sudden changes of mode occur during the heating-up period.

6.5.3 The initiation of vibrations in pipes by edge tones

The earliest method of producing a musical sound from air vibrations in a pipe or bottle was undoubtedly the simple act of blowing across the opening. This still survives as a method of excitation in the transverse flute but demands considerable skill in execution as the precise shape and position of the mouth and velocity of the air jet are very important. The addition of an "artificial mouth" and a carefully-designed edge led to the recorder or "flute-à-bec" and to the diapason and similar organ pipes. The primary source of excitation is the set of eddies produced when a jet of air impinges on an edge. They have a frequency which depends on the dimensions, on the velocity, and on other factors, but the resonant frequencies of the excited pipe also have a considerable influence. This method is therefore very much on the border line between those in which the primary timing control comes from the period of the main vibrator, which have already been discussed, and those in which the excitor has a strong natural period which will be discussed in the following section.

Edge tones occur whenever currents of air move past edges, thin rods or wires. The whistle of the wind in the rigging of a ship, round the eaves of a house, or through a crack in a door, are all of the same origin. They can probably best be understood by observing a corresponding process in a liquid. If a stick or paddle is made to move rapidly through water, successive eddies can be seen on alternate sides and the reaction on the stick can be felt quite clearly; it tends to develop oscillations in a direction at right angles to the direction of movement (see Fig. 6.6). This effect was recorded by Rayleigh in one of his early note-books and its probable connection with edge and aeolian tones was noted by him. He later (1915) reported experimental and theoretical work and many other investigations have

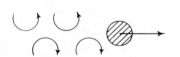

Figure 6.6 Water eddies following a moving object (stable form).

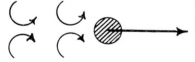

Figure 6.7 Water eddies following a moving object (unstable form).

since been made. Kármán (1912), for example, showed that two systems of vortices are possible, one as shown in Fig. 6.6(a)—which is the stable one—and one as shown in Fig. 6.7, which is unstable. Trains of vortices are also produced when a jet of fluid emerges from a narrow slit, and the result is to make the jet itself follow a curved path (see Fig. 6.8). A survey of the results of experimental work of both kinds of vortices with a useful list of references is given by Wood (1940). When the two effects are combined, i.e. when the jet of air impinges on an obstacle, it is not surprising to find that vortices are produced which tend to travel on alternate sides of the obstacle (Fig. 6.9(a)). If the dimensions, air pressure and velocity are varied conditions can be found under which very strong oscillations, which can be heard as a definite musical note, occur. If the obstacle is the edge separating the outside from the inside of a pipe alternate vortices will pass along the inside and the outside of the pipe, and hence periodic pulses are applied to the air in the pipe (Fig. 6.10). If their frequency of generation is comparable with a resonant frequency of the pipe combined oscillations can build up. It turns out in practice that the vibration of the air in the pipe itself has a strong reflex action on the period of the vortex formation and tends to dominate its frequency of production. The starting conditions depend very much on how near the natural period of vortex formation is to the natural period of the pipe; it is clear, therefore, that the shape of the edge and slit and the air velocity conditions can have a profound influence on harmonic content and on the initiation of the note. Richardson (1953b) gives a summary of experiments using smoke mixed with the air supply to make the vortices visible. It can be shown that the spacing—or wavelength—of the vortices is roughly equal to the separation of the slit and the edge or to some fraction of this separation. For example, in Fig. 6.9(a), a second vortex is just being formed at the slit as the first on the outside is reaching the edge. In practice there is a minimum separation for which vortices can be produced. If the distance from the slit to the edge is d and the velocity of efflux is v then the frequency of sound produced—which is the frequency at which the vortices strike the edge—will be proportional to v/d. Thus if the velocity is kept constant and d_0 is the minimum separation at which a note can be produced the frequency will be v/d_0. If d_0 is now increased the frequency falls, and it turns out that d can be in-

Figure 6.8 Train of vortices from a fluid jet.

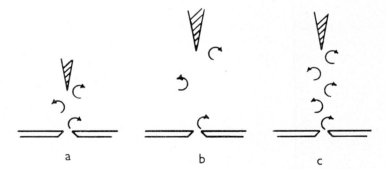

a   b   c

Figure 6.9 (a) Vortices with minimum edge-to-slit separation. (b) Vortices with increased edge-to-slit separation. (c) Vortices just after the first critical edge-to-slit separation.

creased to approximately double its original value before instability occurs. The pitch of the note, now an octave below the original, will probably then jump back discontinuously to somewhere near the original note. Figure 6.9(b) shows the conditions just before this jump and Fig. 6.9(c) those just after it. The important point stressed by Richardson is that not only does the wavelength of the vortices jump back to approximately half its value just before the critical point, but also the angular spread of the vortices decreases very considerably. It is important that the edge should bisect the two rows of vortices and this adjustment is clearly more critical in Fig. 6.9(c) than in Fig. 6.9(b). Thus if the edge is moved to one side, or if the stream is deflected by means of an obstacle placed near to the side of the orifice, it may be possible to prevent the transition, and to maintain the original mode of lower frequency. This principle is of great importance in organ-building and will be discussed again in Chapter 10.

Brown (1937) has made a complete study of the phenomenon and suggests that the quantitative aspects of the outlines already given are grossly over-simplified. He shows that the frequency of an edge tone depends on the velocity of efflux and on the distance from the slit to the edge. He accepts the evidence of frequency jumps as the slit-to-edge distance is increased, but his work demonstrates that the first jump is not an octave, and further that each successive step is less than the previous one. He shows also that the jumps occur under quite different conditions when the distance is being decreased and that the phenomenon exhibits strong hysteresis. Figure 6.11 shows some of his results for relatively high velocities. He has also written a delightful account of the history of all kinds of applications of jets and edge tones in the production of musical sounds (Brown, 1938).

Figure 6.10 Excitation of an organ pipe by edge tones.

6.5.4 Reeds and related devices

Reeds are usually small, thin strips of cane, metal or plastic, clamped at one end and free to vibrate at the other, in which vibrations are induced by an air stream. There are many ways of classifying reeds, but perhaps the most important for our purpose is the distinction between so-called idiophonic and heterophonic reeds. Idiophonic reeds have a very specific vibration frequency of their own; they are usually made of metal. They may be used as a source of sound as for example in the mouth-organ, piano-accordion, and harmonium, or in association with a tuned resonator as in the reed group of organ pipes. Heterophonic reeds on the other hand have no very specific frequency of their own; they are usually much softer, more flexible and are often made of cane. They can be made to vibrate over a very wide range of frequencies by adjustments of wind pressure, clamping, etc. Examples of heterophonic reeds are those of the oboe and clarinet families of woodwind instruments. In the brass family of wind instruments the lips of the player have much of the character of heterophonic reeds. In the human voice, however, the vocal chords are probably somewhere between the two categories as the basic pitch of the voice appears to be controlled by the tension of the chords, although the adjustment of the resonant cavities of the nose and throat also has considerable influence. We shall consider the individual characteristics of reeds in particular instruments in more detail in Chapter 10. In the present chapter we are more concerned with their basic mechanism.

Crudely speaking a reed is an automatic switch for turning on and off a current of air. There are two principal ways in which it can operate. The so-called "free" reed—of which most idiophonic reeds are examples—consists of a rectangular strip clamped to a plate covering a hole which is slightly larger than the reed. At rest the reed lies nearly in the plane of the plate although a slight curvature is usually found necessary to assist in starting the vibration. The plate forms one wall of an air chamber and, when the pressure is increased, the air in trying to escape forces its way past the reed. The elasticity of the reed then returns

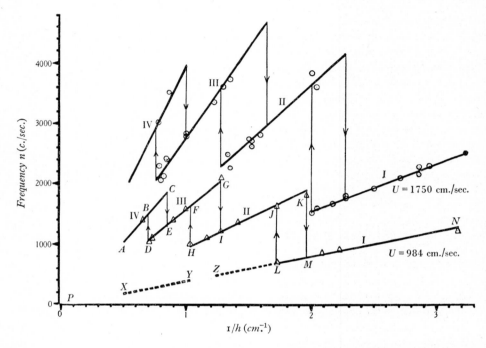

Figure 6.11   Variation of frequency with reciprocal of edge-to-slit distance for high velocities (from Brown, 1937).

it and it is able to pass freely through the hole, and thus in vibration it enlarges and diminishes alternately the space available for the passage of air. It is thus possible to maintain a continuous vibration at almost the natural period of the reed; the air damping first discussed in section 5.7 modifies the natural frequency slightly. The plate to which the reed is clamped acts as a sound board to enhance the note produced. There is thus a periodic force applied to a damped vibrator and the result will involve a transient. Since, however, the period of the force is determined largely by the natural period of the reed there will be no beats and the transient will be almost an exponential rise. The parallel computed example would be that of Fig. 5.6(*a*). Complications can arise if the reed is deliberately bent or made non-uniform, but the tendency is for the wave form produced to be relatively pure for weak excitation and for the relative proportion of higher harmonics to increase considerably as the wind-pressure is increased.

If the idiophonic reed is being used as an initiator for a pipe or resonant cavity—as for example in the reed family of organ pipes—then we must treat the system so far described as a source of periodic puffs of air which are then applied to the pipe. The transient effects which arise will now depend on how closely the pipe and reed are tuned to the same note. Some very curious transient "squawks" can be produced on a reed organ pipe if the two systems are deliberately adjusted to be out of tune with each other.

Heterophonic reeds are more usually of the "beating" type in which the action is almost exactly the reverse of that just described. The air passage is normally open but a high-velocity air stream tends to close it against the elasticity of the reed. Once closed, however, the air flow ceases and hence the force is reduced; the elasticity of the reed then opens the passage and the cycle repeats. In this case the air is cut off rather abruptly and the oscillation is non-symmetrical. The result is, therefore, a set of asymmetric puffs of air whose precise

wave form depends on the physical shape and properties of the reed. It will always, however, tend to have a spectrum which is rich in harmonics because of the relatively steep slope of the wave front just before the abrupt closure of the passage, and it is this richness in harmonics which makes it valuable for exciting vibrations in the reed family of orchestral woodwind instruments. Although the wave form depends largely on the reed the fundamental frequency is very considerably influenced by the pipe or resonator to which it is attached. The back reaction on the reed (or feedback in electronic terms) in the early

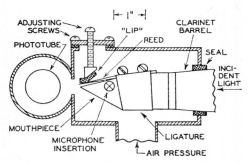

Figure 6.12 Apparatus for observing vibration of a clarinet reed (from Backus, 1961).

stages gives the characteristic transient to which reference was made in the first section of this chapter.

Various experimentalists have attempted to study the mechanism of reed operation. One recent example is the study by Backus (1961) of the vibration of a clarinet reed. The main experimental problem is of course to find a means of examining the behaviour of a reed while it is in the mouth of a player. Backus circumvented this difficulty by the ingenious arrangement shown in Fig. 6.12. An air chamber supplied from a vacuum-cleaner blower surrounds a standard clarinet mouthpiece, and the action of the player's lower lip is simulated by a pad of soft rubber and an adjusting screw (in the figure the mouthpiece is shown upside down relative to the normal position in the mouth of a player). A beam of light is sent down the bore from the open end and passes through the gap (if any) between the reed and the mouthpiece to a photomultiplier tube. Preliminary investigations were made with the photo-tube replaced by a glass window and by observing the motion of the reed under stroboscopic illumination. It was shown that when normal sounds (i.e. not squeals or squeaks) were being produced there was no transverse vibration in the reed, and it could be assumed that the area of the aperture as measured by the response of the photo-tube was proportional to the reed displacement. Backus found that for weak blowing the reed aperture never quite closed and that the motion was almost sinusoidal. For louder sounds, however, the aperture did close and the trace became asymmetric. For extremely loud sounds the aperture was found to be closed for up to half a cycle.

Two other related methods of exciting vibrations in pipes should be mentioned for completeness. The first is the pistonphone (Wente, 1922) which appears to be used only for scientific work at very low frequencies. It consists (see Fig. 6.13) of a piston driven by a rotating cam which permits the generation of sinusoidal variations in pressure of accurately-controlled form. Excitation of a pipe by this method would approach very closely to the theoretical behaviour of a system undergoing sinusoidal forcing and hence its transients would resemble those of Fig. 5.6. The other is the diaphone which is sometimes found as an alternative to a reed as the initiator for organ pipes of very low pitch. It has the advantage of quicker and surer starting and is capable of a great volume of sound; it has also been used as the primary generator for fog-horns. It is in effect a loaded reed; in Fig. 6.14 A is a relatively heavy valve disc (which can completely close the port B) mounted on a spring C. The inertial mass of the disc and the characteristics of the spring determine the period, and the output is almost a square wave. A flexible membrane D is provided

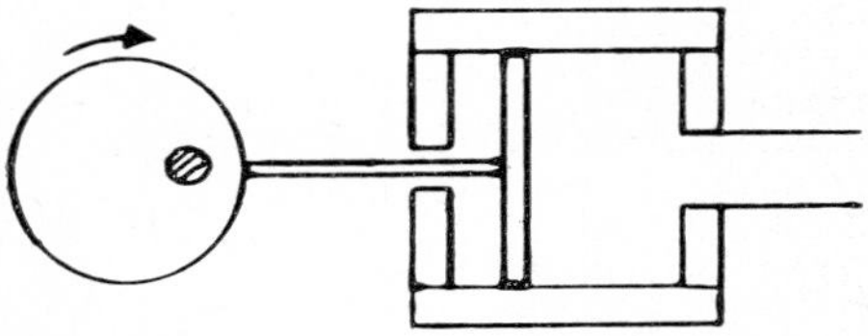

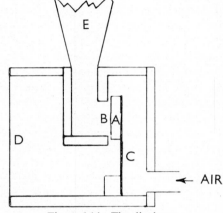

Figure 6.13   The pistonphone (Wente, 1922).

Figure 6.14   The diaphone.

mainly to assist in minimising the back reaction on the main air reservoir resulting from the sudden closure of the valve.

6.6   The analysis of transients

In Chapter 3 we discussed the harmonic content of a complicated periodic sound as the source of its characteristic quality, and this led to the discussion in Chapter 4 of harmonic analysis. In the present chapter we have discussed starting transients and the mechanism of initiation as a further source of quality differences, and it is natural to ask whether harmonic analysis of such non-periodic functions is possible. The first necessity of course is to record the transient wave forms. This has been done by a number of workers including, for example, Nolle and Boner (1941a and b) and Richardson (1954a). Nolle and Boner confined their attention to organ pipes and showed that in general the transient period is longer for flute and diapason pipes than for reed pipes, and that in the early stages of the oscillation very high-frequency components could occur; in some low-pitched pipes it could take as much as half a second for the steady state to become established. Richardson examined various wind instruments as well as organ pipes, and came to the conclusion that during the starting period the wave form is not just a miniature copy of the final steady state as had been claimed by some investigators; he also concluded that it is the starting transients which provide the real distinction between different individual instruments of the same type. The possibility of analysing such non-periodic wave forms has already been suggested in section 4.6.

Any wave can be analysed into harmonics of a fundamental of zero frequency—in other words its spectrum becomes continuous, and the process is one of Fourier transformation rather than Fourier analysis. The optical-diffraction method of analysis introduced in Chapter 4 will be used to illustrate some of the principles involved, and we shall first of all look at the optical patterns produced by various simple functions of the type which occur in musical instruments. In the next section a more mathematical interpretation of the process will be discussed.

The need for analysis arises for three reasons. Firstly, it is part of a proper understanding of their mechanism, secondly it is important in developing new instruments that the transient function should be studied (particularly in electronic or computational synthesisers), and thirdly the effect of the response of recording and reproducing devices can only satisfactorily be considered in terms of the Fourier transforms of the transient terms.

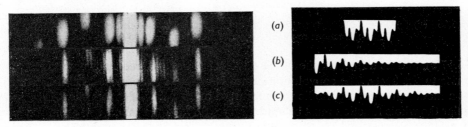

Figure 6.15   (a) Optical-diffraction pattern of a mask representing a limited portion of a periodic wave form. (b) Optical-diffraction pattern of a mask representing the same periodic wave form with instantaneous rise followed by exponential decay. (c) Optical-diffraction pattern of a mask representing the same wave form with exponential rise and fall. The effect is most obvious on the first line on either side of the centre.

The first transient to be studied is really a hypothetical one, since it never arises in practice; it is the result of an instantaneous initiation at a given time of a perfectly periodic wave for a short time followed by an immediate cessation. Figure 6.15(a) is the spectrum of a limited length of a periodic wave form. It can be seen that the original narrow peaks (see, for example, Fig. 4.7) have become broadened and have subsidiary peaks associated with them. Thus the mere act of suddenly initiating and terminating a periodic wave increases the spread of frequencies involved. The widening of the band of frequencies is necessary to carry the information that there is no disturbance from each end of the finite section of the wave form considered up to infinity in either direction. The components making up the spectrum must add up to give the original sinusoidal wave between the two limits and nothing outside it. The second type of transient to be considered is much more likely to occur; it is the exponential rise and fall. Figure 6.15(b) is for an instantaneous rise followed by exponential decay, and Fig. 6.15(c) is for an exponential rise and fall. The various differences in frequency components involved can be clearly seen; the most important point to notice is that the instantaneous rise or fall of (a) and (b) involves a much wider spread in frequency space than the more gradual rise and fall of (c).

In section 4.7 the convolution principle was discussed and we may use it in interpreting these results. Thus it can be seen that the wave shapes used to produce Figs. 6.15(a–c) can all be regarded as products of the continuous wave form and the outline functions shown in

Figs. 6.16(*a–c*). The transforms of the combined functions are thus the separate convolutions of the transforms of Figs. 6.16(*a–c*), each with the sharp peaks from the continuous function. It is thus unnecessary to prepare the whole mask in order to analyse the transient, but merely the mask representing the envelope. As an example of the use of this principle let us suppose that beats occur as well as the exponential rise. The envelope would then be as shown in

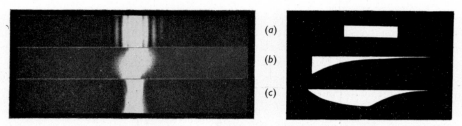

Figure 6.16   (*a*)–(*c*) Optical-diffraction patterns of masks representing the outline functions used to define the functions represented by the masks of Fig. 6.15 (*a–c*).

Fig. 6.17(*a*), and its transform shows the existence of the two frequency components which gave rise to the beats. The convolution principle cannot of course be used if the transient is not a modification of a periodic wave form; in other words, if the transient is completely irregular the whole function must be used. Figures 6.17(*b* and *c*) show two examples of typical instrumental transients; in all these examples the result can be seen to be an extension of the frequencies present. In other words, whenever a non-periodic element is present the band of frequencies required to represent it becomes much greater than that for a periodic

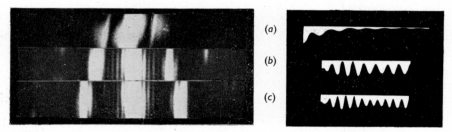

Figure 6.17   (*a*) Optical-diffraction pattern of an outline function representing an exponential rise together with beats. (*b*) and (*c*) Optical-diffraction patterns of masks representing two different instrumental transients.

function. In the next section we shall look at the more mathematical aspects of transient analysis.

*6.7   The mathematical aspects of transient analysis

The transient terms that are of importance in musical instruments can be grouped into several categories. The first group involves modification of the steady state, for example by a sudden rise, by an exponential rise or by a "beat" envelope. In the second group partials, which are not present or which are present in different proportions in the steady state, may make a transitory appearance; these partials may or may not be harmonic. In the third group are those sounds which are quite irregular and which cannot be considered as modifications of a steady periodic wave. In treating the first two groups various properties of Fourier transforms can be used to simplify the mathematical development; in the third group no such simplification is possible. In the first group it is only necessary to compute the transform of the envelope; the complete transform is then the convolution of the transform of the envelope with that of the steady state. In the second group the transforms of the envelopes of the additional partials are required. Each is convoluted with the transform of the partial itself and the sum gives the spectrum of the whole transient. It turns out in practice that the various envelopes involved can also be made up from component parts, again making use of the basic transform properties which were described in sections 4.6 and 4.7. We shall, therefore, first of all deal with one or two basic forms from which more complicated envelopes can be derived.

The first of the forms to be discussed is the step function or instantaneous rise. In practice

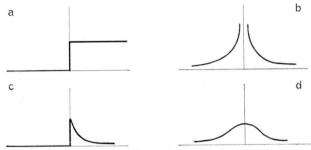

Figure 6.18   (a) Step function in real space. (c) Exponential decay in real space. (b) and (d) Fourier-transform amplitudes for (a) and (c) respectively.

this is never achieved; it would involve the instantaneous transition from zero amplitude to a perfectly periodic wave of constant amplitude. Figure 6.18(a) shows the envelope; it is assumed to be of zero amplitude for $-\infty < x < 0$ and of unit amplitude for $0 < x < \infty$. Such a function presents mathematical difficulties because its area is not finite or, in more mathematical terms, it does not satisfy Dirichlet's conditions. There are various ways of surmounting this difficulty and the reader is referred to mathematical works for a full discussion. From the physicist's point of view the following simple argument is probably satisfactory. We shall first assume that the function is terminated not at $+\infty$ but at some extremely large value of x. Its transform is

$$G(s) = \int_0^\infty \exp(2\pi i x s) \, dx = \left[\frac{\exp(2\pi i x s)}{2\pi i s} \right]_0^\infty.$$

The lower limit can be dealt with satisfactorily, but the upper limit, as already pointed out, causes trouble because the function is oscillatory and changes from -1 to $+1$ as xs changes by an integral number. If we assume, however, that the very large number is an integral number, and that beyond this point the function becomes zero again, the expression becomes zero and the complete transform is merely

$$\frac{-1}{2\pi i s} = \frac{i}{2\pi s}.$$

A more careful mathematical analysis confirms this result. The spectrum is entirely in the imaginary plane: its form is shown in Fig. 6.18(*b*).

The second function to be discussed is not strictly speaking a starting transient. It occurs in termination effects but is also important because it can be used to derive other more complicated functions which do occur as starting transients—it is the exponential decay. Its form is shown in Fig. 6.18(*c*); mathematically it is defined as zero for $-\infty < x < 0$ and $\exp(-\alpha x)$ for $0 < x < \infty$. Its transform is

$$G(s) = \int_0^\infty \exp(-\alpha x) \exp(2\pi i x s)\, dx = \int_0^\infty \exp\{(2\pi i s - \alpha)x\}\, dx$$

$$= \left[\frac{1}{2\pi i s - \alpha} \exp(2\pi i s - \alpha)x\right]_0^\infty$$

$$= \frac{-1}{2\pi i s - \alpha}.$$

(The exponential term can be re-written $\exp(2\pi i x s) \exp(-\alpha x)$; the first term is oscillatory of modulus 1 and the second term is zero if x becomes infinite.) This is clearly a complex function whose amplitude is shown in Fig. 6.18(*d*). It is important to notice that if α becomes zero the exponential decay becomes a unit step function with a transform identical with that derived in the previous paragraph.

With these two functions and the properties discussed in sections 4.6 and 4.7 we can now derive the transforms of a number of useful transient functions. Two examples only will be given here to illustrate the technique. The first is for a single rectangular pulse of the form shown in Fig. 6.19. It can be considered as the difference of two step functions, one of the type discussed earlier in this section translated to a point $-\dfrac{a}{2}$ from the origin, and the other translated to a distance $+\dfrac{a}{2}$ from the origin. The transform of the rectangular pulse is thus the difference of the transforms of the two step functions each multiplied by the exponential phase term to allow for the change of origin. The result is thus

$$\frac{i}{2\pi s} \exp\left(-2\pi i \frac{a}{2} s\right) - \frac{i}{2\pi s} \exp\left(2\pi i \frac{a}{2} s\right) = \frac{\sin \pi a s}{\pi s} = a \cdot \frac{\sin \pi a s}{\pi a s}.$$

This is the well-known sine function multiplied by a, which, because the pulse was of unit height, is in fact the area of the original pulse; the result was shown in Fig. 4.12(*a*). Thus if a pure sinusoidal tone is switched instantaneously on and off for a short period of duration a, its transform, which originally consisted of two single peaks (Fig. 4.12(*a*)), will be convoluted with the sine function and covers a range of frequencies centred on the original one. The second compound function to be considered will be the exponential rise which occurs as an envelope in many transients. It is again a function which does not obey Dirichlet's conditions, but it can be derived from the unit step function and the exponential decay. It is in fact the difference between these two functions (see Fig. 6.20). Its transform is thus the difference between the transforms already derived, namely $G(s) = \dfrac{i}{2\pi s} + \dfrac{1}{2\pi i s - \alpha}$. This is clearly a complex quantity and not a pure imaginary as was the transform of the step function. Its amplitude curve has a very similar form to that of the step function, rising to infinity when $s = 0$ but approaching zero more rapidly as s increases. In other

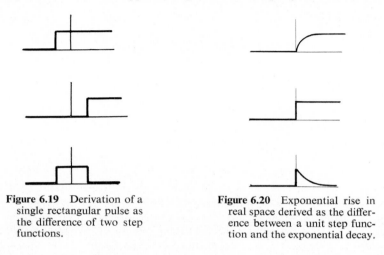

Figure 6.19 Derivation of a single rectangular pulse as the difference of two step functions.

Figure 6.20 Exponential rise in real space derived as the difference between a unit step function and the exponential decay.

words, the high-frequency components are less important; this is clearly reasonable since the rise is much more gradual.

6.8. Summary

This chapter has been concerned with the initiation of musical sounds and we have seen that the principal effect on the spectrum is to increase the spread of frequencies present. Some of the considerations have included termination of sounds as well as initiation, and again we have seen that a sudden termination results in the spreading of frequencies in just the same way as the sudden initiation. Some of the simpler forms of transients have been considered in detail both optically and mathematically, but the more complex forms occurring in practice have been omitted as being beyond the scope of this book. It is clear, however, that both the initiation and termination of musical sounds are extremely important as factors in the recognition of the characteristics of particular instruments. Richardson (1945a) asserts that they are the principal means of distinguishing between instruments of different types. There are, however, still more facts to be considered in determining the quality of the sound produced by an instrument, and the remaining irregular influences will be discussed in the next chapter.

CHAPTER 7

Miscellaneous Other Influences on the Character of a Musical Sound

7.1 Introduction

In our search for the origin of differences in musical quality we have already considered three major factors. We considered first the possibility of vibration in several modes at once, giving rise to a harmonic mixture making a perfectly repetitive wave shape. Secondly, we considered the necessity for amplification and the consequent coupling of vibrating systems which gives rise to transient effects when oscillations are initiated. Thirdly, we considered other transient effects arising from the precise method of initiation. These three are all "necessary" effects; it would be impossible to build a practicable instrument without their presence. It is always difficult to draw hard-and-fast divisions, but there is a fairly clear distinction between these three and the remaining effects which are to be discussed in this chapter; they are the "accidental" effects which nevertheless can have a profound influence on the quality of the sound produced. These effects are often the ones which distinguish one particular specimen of a group of almost identical instruments from others in the same group, or distinguish the sounds produced by different performers on the same instrument. First is the formant, which is the special combination of resonances arising largely from the amplification part of the system. It was tacitly assumed in the chapter on amplification that when broad-band amplification was involved it would be perfectly flat in its response characteristic, that is, that sounds of all pitches would be amplified equally; this in fact is never so, and departures from flatness are partly responsible for the distinction between the tone of individual instruments of the same type.

A second feature which is also characteristic of a particular specimen is the terminal effect, sometimes called the terminal transient. The other two features which will be discussed are partly characteristic of the performer as well as of the instrument; they are incidental noise and vibrato.

7.2 Formants

Richardson (1954b) defines the formant as "... that feature in the sound of an instrument (or of a voice) which distinguishes it from another of the same breed". Other workers have used a slightly narrower definition and have restricted the term formant to non-uniform resonance or amplification effects, and we shall follow this narrower definition. As has already been mentioned, we more-or-less ignored the possibility of an unequal amplification in our consideration of broad-band amplification; it is very clear, however, that a completely flat response curve over the whole of the important frequency range—including, of course, the harmonics as well as the fundamental of the primary vibrator—is unlikely to occur in practice. In general, there will be regions of the spectrum in which amplification peaks or specific resonances will occur. These can have a considerable effect on the quality of sound produced, as in most instruments they tend to remain fixed as the note produced by the primary vibrator is changed in pitch. Thus, for a low note the main amplification might occur in the region of its second harmonic; when a note an octave higher is played the same formant peak would emphasise the fundamental. The harmonic balance is therefore altered and with it the tonal quality. The transient terms are also affected; the formant is in fact a kind of multiplying factor which stamps a definite character on every wave form produced by the instrument.

A crude demonstration of the effect can be based on the familiar trick of talking through a mouth-organ. If a whole "mouthful" of notes is used—that is, no tongue-stopping—and the performer whispers through the instrument, recognisable words emerge which are strongly coloured by the mouth-organ tone. One can consider that the mouth-organ is acting as the resonator with a series of sharp peaks corresponding to the individual mouth-organ notes, and this characteristic is then acting as a formant impressing itself on the wave shape produced by the voice.

The human voice itself depends very much on formants for its character (see Chapter 10). The vocal chords determine the basic pitch of a note, but it is the multiple resonance, of the various coupled cavities of the head which determine the quality of a note. The formants are responsible for the difference between individual voices and also of the difference between vowel sounds. If a particular note, for example, is sung to the vowel "ah" and then to "oh" the basic vibration frequency of the vocal chords does not alter, but the cavity shape—particularly in this example the mouth—provides the distinction between the two vowels. There are two principal formant regions, one at a relatively low frequency and one at a much higher frequency (some workers distinguish two separate high-frequency formants) and they provide the necessary information to the ear and brain which enables the pitch, vowel sound, and voice quality to be recognised more-or-less independently of each other. A very striking demonstration of the influence of formants can be performed if a tuneable filter is available. A recording of a human voice is played back through filters of different band widths set at different mean frequencies. It is astonishing how small a range of frequencies is needed for recognition of the words though the quality of the voice is completely changed. If the filter happens to be tuned to one of the characteristic formant frequencies of a particular sound the result is more like singing than speaking. The same sort of experiment can be performed with a source of white noise; the source is coupled to a loudspeaker via a tuneable filter and the result still resembles white noise, but there is in addition a musical quality. If the frequency of the pass band is lowered, for example, the result is rather like changing a hoarse-whispered "ee" or "ah", to "oh" or "oo". When such a modified recording is played to an audience the reaction is often to describe the sounds as "space noises". Presumably the human vocal quality of the formant in an obviously mechanically-produced basic sound is the source of the rather sinister or mysterious effect.

Most instruments have formants; in the violin family, for instance, they obviously arise from the resonances of the body cavity, and as a result of variations in thickness of the wood. Although not usually classified in this way the "wolf note" (see Chapter 10) is an undesirable peak in the formant characteristic. In wooden instruments the thickness and character of the wood and, to some extent, the head and chest cavities of the player, influence the formant. In the piano the structure of the sound board (and to a very small extent the structure of the case) is involved.

*7.3   Formants considered from the point of view of Fourier transformation

A little earlier in this chapter it was said that the formant is a kind of multiplying factor. The mathematical implications of this can be studied very simply by making use of the

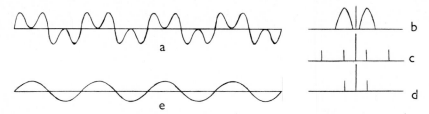

Figure 7.1   (*a*) Primary wave form in time-space. (*b*) Function in frequency-space representing the formant. (*c*) Spectrum of (*a*) in frequency-space. (*d*) Product of (*b*) and (*c*) in frequency-space. (*e*) Transform of (*d*) into time-space.

Fourier-transform properties discussed in Chapter 4. Suppose, for example, that the wave form produced by a primary vibrator is as shown in Fig. 7.1(*a*), and we wish to know what will be the effect on it of a given formant. Let us suppose that the formant is represented by the curve of Fig. 7.1(*b*); it is really a plot of the relative amplification at different frequencies and clearly exists in frequency space. In order to judge its effect we must first transform the curve of Fig. 7.1(*a*) to frequency space—its spectrum is shown in Fig. 7.1(*c*)—then multiply

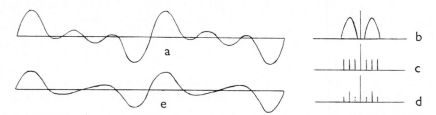

Figure 7.2   (*a*) Primary wave form in time-space. (*b*) Function in frequency-space representing the formant. (*c*) Spectrum of (*a*) in frequency-space. (*d*) Product of (*b*) and (*c*) in frequency-space. (*e*) Transform of (*d*) into time-space.

it by the formant (this product is shown in Fig. 7.1(*d*)) and finally re-transform to time space again. The result is shown in Fig. 7.1(*e*). It is clear that a considerable change in its form has occurred. The effect of the same formant on a different basic wave form is shown similarly in Figs. 7.2(*a*–*e*); although the final result is different the family resemblance implanted by the formant can be seen.

One or two special examples are worth considering. We shall first examine the result when a single sharp pulse is fed into a system with a definite formant. The pulse can be represented mathematically by a peak function (see section 4.9) and its Fourier transform can be derived as follows. Let us suppose that we are dealing with a unit peak function which is zero everywhere except at a time $t = 0$ when it is infinite to such an order that its integrated content is unity, then

$$G(s) = Z_0^1 \exp \{2\pi its\} \, dt$$

which from the definition of Z already adopted is clearly equal to 1 for all values of s. In other words, the Fourier transform of the peak function is an infinite horizontal line at height 1 (see Figs. 7.3(a) and (b)). In physical terms this simply means that a single infinitely-high but infinetisimally wide pulse can only be represented accurately by an infinite number of frequency components infinitesimally close to each other and all of the same amplitude. It may seem rather surprising that such a vast amount of information in frequency space is needed to define such a simple function, until we realise that the large number of terms arises not from the specification of the pulse itself but from the need to specify that the amplitude is completely zero everywhere else.

Suppose now that such a pulse is fed into the system whose formant is indicated by Fig. 7.3(c). The product (Fig. 7.3(d)) is identical with Fig. 7.3(c) and so the final result is

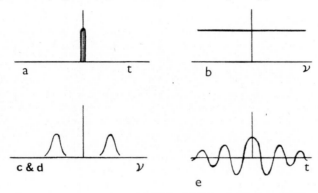

Figure 7.3 (a) Representation of peak function in time-space. (b) Transform of peak function in frequency-space. (c) Function representing a formant in frequency-space. (d) Product of (b) and (c) in frequency-space. (e) Transform of (d) or (c) into time-space.

merely the transform of Fig. 7.3(c)—the formant—which is shown in Fig. 7.3(e). This phenomenon leads to some rather surprising results. Suppose, for example, that a single pulse is fed into a system whose response is perfect resonance at one precise frequency. In theory the spectrum of the single pulse multiplied by the spectrum of this response curve is still the spectrum of the response curve, and hence the result transformed into real space is a sine wave of infinite duration. In electrical terms this is sometimes referred to as a "ringing" circuit. In practice, of course, there is always some damping, which means that the resonance curve—that is the formant—is broadened. Broadening the spectrum corresponds to shortening the length of the sine wave (see, for example, Fig. 4.17), that is, to a musical tone of shorter duration.

This effect—the turning of a single pulse into a musical tone of limited duration—can easily be demonstrated. It is the basis of the well-known production of more or less musical sounds by tapping the teeth or cheeks with a pencil; the pitch can be changed by altering the shape of the resonance cavities of the nose and throat. It is also another way of viewing the ringing tone produced in some narrow passages between buildings (see section 9.2.3 for further details).

It is also important to notice that from the Fourier-transform standpoint white noise, which is a succession of single pulses randomly related in time, has effectively the same transform as that of a single pulse—because of the random phase relationship they merely add in intensity rather than in amplitude (except at the centre—but the formant amplitude is almost certainly zero at zero frequency). Thus, if white noise is fed through a system with a characteristic response curve it takes on more-or-less musical qualities. (Section 7.2.)

7.4 Terminal effects

We have already considered some terminal effects in the section on transients and it was pointed out that they can have an important influence upon the quality of a musical sound. They are perhaps most important in instruments producing a percussive sound, including those involving plucked or struck strings. In such instruments almost the whole sound is termination with no steady state, and the important feature to be studied is the relative damping of the different overtones present. Myer and Buchmann (1931) discuss the differential damping in their study of the tone produced by a piano. Their technique includes recording and subsequent reverse playback (see section 6.2), and this highlights a change in quality with time.

Another terminal effect which is quite significant is the tendency for an instrument with a resonant cavity of some kind to go on radiating a given note for an appreciable time after the primary vibrator has moved to a new frequency. Tape-reversal again provides an excellent way of demonstrating this effect. For example, a passage played on a solo violin when reversed sounds at times as though two violins are involved; the first note is still being radiated by the body of the violin when the string has already begun to vibrate for the next note. Normally one is so used to this effect that it is not noticed; with reversed tape the sounds are much more easily identified. It is, of course, important that recordings for this purpose should be made in an acoustically-dead room, or the reverberation—which is itself a kind of resonance (see Chapter 9)—will mask the effect.

7.5 Incidental noise

All musical instruments produce a surprising amount of pure noise with no musical quality at all, and this plays a considerable part in determining the characteristic sound both of a particular instrument and of a particular player. A very striking method of demonstrating this is to record a long steady note of a certain pitch and then to re-record several times through a tuneable filter set to reject each harmonic of the steady state in turn. In this way all the steady-state components are removed and only the noise (and transients) remains. Friedlander (1953) points out that for very small bowing speeds the proportion of white noise produced by a violin bow is increased, and the "breathy" sound associated with the playing of a flute is another very obvious source of noise; various clicks and squeaks arise in the playing of all woodwind instruments and it is surprising how characteristic these can be of given instruments and given players. Báron (1958) and Bartholomew (1942) discuss the occurrence of noise associated with the piano where the musical sound of the hammer striking the string is an important component of the tone. In most pianos the noise element is greater for the strings of higher pitch. Bartholomew also points out the important part played by deliberate noise—drums, cymbals, etc.—in defining rhythm and in adding to climactic effects with massed instruments.

7.6 Vibrato

Perhaps one of the most controversial subjects in this extremely subjective field is that of the part played by vibrato in instrumental playing and in singing. Vibrato is the term given to a periodic modulation—usually of both amplitude and frequency—of a sound which can, if used discreetly, enhance the pleasing quality. The phenomenon has been studied by numerous workers although more attention has been paid to vibrato in singing than in instrumental playing. The observed effects seem to be that a frequency of 6–8 c.p.s. is the optimum, that usually both amplitude and frequency are modified—normally either in-phase or 180° out-of-phase—and that, contrary to the belief of many critics and performers, practically all singers use vibrato. Even those who claim not to do so can usually be shown by oscillograph studies to produce quite large modulations. The limit of the frequency modulation is often about a quarter of a tone each way.

There have been many suggestions to account for the pleasing effect of vibrato. Sacerdote (1957) quotes Fournier's assertion that vibrato in the human voice is part of the frequency-regulating mechanism. It can easily be shown (by producing loud masking sounds in ear-phones) that feedback is necessary either through the air or by tone conduction in order to maintain control of the pitch of the voice. The time delay in this feedback mechanism is about 0·15 seconds and this fits in very nicely with the 6·5-cycle modulation frequency that has already been mentioned; in other words it reflects a kind of "hunting" of the stabilising mechanism. The dependent suggestion is that since vibrato is so universal in the human voice, instrumental players tend to achieve a human quality by making use of it.

Another view is that the ear finds absolutely steady sounds tedious. It is certainly true that a steady pure tone can be very unpleasant if sounded for a long period. Several auxiliary effects arise; one simple one is that a definite standing wave pattern may be created in the room, and hence a steady note of mixed harmonic content can apparently change in quality if the observer's position is changed very slightly. A slight frequency wobble of the vibrato keeps the standing wave pattern moving, and hence the effect of the observer's movements is minimised. Winckel (1960) points out that all natural animal sounds involve modulation of some kind. No completely steady note is ever produced by an animal, and in fact an artificially-produced steady note is completely ignored. The familiar notion that one "hears" a clock stopping, or that one becomes conscious of a fan only when it is switched off, further illustrates this point. It is interesting also to note that a steady hum or whine is always instinctively associated with machinery rather than with a sound of animal origin.

A further possibility is that vibrato heightens concentration. If a sound is completely steady the brain loses interest in it; if it varies then concentration is enhanced because a definite activity is involved in following the changes. It is possible that there is a relationship between the decrease in the sensitivity to a steady sound of long duration, and the dis-appearance from perception of a retinal image which is artificially fixed in relation to the retina instead of being scanned by the normal eye movements (e.g. Ditchburn, 1955). The vibrato may in other words be a means of providing a scanning mechanism.

Whatever the true explanation, the importance of the right frequency of modulation and the undoubted improvement in general tone resulting from the application of vibrato is universally accepted. The frequency can be studied by playing-back recordings at different speeds. For example, if a recording of a cello playing a slow passage is played back at twice the speed the pitch goes up to that of a violin, but the rapid vibrato is quite unpleasant. Similarly, if a violin recording is slowed down it does not sound like a cello because the vibrato is too slow. This technique was suggested by Seashore (1938) who has made a very full study of the psychological aspects of music and devotes much attention to vibrato. His analyses, note by note, of actual performances by singers and instrumentalists illustrate the surprising extent both of pitch and intensity variations and the extremely wide incidence of vibrato. He supports the general thesis put forward by other workers that one is often not conscious of it as changes of pitch or intensity but rather as an additional warmth of tone.

7.7 The effect of vibrato on the spectrum of a sound

From the point of view of Fourier transformation vibrato involves the multiplication of the original steady wave form by a modulating function at the vibrato frequency. In

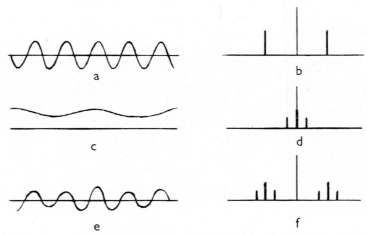

Figure 7.4 (a) Basic wave form in time-space. (b) Transform of (a) in frequency-space. (c) Function representing vibrato-modulation in time-space. (d) Transform of (c) in frequency-space. (e) Product of (a) and (c) in time-space. (f) Convolution of (b) and (d) in frequency-space.

frequency space therefore a convolution is involved—the convolution of the transform of the unmodified tone with that of the modulating wave form. If only amplitude modulation is involved the result is to introduce two "side-band" frequencies corresponding to the sum and difference of the basic frequency and the vibrato frequency; Fig. 7.4 illustrates this. (This effect is precisely the inverse of the "beat" effect which is discussed in the next chapter. Here the beat modulation is imposed and the result is the presence of extra frequencies; in the next chapter the effect of adding extra frequencies to produce variations of amplitude will be discussed.) If, as is usually the case, frequency modulation is involved, the result is much more complicated. It can be interpreted as a convolution in time space. The frequency-modulated wave can be considered as the convolution of a repetitive peak function defining the vibrato period and a function representing the frequency changes involved in a single cycle of the vibrato. Figure 7.5 illustrates the derivation, and it can be seen that the result is a product of the transforms of the two functions; in other words, a fairly large number of extra frequencies are introduced, and these extra frequencies are spaced at the vibrato-frequency apart. Suppose we consider a note of 440 c.p.s. with a vibrato period of 7 c.p.s.; this would lead to a series of notes on either side of the basic note spaced at about 1/8th of a tone from each other. It is thus possible that the ear hears this as a blended tone as though several performers were playing at once.

Clearly there is no one answer to this extremely complex psychological problem, but all the above interpretations seem to have some relevance.

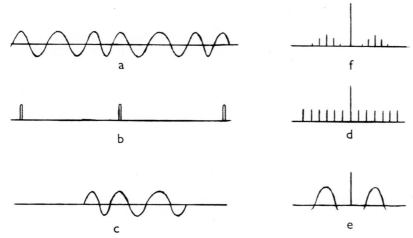

Figure 7.5 (*a*) Basic wave form with frequency vibrato in time-space. (*b*) Peak function representing vibrato period in time-space. (*c*) Function representing the wave form within one cycle of vibrato in time-space. (*d*) Transform of (*b*) in frequency-space. (*e*) Transform of (*c*) in frequency-space. (*f*) Since (*a*) is the convolution of (*b*) and (*c*) its transform is the product of (*d*) and (*e*) which is shown here in frequency-space.

7.8 Non-harmonic partials

In the sections on simple vibrating systems (2.6–2.10 inclusive) it was shown that the partials of a string or pipe should in theory be harmonically related to the true fundamental. In practice, however, the conditions under which these results were derived rarely hold. For example, the string is never anchored completely rigidly at each end—there is always some movement of the supports or of the bridge. Also the string has some lateral stiffness which has not been taken into account, and hence the higher partials for most stringed instruments may not be precisely harmonic. In wind instruments the precise point at which the reflexion occurs at an open end is difficult to define. Clearly the wave emerges a little and there is an "end correction" which depends on the relative diameter of the bore in relation to the wavelength involved, and which also may be influenced by the presence of any kind of flare of bell. The high notes of a woodwind instrument are produced by opening or closing side holes and so the thickness of the wall, the shape of the hole and the valves will all have an effect The important point is that the effects both in strings and woodwind will differ according to the wavelength of sound involved. In other words, they will differ for different modes of vibration of the same instrument, and hence lead to the possible existence of non-harmonic partials. The extent of the departure from harmonicity varies from instrument to instrument, and is often characteristic of individual specimens. The discordant partials add further character to the tone colour produced by the instrument. Nolle and Boner (1941*a*) have in fact demonstrated that the first four partials of an organ pipe and of a violin string are strictly harmonic once the steady state has been achieved.

CHAPTER 8

Combinations of Notes

8.1 Introduction

We have now reached a significant stage in the collection of design data for a new musical instrument. Many facets have been considered, and if we were merely concerned with the limited definition of a musical instrument put forward in Chapter 1 we should now be in a position to proceed with a design. The definition called for a device "for producing musical sounds that can be varied in order to play tunes". If our interest stops at melody—i.e. the building-up of sequences of single notes in time—the present chapter could be omitted. However, most music—particularly in the West—involves harmony as well as melody; in other words our music demands the simultaneous sounding of different notes by different instruments. This at once introduces complications, and we shall see that these are not only important for themselves but also shed light on some features of instrumental tone that have not yet been fully developed. We need, for example, to consider not only the effects of notes on separate instruments played together, but to investigate some of the effects of the simultaneous sounding of several partials in a single instrument. From some points of view one can consider a single note played by a single instrument as a chord, and hence the considerations of this chapter may be said to apply to melodic music if performed with anything other than a single pure tone.

We shall first consider the physical effects which can occur when two or more notes are sounded together. We shall then try to discover the connections between physical principles and the musician's search for a convenient standard sequence of notes in which to record his music, i.e. the concept of the musical scale. Finally we shall try to discover why certain combinations of notes sound pleasanter to the ear than others.

8.2 Beats

The phenomenon of beats is very well known and can be demonstrated easily. Any two sources of musical tone differing in frequency by a few c.p.s. give rise to a combined sound which to the ear and brain is recognised as a single tone of frequency midway between the two, pulsating in amplitude at a rate which turns out to be the difference of the frequencies of the two tones (two tuning-forks of the same pitch, one of which is loaded with a piece of plasticine on one of the prongs, or two organ pipes of nominally the same pitch, are probably the best sources to use if two electronic signal generators are not available). The phenomenon is of wide practical application as it provides a precise method of tuning two sources to the same frequency. It is used, for example, by organ- and piano-tuners for this purpose. It also provides an exact way of tuning the two generators to give notes which are a given amount different in pitch, provided that the difference is only a few c.p.s. This again is useful in tuning instruments to particular temperaments (see section 8.6). From time to time rather meaningless discussions have arisen concerning which is the reality, the two separate tones or the pulsating single tone. The Fourier-transform viewpoint clarifies the issue (see next section for fuller details). It was made clear in section 4.5 that the two alternative representations of a function in time space or frequency space are in every way equivalent as far as their information content is concerned. The two-tone aspect is the frequency-space representation of the combined function, the pulsating single tone is clearly the time-space representation, and they are completely equivalent (Fig. 8.1). An extremely interesting point arises when one considers the ear and the brain mechanism involved. If two tones are far apart in pitch the physiological response appears to be controlled by the frequency-space representation; if they are very close together the response appears to be controlled by the time-space representation. This point will be considered again in the discussion of the hearing process in section 9.4.5.

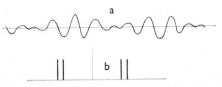

Figure 8.1   Beats. (*a*) In time space. (*b*) In frequency-space.

*8.3   Mathematical treatment of beats

The mathematical treatment is extremely straightforward. Suppose that the two tones involved are represented by equations of the same form as equation [2.13],

$$y_1 = a \sin 2\pi(\kappa_1 x - v_1 t) \qquad [8.1]$$

$$y_2 = a \sin 2\pi(\kappa_2 x - v_2 t). \qquad [8.2]$$

They are assumed to have the same amplitude but different wave numbers and frequencies κ_1, κ_2 and v_1, v_2 respectively. If we assume a linear system the principle of superposition (section 3.6) holds and the resultant is obtained merely by adding

$$y_1 + y_2 = 2a \sin 2\pi \left\{ \frac{\kappa_1 + \kappa_2}{2} x - \frac{v_1 + v_2}{2} t \right\} \cos 2\pi \left\{ \frac{\kappa_1 - \kappa_2}{2} x - \frac{v_1 - v_2}{2} t \right\}. \qquad [8.3]$$

If we combine the term $2a$ with the cosine term and treat this as the amplitude the equation is then of the same form as [8.1] and clearly corresponds to a wave of wave number and frequency which is the mean of [8.1] and [8.2], but with an amplitude that varies cosinusoidally with a wave number and frequency equal to *half* the difference between those of [8.1] and [8.2]. A moment's reflexion will show that although the frequency of the beats appears to be $\dfrac{v_1 - v_2}{2}$ in point of fact this refers to a full cycle; the ear cannot distinguish between positive and negative amplitude maxima and hence two maxima per cycle are heard, and the effective frequency is just $v_1 - v_2$.

It is convenient—particularly as an introduction to the next section—to consider the phenomenon of beats from the point of view of Fourier transformation. The problem is to find the transform of a function which represents the sum of two tones. Figures 8.2(*a*) and (*b*) are the frequency-space representations of the two tones and Fig. 8.2(*c*) is their sum. Figure 8.2(*c*) can be regarded as the convolution of two functions shown in Figures 8.2(*d*) and (*e*). In time space, therefore, the transform of the convolution is the product of the transforms of Figs. 8.2(*d*) and (*e*). The transform of Fig. 8.2(*d*) is a sine wave of frequency intermediate between that of the two separate tones, and the transform of Fig. 8.2(*e*) is a sine wave with a frequency equal to the difference of the two original tones; the final product, as in Fig. 8.1(*a*), agrees with that predicted by equation [8.3]. This way of considering the process emphasises the equivalence of the representations in time and frequency space.

8.4 Combination tones

It is interesting to consider what happens if two tones are sounded simultaneously and their pitch separation is then gradually increased. At first beats will be heard but their frequency will increase until they are too rapid to be heard. If very loud sounds are used and the difference in the pitches of the notes is still further increased one becomes conscious of at least one further sound in addition to the two basic tones. Careful listening—which is difficult because of the probable existence of harmonics of the basic tones—shows that in fact at least two new tones are present, neither of which is present when the tones are sounded separately. The two new tones have frequencies equal to the sum and to the difference of the two basic tones. The simplest way to demonstrate their existence is to use two audio-signal generators feeding a loudspeaker. One generator is kept at a fixed frequency of about 1,000 c.p.s., and the other fixed at 500 c.p.s. is switched on and off intermittently. The audience hears in addition to the two basic sounds an intermittent high tone at 1,500 c.p.s. This of course is the sum tone; the difference tone is equal in frequency to one of the exciting tones and hence does not distract attention. If the experiment is repeated with a fixed tone of 1,000 c.p.s. and an intermittent tone of 1,500 c.p.s. the audience will have the impression of an intermittent 500-cycle tone; in this case the difference tone is heard and the sum tone which is now at 2,500 cycles is high enough not to distract attention. An even more striking demonstration can be given by holding one generator fixed at 1,000 c.p.s. and changing the frequency of the other generator slowly from 500 cycles to 1,000 cycles; if the sounds are sufficiently loud the audience will hear an additional tone starting at 500 cycles and descending gradually to zero frequency. If the composite sound is recorded and played back to an audience at fairly high level the phenomenon is even more pronounced.

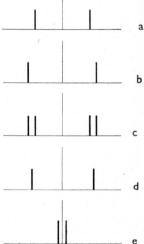

Figure 8.2 (*a*) and (*b*) are the frequency-space representations of two simple tones, and (*c*) is their sum. (*c*) May be regarded as the convolution of the two functions shown at (*d*) and (*e*).

In order to clarify the issue at stake let us go back to the question with which this section commenced. What really happens when the pitch separation is increased? If an oscillograph is connected to the output of the two generators no discontinuity is apparent; the beat wave form—one sine wave modulating another—continues smoothly. The mean frequency and the modulating frequency both change, but no matter how large an interval of pitch there is no discontinuity. Young (1784) sought to explain the difference tone merely as beats of such rapid occurrence that they became blended into a sound of definite pitch. Helmholtz

(1877), however, rejected this explanation because it failed to account for the sum tone. There is clearly some connection between the two phenomena however. A clue to the connection is contained in the reference already made to the fact that sum and difference tones— or combination tones—are more clearly heard for very loud sounds, and also to the fact that the experiment works better if the combined sounds are recorded and played back. The solution lies in the non-linear response of the ear, which is more apparent at high intensities; recording and reproduction also tend to involve non-linearities unless very great care is taken and this effect is still further enhanced.

We have so far assumed that the principle of superposition applies to all our considerations, i.e. if two disturbances y_1 and y_2 are applied to a system the combined result is merely $y_1 + y_2$. If the system is non-linear this is no longer true. For example, if a particular system responds to the square of the displacement it is clear that $y_1^2 + y_2^2$ is not the same as $(y_1 + y_2)^2$. A complete understanding of the phenomenon depends on a mathematical approach, one form of which will be given in the next section. However, a parallel from modern everyday life may help to clarify the phenomenon for non-mathematicians. It is well known that useful audible signals transmitted by radio are conveyed as modulation of a basic carrier wave. If the modulated carrier wave is fed straight to the loudspeaker no sound will be heard although if it is fed to an oscillograph of suitable characteristics the modulations can be clearly seen.

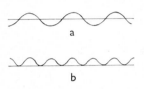

Figure 8.3 (*a*) Sinusoidal wave. (*b*) Function representing the square of the function shown in *a*.

This is analogous to the condition when the separation of the two tones is too far apart for beats to be heard; an oscillograph shows that they exist as a modulating envelope. In the radio-receiver a "detector" or demodulator is necessary—often a valve used on a non-linear part of its characteristic or a crystal with non-linear response—in order to produce a signal proportional to the modulation envelope. The non-linear properties of the ear or of a recording system act as a detector in just the same way and make the modulation—in this case the difference tone—apparent. There is also a further complication: if a sine wave—complete with the negative parts of its cycle— is squared the result is a sine wave of twice the frequency with no negative component (see Fig. 8.3). Thus even a single pure tone will have the second harmonic added to it if there is any element of "squaring" in the response. This results in what are called aural harmonics, i.e. harmonics which are only present as real components after a wave has passed through a non-linear system such as the ear.

We thus see that, in the presence of even a small amount of square-law distortion, a wave which started out as the simple sum of two tones can have added to it sum and difference (combination) tones and second harmonics of both basic tones (aural harmonics). Just as in considering the beat phenomenon, the question of the real existence of the tones can be examined in terms of Fourier transforms. The frequency-space representation after passage through a non-linear system now includes the separate components and in this sense they can be regarded as real. In time space the original wave form symmetrical above and below the horizontal axis is now replaced by an asymmetric wave form. It is also important to notice that the process may be cumulative. Once the extra components—combination tones or aural harmonics—have been established, if the wave then passes through further non-linear systems, sum and difference tones and aural harmonics of the existing components may be produced. The resulting structure can clearly become very complex indeed.

The influence of non-linearity in introducing extra components can be demonstrated by means of optical transforms. Figure 8.4(b) shows the transform of the simple wave form shown in Fig. 8.4(a). It consists of two components of relative frequency 2:3. Figure 8.4(c) shows the same wave form squared and the resulting transform—Fig. 8.4(d)—shows peaks at frequencies corresponding to 1, 4, 5 and 6.

*8.5 Mathematical treatment of combination tones

The mathematical treatment will be confined to a Fourier-transform interpretation. A full analysis would involve a detailed knowledge of the precise form of non-linearity which occurs in the ear and in the hearing mechanism, and since there are considerable doubts about many factors in this process (see Chapter 9) we shall confine our attention to demonstrating the

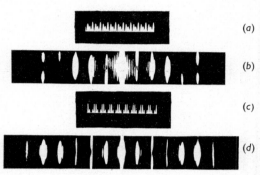

Figure 8.4 (a) Mask representing the sum of two sinusoidal waves of frequency ratio 2:3. (b) Optical transform of (a). (c) Mask representing the square of (a). (d) Optical transform of (c).

general lines along which the explanation might proceed. It may ultimately turn out that a more precise study of the exact nature of the relative intensities of combination tones and aural harmonics might lead to a more detailed knowledge of the hearing mechanism. Whatever the form of the response it can be expressed as a power series, and we shall content ourselves with a demonstration that even squared terms are enough to account for sum and difference tones.

Let us suppose that the response ϕ of the ear can be represented by an equation of the type

$$\phi = ay + by^2 + cy^3 + dy^4 \ldots \qquad [8.4]$$

where y is the instantaneous pressure or displacement in the sound wave. For our present purpose we shall assume that $c = d = e$, etc. $= 0$. The problem to be considered is clearly the nature of the operation in reciprocal space corresponding to squaring in real space. Squaring is simply self-multiplication and hence in the reciprocal space the corresponding operation is self-convolution. Let us consider the consequence of applying this principle to the problem of two pure tones of different frequencies applied to a square-law system. Figure 8.5 demonstrates the result; Fig. 8.5(a) is the Fourier transform—i.e. the frequency spectrum—of the original two waves. It is now necessary to convolute (Fig. 8.5(a)) with itself. Two steps in this process are illustrated in Figs. 8.5(b) and (c); the function (a) is placed successively at each point of the function (a) and the sum of all four operations is shown in Fig. 8.5(d). The combination now involves a steady term which arises from the rectification process since squaring removes the negative parts of the cycles. It also includes the sum and difference tones and the aural harmonics. These are now actual constituents of the tone. In a real system there would of course be linear as well as square-law terms, and if, for the sake of argument, we let $a = b$ in equation [8.4] the total result can be found by adding Figs. 8.5(a) and (d), and is shown in Fig. 8.5(e). We now see that in the presence of a square-law term the sum and difference components assume real existence.

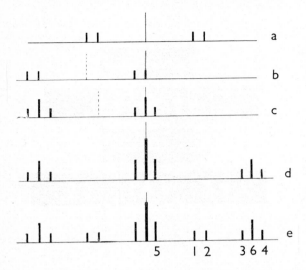

Figure 8.5 (a) Frequency-space representation of the sum of two waves of different frequencies. (b) and (c) The first two steps in the process of self-convolution of (a). (d) The final self-convolution which is the frequency-space representation of the square of the sum of the two waves. (e) Frequency-space representation of a combination of (a) and (d); the numbered elements have the following significance (1) basic tone of frequency A, (2) basic tone of frequency B, (3) aural harmonic of frequency 2A, (4) aural harmonic of frequency 2B, (5) difference tone of frequency B−A, (6) summation tone of frequency B + A.

The aural harmonics would arise for just a single tone, and the corresponding development is shown in Figs. 8.6(a–c).

8.6 Musical scales—introduction

We shall shortly consider the extremely interesting problem of why certain combinations of notes sounded simultaneously have a pleasant effect whereas other combinations are harsh and unpleasant. Before proceeding to that discussion, however, it will be helpful to consider the origin of the musician's classification of notes and intervals, in other words the

Figure 8.6 (a) Frequency-space representation of a single tone. (b) First step in the self-convolution process applied to (a). (c) Completed self-convolution which is the frequency-space representation of the square of the single tone, and clearly consists of a tone of twice the frequency of (a).

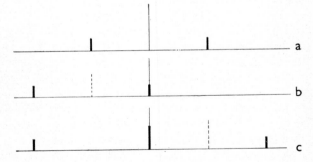

origin of the idea of a musical scale. Why is a scale necessary at all? Clearly, from the scientific point of view, an infinite range of frequencies between the lowest and the highest to which the ear is sensitive can be produced. Music can in fact be written for electronic performance (see Chapter 11) by specifying simply the frequencies required. For most conventional instruments, however, all possible frequencies cannot be produced nor could a musical score in this form be read quickly enough. Some form of standardisation of notes is thus necessary, both for writing and for performance, and the result is a musical scale. The complications and difficulties arise when one attempts to form a scale which will, on the one hand, provide the necessary flexibility in use, permit the performance of music at different basic pitches on the same instrument, and include some of the steps which seem to be accepted by most people as pleasant, and on the other hand not require an impracticable number of notes. A great many possible solutions have been put forward, many of which are purely theoretical. There are also many technical factors—such as the size of the fingers in stringed instruments, and the precision of location and size of holes in woodwind instruments—which make it completely unrealistic to discuss scales involving ratios specified to one part in 100,000 as has been done on occasions. We shall confine attention to three of the solutions that have been put forward, the first of which arises from the earliest recorded scientific work in this field.

8.7 Pythagorean scale

As has already been mentioned Pythagoras investigated the ratios of the vibrating lengths of a string under constant tension which give rise to pleasing intervals of sound. He soon discovered that the interval which is now called the octave seemed to define a natural scale. If the note given by a string is observed as it is successively shortened a feeling of completion seems to occur every time the length is halved. Although Pythagoras worked in terms of length of string it is now more convenient to translate his lengths into the corresponding frequencies which—as we found in Chapter 2—are inversely proportional to the length of the wire in use. He further found that certain other simple ratios led to natural pauses at smaller intervals than those of the complete cycle of the octave; these had frequency ratios of 3:2 and 4:3. Starting from a given base note and ascending by first one and then the other of these two intervals leads to two notes whose pitch difference is small but clearly recognisable. This interval has a ratio of $\dfrac{3}{2}\Big/\dfrac{4}{3} = \dfrac{9}{8}$. This seemed to be a suitable small step into which to divide up the much larger interval of the octave, and Pythagoras sought ways of dividing up the octave into steps of about this size. Steps having some simple frequency relationship were sought in order to fit in with his ideas about the perfection of small numbers. His divisions are based entirely on powers of 3 and 2. Let us take a certain base note of frequency represented as 1 and then ascend by successive intervals having a frequency ratio $\frac{3}{2}$. The result is the sequence of notes shown in Table 1.

Table 1

$$1 \qquad \frac{3}{2} \qquad \left(\frac{3}{2}\right)^2 \qquad \left(\frac{3}{2}\right)^3 \qquad \left(\frac{3}{2}\right)^4 \qquad \left(\frac{3}{2}\right)^5$$

$$= 1 \qquad \frac{3}{2} \qquad \frac{9}{4} \qquad \frac{27}{8} \qquad \frac{81}{16} \qquad \frac{243}{32}$$

All except the first two lie outside the range of a single octave, but if we descend from each of these notes by octaves (i.e. multiply successively by $\frac{1}{2}$) until all the resulting notes lie between 1 and 2, the result, rearranged into ascending order of frequency, is the sequence shown in Table 2.

Table 2

1	$\dfrac{9}{8}$	$\dfrac{81}{64}$	$\dfrac{3}{2}$	$\dfrac{27}{16}$	$\dfrac{243}{128}$
1	1·12	1·26	1·5	1·68	1·90

If such a sequence of notes is played the gap between the third and fourth members seems to be greater than any of the others, and furthermore the interval already mentioned as a pleasant one, $\frac{4}{3}$, is not included. It fits conveniently into the gap between the third and fourth members, and in fact it can be derived from the sequence of powers of $\frac{3}{2}$ if one permits the descent of one such step from the base note instead of an ascent. The sequence of powers becomes as shown in Table 3.

Table 3

$$\frac{2}{3} \quad 1 \quad \frac{3}{2} \quad \left(\frac{3}{2}\right)^2 \quad \left(\frac{3}{2}\right)^3 \quad \left(\frac{3}{2}\right)^4 \quad \left(\frac{3}{2}\right)^5$$

The resulting series of frequencies, on transferring to the same octave, as before, and completed by adding the octave above the base note, becomes the sequence known as the diatonic scale; its eight steps as shown in Table 4 give rise to the name octave.

Table 4

1	$\dfrac{9}{8}$	$\dfrac{81}{64}$	$\dfrac{4}{3}$	$\dfrac{3}{2}$	$\dfrac{27}{16}$	$\dfrac{243}{128}$	2

There are other ratios which form the diatonic scale of eight notes as will be seen later, but this is the Pythagorean version. Musicians give names to the intervals between notes based on the position in such a diatonic scale. For example, the interval between 1 and $\frac{9}{8}$ would be called a second, that from 1 to $\frac{4}{3}$ a fourth, etc. It could thus be said that the Pythagorean scale is built entirely on the basis of fifths and octaves.

Let us now examine the ratios between successive steps in this scale; they are shown in Table 5.

Table 5

1	$\dfrac{9}{8}$	$\dfrac{81}{64}$	$\dfrac{4}{3}$	$\dfrac{3}{2}$	$\dfrac{27}{16}$	$\dfrac{243}{128}$	2
$\dfrac{9}{8}$	$\dfrac{9}{8}$	$\dfrac{256}{243}$	$\dfrac{9}{8}$	$\dfrac{9}{8}$	$\dfrac{9}{8}$	$\dfrac{256}{243}$	

The ratio $\frac{9}{8}$ is called a tone or whole tone and $\frac{256}{243}$ is a semi-tone. The sequence of notes corresponds roughly to the white notes on the piano beginning on C. Scales starting at other points in this sequence, and hence having a different succession of tones and semi-tones, later gave rise to the various so-called modes culminating in the full series of "Gregorian" modes used by the mediaeval church. The reader is referred to various encyclopaedias and dictionaries of music for fuller discussion of these.

Two important points about the Pythagorean scale must now be made: the first is that no matter how far (in either direction) one proceeds in steps of consecutive fifths (powers of $\frac{3}{2}$ or $\frac{2}{3}$) one can never reach a note which is a whole number of octaves above or below the base note; the second is that, by extending the powers of $\frac{3}{2}$ and $\frac{2}{3}$, a fuller sequence of notes which are roughly a semi-tone apart can be derived, as shown in Table 6.

Table 6

$$\left(\frac{2}{3}\right)^6 \quad \left(\frac{2}{3}\right)^5 \quad \left(\frac{2}{3}\right)^4 \quad \left(\frac{2}{3}\right)^3 \quad \left(\frac{2}{3}\right)^2 \quad \left(\frac{2}{3}\right) \quad 1 \quad \frac{3}{2} \quad \left(\frac{3}{2}\right)^2 \quad \left(\frac{3}{2}\right)^3 \quad \left(\frac{3}{2}\right)^4 \quad \left(\frac{3}{2}\right)^5 \quad \left(\frac{3}{2}\right)^6$$

If this sequence is treated as that in Table 1 (i.e. by multiplying by appropriate powers of 2 or $\frac{1}{2}$) and rearranged in ascending sequence it becomes as shown in Table 7.

Table 7

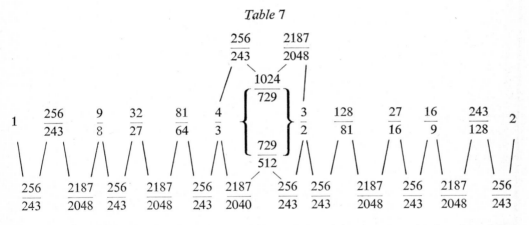

It will be seen that two different values arise for the note lying between the fourth and fifth members of the diatonic scale. In fact, if Table 6 had been extended further in both directions two different notes would occur in each of the whole-tone intervals of the diatonic scale. The musician's convention is that those derived by moving upwards in fifths are called sharps (♯) and take the letter of the note below, and those derived downwards in fifths are called flats (♭) and take the letter of the note immediately above. Table 7 includes the intervals between the notes of the new scale, and it can be shown that wherever a sharp is involved it bears a ratio $\frac{2187}{2048}$ to the note below, from which it takes its name, and where a flat is involved it bears a ratio $\frac{2187}{2048}$ to the note above, from which it takes its name. Table 8 shows the symbols corresponding to the scale of Table 7—the so-called chromatic scale—completed to the same extent as Tables 6 and 7.

Table 8

$$C \quad D^\flat \quad D \quad E^\flat \quad E \quad F \left\{ \begin{array}{c} G^\flat \\ \hline F^\sharp \end{array} \right\} G \quad A^\flat \quad A \quad B^\flat \quad B \quad C$$

The disadvantages of the Pythagorean method of dividing the scale are first that no succession of fifths leads back to the octave, and second that when used in harmony—i.e. when two or more notes are sounded simultaneously—some of the intervals are rather harsh. The precise reasons for this will be discussed in more detail later, but it will be noticed that the sequence of harmonics produced by a string or pipe leads naturally to notes which do not fit exactly in the Pythagorean system. If one attempts to build a scale into which most of the harmonics would fit the result is the system known as Just intonation.

8.8 Just intonation

The precise origin of the various musical scales is often very difficult to reconstruct. Indeed, it is important to heed the warning given by Parry (1930) and stressed by Bartholomew (1942) ". . . to guard at the outset against the familiar misconception that scales are made first and music afterwards. Scales are made in the process of endeavouring to make music and continue to be altered and modified, generation after generation, even till the art has assumed a high degree of maturity." We shall be concerned now with one possible method of constructing the diatonic scale of Just intonation, but it is unlikely that this in fact was the method by which it was originally developed.

We begin by taking a base note and two other notes a fifth above and a fifth below. On each of these three notes the first five members of the harmonic series are produced, and then all the resulting notes are reduced to within the same octave by the process already used in developing the Pythagorean scale. The result is a set of eight notes which are not completely different from those of the Pythagorean scale but which nevertheless blend in harmony much more satisfactorily. If we take as before a base note of frequency 1 the derivation proceeds as shown in Table 9.

Table 9

	First Harmonic	Second Harmonic	Third Harmonic	Fourth Harmonic	Fifth Harmonic
Base note	1	2	3	4	5
Fifth below base note	$\frac{2}{3}$	$\frac{4}{3}$	$\frac{6}{3}$	$\frac{8}{3}$	$\frac{10}{3}$
Fifth above base note	$\frac{3}{2}$	$\frac{6}{2}$	$\frac{9}{2}$	$\frac{12}{2}$	$\frac{15}{2}$
Harmonics of base note reduced to one octave	1	1	$\frac{3}{2}$	1	$\frac{5}{4}$
Harmonics of fifth below base note reduced to one octave	$\frac{4}{3}$	$\frac{4}{3}$	1	$\frac{4}{3}$	$\frac{5}{3}$
Harmonics of fifth above base note reduced to one octave	$\frac{3}{2}$	1	$\frac{9}{8}$	$\frac{3}{2}$	$\frac{15}{8}$

When the different notes from this table are rearranged in sequence they become as shown in Table 10, in which the corresponding Pythagorean frequencies are also shown for comparison.

Table 10

Just intonation	1	$\dfrac{9}{8}$	$\dfrac{5}{4}\left(=\dfrac{80}{64}\right)$	$\dfrac{4}{3}$	$\dfrac{3}{2}$	$\dfrac{5}{3}\left(=\dfrac{26\frac{2}{3}}{16}\right)$	$\dfrac{15}{8}\left(=\dfrac{240}{128}\right)$	2
Pythagorean	1	$\dfrac{9}{8}$	$\dfrac{81}{64}$	$\dfrac{4}{3}$	$\dfrac{3}{2}$	$\dfrac{27}{16}$	$\dfrac{243}{128}$	2

The intervals between these notes are much more complicated than for Pythagorean intonation, and in fact two different kinds of whole tones occur to which the names major and minor are usually applied. The intervals are shown in Table 11.

Table 11

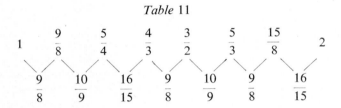

Although much pleasanter in harmony this scale becomes completely impracticable if used with instruments having fixed notes. Thus if one wished to play the same sequence of ratios but starting on the second member of the scale instead of the first the sequence of frequencies which would result would be as shown in Table 12.

Table 12

$$\frac{9}{8} \quad \frac{81}{64} \quad \frac{45}{32} \quad \frac{3}{2} \quad \frac{27}{16} \quad \frac{15}{8} \quad \frac{135}{64} \quad \frac{9}{4}\left(=\frac{9}{8} \text{ in the normal octave}\right)$$

It can be seen that this requires four additional notes beyond those already established in Table 10. The complications grow extremely rapidly as one attempts to extend the scale to other base notes, and an impossibly large number of fixed notes would be required in order to play satisfactorily in tune at any pitch or key. This scale also suffers from a similar defect to that of the Pythagorean scale in that no succession of fifths and thirds leads one back to an octave.

In order to extend the scale of Just intonation to include chromatic notes the simplest procedure is to begin with the diatonic scale and to move upwards and downwards by an interval of a major third (two whole tones—a ratio of $\frac{5}{4}$); this was the characteristic interval introduced to distinguish the Just scale from the Pythagorean scale. As before, the additional notes derived by *upward* movement are called sharp and those by *downward* movement are called flat. Table 13 shows the resulting notes, their method of derivation and their frequencies with a base note of frequency 1.

Table 13

	E	F♯	G♯	A	B	C♯	D♯
Major third up	$\frac{5}{4}$	$\frac{45}{32}$	$\frac{25}{16}$	$\frac{5}{3}$	$\frac{15}{8}$	$\frac{25}{12}$	$\frac{75}{32}$

	C	D	E	F	G	A	B
Basic Just scale	1	$\frac{9}{8}$	$\frac{5}{4}$	$\frac{4}{3}$	$\frac{3}{2}$	$\frac{5}{3}$	$\frac{15}{8}$

	A♭	B♭	C	D♭	E♭	F	G
Major third down	$\frac{4}{5}$	$\frac{9}{10}$	1	$\frac{16}{15}$	$\frac{6}{5}$	$\frac{4}{3}$	$\frac{3}{2}$

As with Pythagorean intonation it can be seen that each whole-tone interval now has two possible extra notes—for example C♯ and D♭—which are not the same.

Apart from the difficulties of providing for these two extra notes per whole tone it is soon discovered that, if this procedure is extended still further, more and more notes are produced, and it can be seen by comparison with Table 12 that even those of Table 13 are not sufficient to play correctly starting on any given base note. The most usual method of overcoming this kind of difficulty will now be discussed.

8.9 Equal temperament

If it is desired to play on one instrument in different keys—i.e. with different starting points and hence to use different members of the chromatic scale—both the Just and the Pythagorean scales need to be modified or tempered. The most universally-accepted compromise is that known as Equal Temperament, in which the octave is divided into 12 exactly equal semi-tones. The distinction between sharps and flats thus disappears and only one extra note occupies the whole-tone intervals of the diatonic scale. The chromatic scale in equal temperament thus consists of a succession of notes whose frequencies all bear to that of the one immediately below the ratio $2^{\frac{1}{12}}:1$. The diatonic scale can be selected by including whole tones of ratio $2^{\frac{1}{6}}:1$. As has already been said it is a compromise, but as J. S. Bach demonstrated by writing his forty-eight preludes and fugues "für das Wohltemperierte Klavier" it is an extremely acceptable and successful one.

Arguments about the relative merits of various scales and temperament will go on, but a number of authors have pointed out (e.g. Milbourn, 1962) that much of the argument is highly theoretical, and many music lovers would have considerable difficulty in distinguishing, for example, between the D♯ or E♭ of Pythagorean or Just intonation, and the note of the equal-temperament scale which does duty for both. Lloyd and Boyle (1963), on the other hand, point out that equal temperament is a purely theoretical compromise and that it would take far more skill for a singer—unaccompanied by a keyboard instrument—to sing in exact equal temperament than in Just intonation. As with most controversial subjects it seems that there is a measure of truth in all the contentions, and it may well be true that the differences only become important with the very highest class of performers and the most advanced listeners. It is, of course, perfectly possible for players of non-fretted stringed instruments (see Chapter 10) to play in Just intonation since there is no quantisation of the positions of the fingers on the string and an infinite variation of notes is possible. Table 14 gives the frequencies of the notes of the chromatic equal-tempered scale using a base note of frequency 1. Also included are the frequencies of the corresponding Pythagorean and Just intonation scales.

In comparing the notes derived in various systems it is convenient to use a much finer sub-division of the octave than the semi-tone or whole-tone. Various numerical methods have been put forward, but the most convenient is that based on a logarithmic scale leading to the unit known as the cent. If two notes have an interval of 1 cent between them their frequency ratio is $2^{\frac{1}{1200}}$. Thus if an interval with a ratio I contains C cents then

$$I = (2^{\frac{1}{1200}})^C$$

or

$$\log I = \frac{C \log 2}{1200},$$

i.e.

$$C = \frac{1200}{\log 2} \log I.$$

Because the unit is logarithmic, intervals expressed in cents can be added rather than multiplied. In Table 14 the number of cents in the interval between each note and the base note is given for each of the three scales.

It is of interest to notice the differences between the disposition of sharps and flats in the Pythagorean and Just scales. If the procedure outlined for developing the Just scale is extended and, as for the Pythagorean scale, those developed in the upward direction are specified as sharps and those developed in the downward direction as flats, the resulting notes and intervals are found to occur in a different order from those of the Pythagorean system. Values derived in this way are included in Table 14.

8.10 Consonance and dissonance

It is interesting to consider how the use of various harmonic intervals may have arisen. It is conceivable that when two similar instruments were being played and one was accidentally over-blown, or when a man and a woman attempted to sing the same melody, the idea of singing in octaves arose. The fifth occurs quite early in written music, and some writers have claimed that its occurrence as the interval between the second and third harmonics of a pipe accounts for its experimental use in harmony. It is worth noting, however, that students who have no musical training or experience often tune a monochord and a tuning-fork a fifth apart and claim them to be in unison. Untrained singers too sometimes sing a melody a fifth lower than written, and think that they are singing in tune. It is thus possible that the fifth might have been introduced as a result of mistakes of this kind. These are perhaps idle speculations, and we shall never know how the development really came about. The important question for us at the moment is why two notes an octave or a fifth apart sound relatively pleasant together, whereas two notes a semi-tone apart sound extremely unpleasant.

Table 14

Note	Pythagorean Frequency	Cents	Just Intonation Frequency	Cents	Equal Temperament Frequency	Cents
C	1	0	1	0	1	0
C$^\sharp$	$\dfrac{2187}{2048}$	114	$\dfrac{25}{24}$	71	$2^{\frac{1}{12}}$	100
D$^\flat$	$\dfrac{256}{243}$	89	$\dfrac{16}{15}$	112		
D	$\dfrac{9}{8}$	204	$\dfrac{9}{8}$	204	$2^{\frac{1}{6}}$	200
D$^\sharp$	$\dfrac{19683}{16384}$	317	$\dfrac{75}{64}$	275	$2^{\frac{1}{4}}$	300
E$^\flat$	$\dfrac{32}{27}$	294	$\dfrac{6}{5}$	316		
E	$\dfrac{81}{64}$	409	$\dfrac{5}{4}$	386	$2^{\frac{1}{3}}$	400
E$^\sharp$	$\dfrac{177147}{131072}$	522	$\dfrac{125}{96}$	457		
F$^\flat$	$\dfrac{8192}{6561}$	385	$\dfrac{32}{25}$	427		
F	$\dfrac{4}{3}$	498	$\dfrac{4}{3}$	498	$2^{\frac{5}{12}}$	500
F$^\sharp$	$\dfrac{729}{512}$	612	$\dfrac{45}{32}$	590	$2^{\frac{1}{2}}$	600
G$^\flat$	$\dfrac{1024}{729}$	588	$\dfrac{36}{25}$	631		
G	$\dfrac{3}{2}$	702	$\dfrac{3}{2}$	702	$2^{\frac{7}{12}}$	700
G$^\sharp$	$\dfrac{6561}{4096}$	816	$\dfrac{25}{16}$	773	$2^{\frac{2}{3}}$	800
A$^\flat$	$\dfrac{128}{81}$	792	$\dfrac{8}{5}$	814		

Table 14—*contd.*

Note		Pythagorean		Just Intonation		Equal Temperament	
		Frequency	Cents	Frequency	Cents	Frequency	Cents
A		$\frac{27}{16}$	906	$\frac{5}{3}$	884	$2^{\frac{3}{4}}$	900
	A$^\sharp$	$\frac{59049}{32768}$	1019	$\frac{225}{128}$	977	$2^{\frac{5}{6}}$	1000
	B$^\flat$	$\frac{16}{9}$	996	$\frac{9}{5}$	1018		
B		$\frac{243}{128}$	1109	$\frac{15}{8}$	1088	$2^{\frac{11}{12}}$	1100
	B$^\sharp$	$\frac{531441}{262144}$	1228	$\frac{125}{64}$	1159		
	C$^\flat$	$\frac{4096}{2187}$	1086	$\frac{48}{25}$	1129		
C		2	1200	2	1200	2	1200

Helmholtz (1877) made a thorough investigation of the problem of consonance and dissonance and suggested that the primary factor is the occurrence of beats between the notes themselves or between their upper harmonics. If the beats are rapid the result is a kind of roughness. Let us consider a few examples. A note and its octave do not produce beats directly, but Table 15 shows the sequence of harmonics likely to be produced if the sources are ordinary musical instruments.

Table 15

1	2	3	4	5	6	7	8
	2		4		6		8

Clearly there are a great many in common and, if either the note or its octave are a little out of tune, all these pairs will tend to produce beats. Notes a fifth apart give the same sort of result, as shown in Table 16.

Table 16

1	2	3	4	5	6	7	8	9
$\frac{3}{2}$		3		$\frac{9}{2}$	6		$\frac{15}{2}$	9

Helmholtz calculated the result of a hypothetical experiment with two violins, in which one sounded a steady note of fixed pitch and the other sounded a note of increasing pitch covering the range of one octave. He plotted a curve predicting the relative unpleasantness of the pairs of notes as shown in Fig. 8.7.

This idea undoubtedly goes a considerable way towards explaining the full effect. It turns out, however, that consonance and dissonance effects are produced even with pure tones. The question is, then, where do the beats come from if two perfectly pure tones an octave apart are pushed a little out of tune? The aural harmonics and combination tones discussed in section 8.4 may provide an answer. It was shown there that even pure tones are not heard as pure tones because of the non-linear properties of the ear, and harmonics are actually introduced even if they do not exist before. Extra notes—the sum and difference

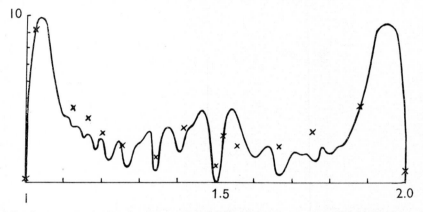

Figure 8.7 Curves representing the degree of dissonance between a note of fixed frequency *A* and a second note *B* which changes smoothly from a frequency equal to that of *A* to one octave higher. The crosses represent experimentally-derived points and are the mean of experiments with a large number of observers. The line represents the results as calculated by Helmholtz. This diagram is on the same scale as Figs. 8.8, 8.9 and 8.10.

tones—are also introduced, and it can be seen fairly easily that the more complicated the interval ratios the more numerous are the sum and difference tones introduced. Thus if we consider just the first-order sum and difference tones and the aural harmonics, the octave, fifth and fourth lead to the series of tones shown in Table 17.

Table 17

Basic notes n_1 and n_2	Sum	Difference	$2n_1$	$2n_2$
1 + 2	3	1	2	4
2 + 3	5	1	4	6
3 + 4	7	1	6	8

Only two new notes are introduced with the octave and four new ones appear with the fifth and the fourth. The complete picture can only be obtained when all the additional tones arising from combinations of these new notes are included.

An experiment with pure tones on the same lines as the Helmholtz violin experiment has been carried out with several classes of students in succession, and the combined result is shown in Fig. 8.7. In performing the experiment the students were asked to give marks from 0 to 10 to correspond to the relative level of roughness of the resulting sounds. The tones were sounded simultaneously for a short period but the pairs were introduced in a random order. There was quite reasonable agreement between various participants provided one asked a specific question regarding a relatively objective quality. For example, if the degree of *roughness* was replaced by the degree of *unpleasantness* the results became very inconsistent. This point has been investigated by a number of authors. Seashore (1938), for example, introduced four different qualities that can arise in assessing the quality of a particular group of notes sounded together. These are smoothness, purity, blending and fusion, and he claimed that it is possible to make a logical judgment on the basis of one or other of these criteria without letting emotion or feeling come in at all. In his final table the octave is placed first in all four categories, and the fifth is placed second in all except the "fusion" category, where it is placed seventh; the second place for fusion goes to the minor second which came last in all the other categories. Whatever the true explanation, beating between high harmonics, beating between sum and difference tones, aural harmonics, and the introduction of extra notes adding to the general complexity of sound, all play a part in determining the relative consonance or dissonance of a note. One of the simplest ways of viewing the possible composite effect of all these influences is to draw a diagram which I have not seen in print before, although it seems so straightforward that I feel sure it must have been used on some other occasion. The diagram is intended to illustrate the Helmholtz-type experiment of keeping one note fixed and allowing the other to rise from unison to an octave above; these two notes are represented by the lines A and B in Fig. 8.8. The harmonics or aural harmonics of these notes are represented by lines such as A_2, A_3, B_2, B_3, etc., the sum tones by lines such as $A + B, A_2 + B, A_3 + B_2$, etc., in Fig. 8.9, and difference tones by lines such as A_2B, AB, etc. An enormous number of lines can be introduced into one diagram, and of course in any one example the relative proportions of the different components will vary. The full diagram, Fig. 8.10, is, however, a useful means of assessing the possible participants arising from any pair of notes.

The important points to be noticed in assessing this diagram are first the great "simplification" that occurs at the octave and unison; the number of notes present suddenly becomes very small. Secondly, on either side of these intervals there is a very large number of notes with very small intervals between, which would obviously give rise to rapid beating. This may account for the extremely high dissonance rating of intervals on either side of the octave and the unison in Helmholtz's curve. Almost the same effect occurs at the fifth and the fourth, but the simplification is not quite so great; in the neighbourhood of the third and sixth the region of clarification is more diffuse.

Bartholomew (1942) discusses the possibility that our idea of what is a consonant interval may change with time, and points out that thirds have now largely superseded fourths and fifths as the most pleasant intervals and that seconds and sevenths are being used increasingly in final chords in modern music. He also points out that other workers believe that thirds and sixths will always be the most satisfactory intervals. It is obvious that we are now entering a highly subjective field in which individual psychology, "taste", and many other factors are involved. The psychological and physiological aspects will be discussed a little further in section 9.4.

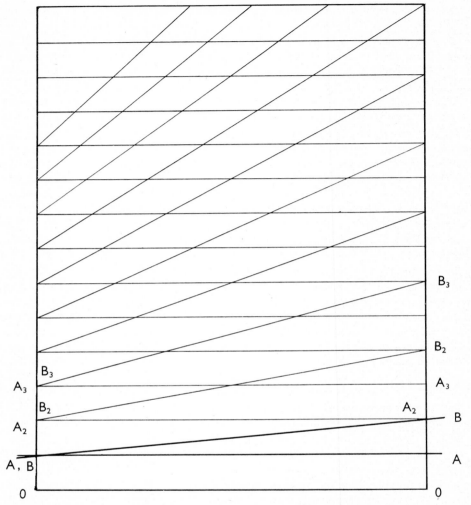

Figure 8.8 The lines AA, BB represent the two tones in the experiment illustrated in Fig. 8.7. The lines A_2A_2, B_2B_2, etc., represent the harmonics or aural harmonics of the two basic notes.

8.11 The musical character of different scales

From time to time interesting discussions arise concerning the different character or quality of music played in different keys. The Gregorian modes mentioned earlier do have completely different characteristics because the succession of whole-tones and semi-tones is different in each. If an equal-tempered instrument is being used, however, there should be no difference between diatonic scales starting on different notes, as all the semi-tones are equal, and it is therefore possible to select from the 12 notes available the same sequence of whole-tones and semi-tones starting on any given note. Nevertheless, many musicians claim that there is still a specific character associated with each key. As an amateur musician I am in-

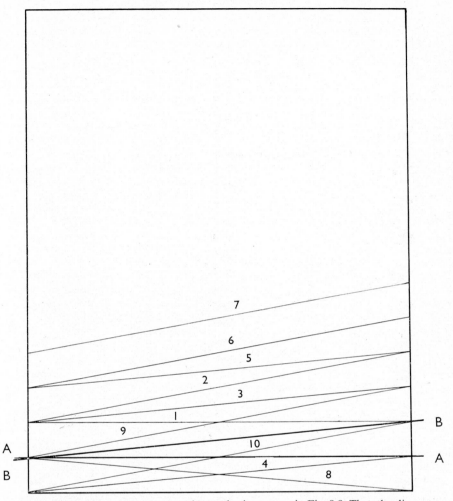

Figure 8.9 The lines AA and BB represent the two basic notes as in Fig. 8.8. The other lines represent the following aural harmonics and combination tones. (1) 2A, (2) 2B, (3) A + B, (4) B − A, (5) 2A + B, (6) 2B + A, (7) 2B + 2A, (8) 2A − B, (9) 2B − A, (10) 2B − 2A.

clined to agree with this feeling, although as a scientist I find it difficult to substantiate or explain. Many suggestions have been put forward. For example, it is well known that piano-tuners "lay-out" the temperament by fairly standard methods, and it may be that slight departures from precise equality of the semi-tones always occur in the same way. Perhaps the fact that the quality associated with a given key on the piano is different from that associated with the same key on the organ (a subjective observation with which many writers agree) lends a little support to this contention, since organ-tuning follows a somewhat different routine. Again, the peculiarities of different keys played on the piano have been explained in terms of the dynamic differences between the operation of the black and the white notes. There have also been discussions in terms of the formant regions of the sounding board

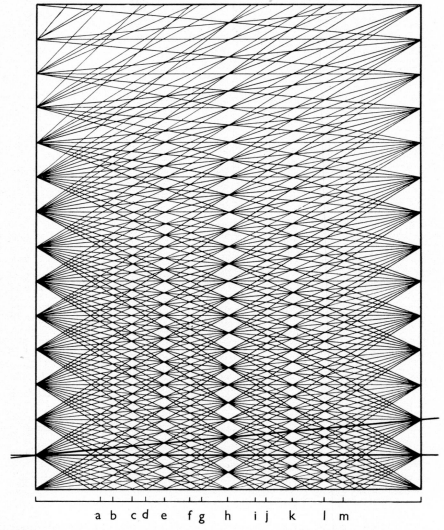

a b c d e f g h i j k l m

Figure 8.10 Continuation of the development shown in Fig. 8.9 to include a large number of harmonics and sum and difference tones. The intervals between the basic notes A and B at the lettered points are as follows: (*a*) Pythagorean minor third (C–E♭). (*b*) Just minor third (C–E♭). (*c*) Just major third (C–E). (*d*) Just diminished fourth (C–F♭). (*e*) Fourth (C–F). (*f*) The Pythagorean diminished fifth (C–G♭). (*g*) Just diminished fifth (C–G♭). (*h*) Fifth (C–G). (*i*) Pythagorean minor sixth (C–A♭). (*j*) Just minor sixth (C–A♭). (*k*) Just major sixth (C–A). (*l*) Just augmented sixth (C–A♯). (*m*) Just minor seventh (C–A♭).

It is helpful to view this diagram obliquely with the page tilted backwards.

which may enhance harmonics in the same frequency region whatever the scale being played. The real difficulty is the consistency of observation by any one observer in changing from one piano to another. Another possibility that has been suggested is that the actual "feel" to the fingers of the combinations of black and white notes which commonly occur in different keys has a strong sub-conscious association with particular pieces written in those keys, and tends to establish a mood without conscious recognition of the particular piece from which it derives. I am inclined to think that in my own case this factor is a significant one though it may not be the only one. (For example, whenever I hear the slow movement of Dvorak's New World Symphony my fingers want to take up the "black-note" positions of the key of D♭!).

For music played on other instruments the formant may be largely responsible; certainly a change of pitch of only a semi-tone or two will alter the position in the scale at which the formant emphasis is most prominent, and hence may change its character. Bartholomew (1942) discusses the effect of the actual mechanics of playing the instruments. For the piano this involves the shape of the fingers in playing black or white notes, in the violin the occurrence of different numbers of open strings in different keys, and in general the different degrees of facility with which different scales can be played. The discussions will undoubtedly go on for some time to come.

CHAPTER 9

Influences on the Perception of Sound

9.1 Introduction

Up to this point we have been investigating the problem of producing a given wave form in the air and have tried to find what are the important factors which govern its characteristics. It is certain, however, that there are many influences at work during the transit of the sound from the instrument through the air and through the mechanism of the ear until it becomes a "perception" in the brain. These influences may have as profound an effect on the quality of the perception as any of the factors considered up to this stage. In this chapter we shall consider three such external influences. First, it is clear that the acoustic properties of the room in which the instrument and the observer are placed can cause considerable modification of the sound wave itself. Secondly, the effect of transmission via electrical reproducing systems will be considered since it plays such an important part in modern life. Finally, the physiological and psychological aspects of the hearing process itself must be taken into consideration.

9.2 Room acoustics

The study of the acoustics of rooms has tended, for some reason, to be shrouded in mystery, and only in relatively recent years has it become part of the curriculum of science students. The basic principles are extremely simple—the difficulties only begin to arise when the principles are applied to large complicated structures. We shall start by considering a source of sound in the open air infinitely removed from all other objects and see what happens when walls are created round it. The waves produced by an isolated source would travel out at a uniform velocity in all directions, giving rise to spherical waves; in other words, at a given instant t seconds after the wave has been initiated, all points on the surface of any sphere of radius less than ct, with the source as centre, will be in the same state of vibration (Fig. 9.1(a)). Under these conditions the energy is distributed over the surface of the sphere, and hence the energy flow per unit area decreases as the square of its distance from the source; in other words, an inverse square law is obeyed. Without any artificial aids it would be quite difficult to carry on a conversation over distances of greater than 20–30 ft. under otherwise normal conditions. If, however, a flat surface is added below the source of sound use can be made of reflected waves and so the level perceived is increased (Fig. 9.1(b)). If, in addition to providing a floor, the source and observer are placed near to a vertical wall the additional reflection from the wall itself enhances the sound, but there is also one arising from reflection at both surfaces (Fig. 9.1(c)). This process goes on each time an additional surface is added, and it can be seen that the sound level will rise rapidly. Figure 9.1(d) shows the conditions when four walls have been added to surround the source and the observer. In theory there can now be an infinite number of reflections and hence a high level of sound can be reached. The arrangement is analogous to the well-known experiment, described in textbooks on light, in which a candle flame is placed between two facing parallel mirrors and an infinite series of reflections may be seen if the eye is applied to a hole in one of the mirrors. If two remaining surfaces are added the source and observer are completely enclosed in the room. Then, if the walls could be of perfectly reflecting material, no sound would ever escape, but the level would increase to infinity. In practice, of course, this situation never arises, but smooth plaster walls can have a very high reflection coefficient, and if there is little absorbent material present in the room an extremely high level of sound can result. In a large room where speech or music is to be heard in all parts the high level is desirable, but a moment's thought will show that there are also disadvantages in achieving it in this way. The high level occurs because of successive reflections, and

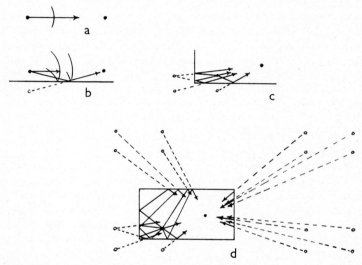

Figure 9.1 Transmission of sound from a source to an observer. (*a*) In the absence of any reflectors. (*b*) With one reflector (the floor). (*c*) With two reflectors (floor and one wall). (*d*) With four reflectors (floor, walls and ceiling).

therefore sounds become spread out in time; the result, although of high level, may be blurred and unintelligible. For example, in speech the first syllable uttered may well persist at quite a high level while subsequent ones are being uttered; the effect is usually described as reverberation and is a very familiar, though often unrecognised, phenomenon. In a normal room of a house the carpets, wall coverings, curtains, and other soft furnishing materials absorb a large proportion of the sounds produced and hence they die away quite rapidly. In the bathroom, however, where there are probably hard tiled walls and no soft furnishings, the reverberation may be quite high; this may be why many people enjoy singing in the bathroom—quite a loud sound can be produced with relatively little effort and the quality may also be affected (see section 9.2.3).

It is obviously necessary to arrive at some suitable compromise between the requirement of an adequate sound level and the requirement of intelligibility, and this—the achievement of an acceptable reverberation characteristic—is one of the first conditions for good acoustics.

9.2.1 The basic conditions for good acoustics: (i) acceptable reverberation

It has already been pointed out that the amount of absorbent material present in a room has a profound effect on its reverberation characteristics, and it ought to be possible to adjust the conditions by introducing additional absorbent—acoustic tiles, carpets, curtains, etc.—or to decrease it by introducing additional hard reflecting surfaces. Sabine (1922) was the first to put this possibility on a quantitative basis; he showed that the amount of re-verberation was proportional to the volume of the room and inversely proportional to the total amount of absorbent present. In order to make his investigation quantitative he introduced the term "reverberation time". He defined it as the time taken for a sound of 10^6 times the loudness of the smallest sound that the observer can just perceive to fall to the level of that smallest sound. In an average sitting-room this will be about $\frac{3}{4}$ of a second, whereas in an average bathroom it might be 2–3 seconds. Sabine found that if V is the volume of the room in cubic feet and A is the total absorbent present, expressed in terms of the equivalent area (in sq. ft.) of 100 per cent absorbent, then T, the reverberation time in seconds, is given by

$$T = \frac{0 \cdot 053 V}{A},$$

which for practical purposes can be taken as $\dfrac{V}{20A}$.

The value of T to be attained depends considerably on taste, though for relatively small rooms it is usually about 1 second, going up to 1·8 seconds for very large concert halls. The precise purpose for which the hall is required also influences the selected value. It is usually found that, for successful musical use, a rather longer time of reverberation is desirable than for speech. If the room is already built the time of reverberation may be measured either crudely by firing a pistol and timing the interval between its firing and the complete cessation of noise, or more precisely by using microphones and a cathode-ray oscillograph. The decay of the sound used for measuring purposes is of course exponential; it therefore does not matter very much if the starting level of the sound is not quite correct. In the early stages the slope is so steep that a small error results only in second-order errors in the time measurement. At the other end, however, the precise level at which the sound is thought to reach the threshold is much more difficult to determine. Since the curve is approximately horizontal the errors in time can be very large indeed. It is particularly important therefore, even in rough measurements, to make sure that the source used as the test sound is at least 10^6 times the ambient noise level in the room. Many short measured times of reverberation result from a high level of ambient noise which makes the test sound appear to sink below the threshold at much too high a level. From the measured time and the volume the total absorbent already present can be calculated, and hence the additional quantity required to achieve the desired value of T may be found. If the hall is only at the design stage then it is necessary to add up the total area of absorbent likely to be present, multiplying each area by the appropriate absorption coefficient (available from tables).

For example, a small room 20 ft. × 30 ft. × 10 ft. has a volume of 6,000 cu. ft. Let us suppose that the walls and ceiling are of plaster with an absorption coefficient of 0·03, that the floor is of wood with an absorption coefficient 0·05 and that there are to be 11 chairs each of equivalent absorption 2 sq. ft. The total absorption equivalent is thus

$$(20 \times 30) \times 0·05 + 20 \times 30 + 2(20 \times 10) + 2(30 \times 10) \times 0·03 + 2 \times 11 = 100 \text{ sq. ft.}$$

Thus
$$T = \frac{1}{20} \times \frac{6000}{100} = 3 \text{ seconds.}$$

If a time of reverberation of 1 second is required the total absorbent necessary is clearly 300 sq. ft., and hence 200 equivalent sq. ft. of additional absorbent are required. A very thick carpet and underfelt of absorption coefficient 1/3rd covering the whole 600 sq. ft. of floor would supply this. (Strictly speaking, an absorption coefficient of 0·383 would be required to compensate for the loss arising from the covering up of the floor of absorption coefficient 0·05.)

The next question to be considered is the location of the extra or existing absorbent material. Does it in fact matter very much where the absorbing and reflecting areas are in relation to the source and audience? For very small rooms it turns out to be of little significance because the velocity of sound is such that in a very short time the wave has impinged on all surfaces in the room and the precise order does not matter very much. However, in a lecture theatre or concert hall the distribution of absorbers and reflectors can be important. The correct value of reverberation time is not the only condition; it is also necessary to ensure that the sound produced is properly distributed throughout the hall and that there are no unwanted concentrations, dead spots, or echoes. We shall now consider how these further requirements may be fulfilled.

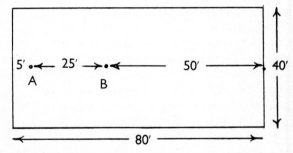

Figure 9.2 Diagram of large hall to show the origin of long path differences in transmission from (a) to (b).

9.2.2 The basic conditions for good acoustics: (ii) uniform distribution

So far we have ignored the time element more-or-less completely and have assumed that if enough reflections occur the sound will be reinforced to give adequate loudness. The ear, however, is quite sensitive to small delays and, if the time elapsing between the receipt of an initial sound and of its reflection from a wall increases beyond about 1/15th of a second, the two will cease to fuse together as one sound and the ear will perceive the reflection separately as an echo. This time interval corresponds to a path length of about 75 ft. under normal conditions, and hence any wall more than 35–40 ft. from the source can be a potential source of echo if the observer is close to the source. For example, in Fig. 9.2 if A is the source and B the observer the direct path is 25 ft., the path via the wall nearest the source is 35 ft., that via the side walls is 48 ft., and that via the opposite wall is 125 ft. Clearly the direct sound and that reflected by the nearer wall and the side walls will fuse and become usefully enhanced in loudness, but the reflection from the end wall will be a distinct echo and therefore undesirable. In this simple example the obvious place for any necessary extra absorbent to adjust the reverberation time would be on the back wall whose reflections are undesirable. The general rule is thus to place the tile on the least useful reflecting surfaces.

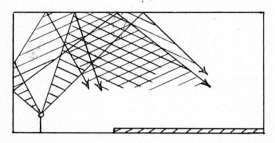

Figure 9.3 (*a*) Vertical section of hall with audience represented by the shaded portion on the floor; only the shaded portions of the radiated sound from the source are useful.

The purpose for which the room is used therefore becomes important. The example already given was of a "single-ended" room in which the source is always expected to be at one end and the audience at the other. If, on the other hand, a room is to be used for committee purposes in which the speakers may be placed anywhere and all must be able to hear, the best solution is to provide a low hard ceiling to be used as a reflector and to place any necessary absorbent material on the walls, all of which are equivalent as far as the speakers are concerned.

The condition may arise, however, that the right reverberation time has been achieved while there are still surfaces which are not being effectively used as reflectors. Consider, for example, Fig. 9.3(*a*); it is a vertical section through a large hall used for lectures in which the positions of the speaker and the audience are fixed. Simple geometry shows that the regions outside the shaded areas are not usefully contributing and might in fact give rise to echo if the distances involved were large. Additional useful reflections could be provided by introducing a flare in Fig. 9.3(*b*). The change in volume is very small and hence the effective loudness has been increased without significantly changing the reverberation time. This procedure is the basis of all good acoustic design and there are many possible extensions of it. It is not, however, within the scope of this book to go into further details. In practically every complicated case there is a great deal of compromise involved, and this necessarily introduces subjective elements into the solution. It

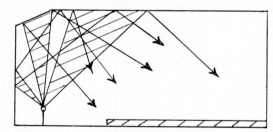

Figure 9.3. (*b*) The effect of adding a small flare to the hall shown in Fig. 9.3(*a*); the increase in useful radiated sound can clearly be seen.

should perhaps be pointed out finally that there are other considerations to be taken into account. For example, it might be thought that the ideal solution for the "single-ended" room might be a complete parabolic reflector round the speaker; the difficulty here is that although it is effective in raising the level of useful sound it also effectively focuses all the unwanted sounds produced by the audience on the speaker with disastrous results!

9.2.3 The effect of acoustic characteristics on the quality of sound perceived

As far as this book is concerned our main interest in acoustics is in the possible modification to a wave form that could arise in transit between the source and the observer.

There are three main ways in which such a modification might arise. First, the dimensions of the room and the distribution of the sources may have an effect because the individual "echoes" making up the reverberation may occur in a regular sequence, and hence introduce or enhance a specific frequency component related to the dimensions of the room. Secondly, even in a room in which the reflection is completely diffuse with no periodicities in the reverberation, the exponential decay curve modifies the wave form. Thirdly, the absorption coefficients of materials are not the same at all frequencies, and hence the time of reverberation—which we have so far tacitly assumed to be the same for all sounds—is in fact frequency-dependent. We shall consider each of these factors in turn, and it will be convenient to make use of the convolution concept (section 4.6) in discussing their effects.

Let us first consider the effect of two parallel walls of very high reflectivity. A source of sound placed between them will give rise to an infinite succession of sound images (like the corresponding optical experiment of the candle flame and mirrors already mentioned), and, because of the constant spacing between the images (see Fig. 9.4) and the constant velocity

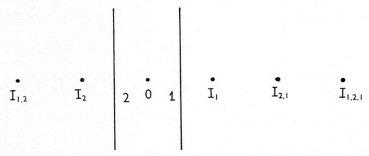

Figure 9.4 Source of sound between high walls showing succession of sound images.

of sound, an observer will hear a given sound repeated with a regular periodicity which depends on the separation of the walls. If the walls are a distance d apart and if the source is midway between them the images will be d apart, and hence an observer between the walls would experience a delay of d/c seconds between each arrival. The resulting wave form is therefore the convolution of the initial wave with a unit peak function of periodicity d/c seconds. In reciprocal space, therefore, its frequency spectrum is multiplied by that of the peak function, which is another series of peak functions occurring at frequencies $c/d, 2c/d$, etc. The result, in other words, consists of a series of harmonics of a fundamental of frequency d/c c.p.s. whatever the form of the original sound (see Fig. 9.5); a musical sound can thus arise from a non-periodic noise. The effect can sometimes be experienced when walking between high walls in a narrow passage; the sound of the footsteps acquires a musical "ring" of definite pitch. I know of one such place where the effect is so pronounced that the local inhabitants believe that the paving of the passage is hollow and that this is the cause of the ringing sound. This is perhaps the most extreme example of the modification of quality by acoustic properties. Another way of considering this effect in a closed room is to calculate its possible natural modes of vibration (see footnote on page 26); the resulting set of specific frequencies at which resonance may occur corresponds to a formant characteristic.

Suppose, however, that because of complex shapes in the room the train of reflections is random and contains no regular periodicities at all. The result is in effect to add an exponential tail to each pulse of sound. Consider, for example, a regular train of pulses (see Fig. 9.6(*a*)); by simple addition it can be seen that if each acquires an exponential decay the net result is as shown in Figs. 9.6(*b* and *c*). Clearly the wave shape has been modified by the acoustics. A detailed investigation would involve consideration of the relative phases and timing of the individual pulses, but the general principles are clear. In convolution

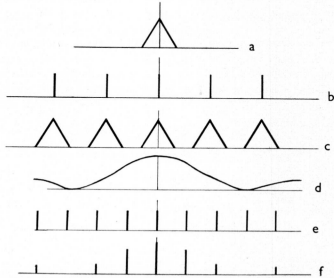

Figure 9.5 (*a*) Original wave form. (*b*) Peak function indicating repetition rate arising from multiple reflexions. (*c*) Convolution of (*a*) and (*b*) representing the resultant wave form. (*d*) Transform of (*a*). (*e*) Transform of (*b*). (*f*) Product of (*d*) and (*e*), i.e. the spectrum of (*c*) the resultant wave.

terms each element of the basic sound is convoluted with the exponential decay, and the result in reciprocal space is the product of the original spectrum with the transform of the exponential function. The transform of the exponential was discussed in section 6.7 and is shown in Fig. 6.18(*d*). Thus when the multiplication occurs the main effect is to attenuate the treble contributions very considerably in relation to the bass; this may account for the "boom" of some rooms and may be one of the contributory factors to the enjoyment of singing in the bathroom to which reference has already been made. Much of the undesirable noise content (section 7.5) of musical instruments has very high-frequency components and hence in a room with moderate reverberation they tend to be attenuated more than in one with a very short reverberation time. This may account for the use of the terms "dry" or "dead" to describe the acoustics of rooms with a very short reverberation time because of the emphasis on the high-frequency, noisy sounds in proportion to the musical—i.e., in general, lower-pitch—sounds.

The frequency characteristics of the absorbent will also affect the spectrum in a similar way. In order to achieve the final result it will be necessary to multiply the spectrum of the basic sound by the response curve of the absorbent as well as by the transform of the exponential decay. For almost all absorbent materials the high frequencies are absorbed much more strongly, and hence when the time of reverberation of a hall is adjusted by the addition of acoustic tile the result can sometimes be an undesirable emphasis on low frequencies. In order to overcome this it is usually necessary to use some other kind of absorber, for example the resonant slot.

Thus we see that the mere act of producing a note in a closed room instead of in the open air can affect its frequency distribution very considerably. Since we have already seen that the harmonic distribution plays an important part in quality determination it is clear that the quality perceived will be modified by the acoustics of the room. It was also shown in Chapters 5 and 6 that transients and other non-periodic elements play a considerable

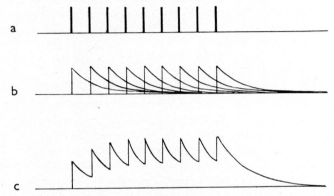

Figure 9.6 (*a*) Regular train of pulses. (*b*) Addition of modified pulses. (*c*) Resultant.

part in defining the quality of a sound, and, since they have continuous frequency distributions often involving important high-frequency components, they will also tend to be modified by the acoustics of the room.

It is important in passing to notice the difference between the effect of the exponential decay term when it arises from damping of the vibration and, as in the case just discussed, when it arises from the effect of the room. In the first case the initial wave form is multiplied by the decay term and hence the frequency spectrum becomes convoluted with the transform of the decay. For example, if the initial wave is a pure sine wave, when it is damped the single harmonic component becomes spread out over a range of frequencies (see section 6.7). In the room example the exponential term is convoluted with the wave form in time-space, and hence multiplication occurs in frequency space.

9.3 Perception via electrical reproduction

9.3.1 Introduction

In the modern world far more people listen to music through some form of electrical reproduction—either "live" through broadcasting, television and public address systems, or after recording on disc, tape and film—than by direct sound transmission through the air. This book would therefore not be complete without a brief reference to this subject. It is not the intention, however, to pursue it in great detail—the reader is referred to the large number of books now available for details of both the theory and practice of electrical sound reproduction and recording. We shall concern ourselves only with the requirements that need to be fulfilled and with the practical results of departures from their strict fulfilment.

The four basic essentials of any sound reproduction system are (1) a converter to change the sound waves in the air into a corresponding electrical wave form (a microphone), (2) an amplification system to increase the amplitude of the electrical signal, (3) a transmission system (which may involve modulation of a carrier wave as in radio, conversion into variations of light and shade as in film recording, or conversion into variations in magnetisation as on a tape, and in each case reconversion into electrical signals) and (4) reconversion into sound waves (by a loudspeaker). The ideal system should obviously be one in which the final sound wave produced by the loudspeaker is identical in every detail with that produced by the original sound. With so many stages of interconversion and transmission, however, considerable deviations inevitably occur.

9.3.2 Imperfections in reproduction systems

These deviations can take several forms. First of all the microphone responds to the pressure variations at a particular point in the room in which the original sound is being produced, whereas an observer using two ears can make some assessment of the directions from which the various components of the wave are arriving. Similarly, the final reconversion into sound is from one relatively small source which may be quite satisfactory for reproducing the sound of a single voice or instrument but is not satisfactory for a complete orchestra. These defects are, of course, to some extent overcome by stereophony—the use of more than one microphone feeding more than one loudspeaker. It is difficult with such a system to produce ideal results for several observers, however, because precise positioning of the microphones relative to the sound source, and of the loudspeakers relative to the observer, is necessary. The acoustic properties of the rooms in which the recording is made and that in which the final reproduction occurs also play an important part in the complex process of creating the illusion of three-dimensional sounds. These considerations, however, are only of importance in the most elaborate reproduction systems, and for most of those used by the general public the defects of the conversion systems themselves are likely to be much more significant. These defects can conveniently be divided into three categories. First, any reproduction system tends to accumulate extra electrical impulses and signals which are not part of the desired wave form. Secondly, the variation of the response of the various components with frequency can lead to distortion of the wave form. Thirdly, lack of proportionality between the input and output signals of any section of the system—i.e. non-linearity in the sense discussed in section 8.2—also leads to complications. The consequences of these effects will be discussed in the next section.

9.3.3 Consequences of defects in reproduction systems

The accumulation of additional signals provides an unwanted background which not only lessens the clarity of the desired sounds, but also destroys the illusion that the sound is "live". White noise arising from thermal and other causes in the various circuits, and "hum" arising from the use of alternating-current power supplies with inadequate filtering, or accidental coupling between circuits, are two of the most common sources of additional noise. They can sometimes be eliminated by suitable filters, but this necessarily affects the useful signal as well. Such defects become really serious if considerable non-linearity is present in subsequent amplifier circuits, since the useful and the unwanted sounds become inextricably entangled. Suppose, for example, that there is an element in the system whose response ϕ in relation to a signal y obeys the equation $\phi = ay + by^2$. If two signals y_1 and y_2 are fed together into the system the result is no longer $\phi = y_1 + y_2$ but

$$\phi = a(y_1 + y_2) + b(y_1 + y_2)^2 = ay_1 + ay_2 + by_1^2 + 2by_1y_2 + by_2^2.$$

The "cross-product" term involving y_1y_2 makes the straight filtering of either y_1 or y_2 impossible.

The variation of response with frequency is perhaps the most potent source of distortion between input and output signals. The best way to approach the problem of interpreting the outcome of such variations is therefore Fourier transformation. The process is exactly parallel to the treatment of formants in section 7.3. When a signal passes through a system with a non-uniform response its transform is multiplied by the frequency spectrum of the system—the so-called response characteristic. Thus the output signal is the convolution of the original signal with the transform of the response characteristic. To take an extreme example, if the response characteristic were finite at only one frequency, and zero everywhere else, then its product with the transform of any incoming signal would only be non-zero if a component of that frequency were present in the signal. The result could therefore only be a signal of the frequency at which the response characteristic is non-zero, in other words the system is a narrow-band filter. In most good reproduction systems the response characteristic can be varied by two or three controls and can be made fairly "flat" over a considerable range of frequencies, say from about 25 c.p.s. to about 5,000 c.p.s. There is usually a tendency for the amplification to be less at the extreme high and low ends. For periodic signals this is quite adequate, but we saw in Chapters 5 and 6 that the transient or non-periodic components of the wave form produced by a musical instrument are important in permitting its identification. We saw in section 6.7 that the spectrum of a step function extends to infinity and that the spectrum of a single narrow pulse or peak function also involves a continuous distribution of all frequencies from zero to infinity. In fact, any transient involving near-vertical portions of its time-space curve needs this wide spread, and it is clear that the adequate response of the system particularly at very high frequencies, is necessary for correct reproduction. The effect of eliminating high frequencies can be shown most vividly by considering a response characteristic with a sharp cut-off, in other words the response characteristic resembles a square wave (see Fig. 9.7(a)). Let us consider the effect of such a system on a pulse of infinitesimal width. The unmodified transform of the input signal is the uniform distribution of intensity to infinity and the modification consists of multiplying it by the square wave. The resulting output is the convolution of the original sharp pulse with the transform of the square wave which is a sine function (see section 6.7). The steps in this process are all shown in Fig. 9.7. It can be seen that the main result is to give a much slower rate of rise, and further that the lower the frequency at which the spectrum is cut off the slower will be the rate of rise. Thus in order to reproduce transients involving rapid rises—which occur, for example, in percussive sounds—a response curve extending to very high frequencies is desirable.

The response characteristic may, of course, be complex; in other words the phase of the transmitted signal may be modified in different ways at different frequencies. Fortunately, this effect is small unless the amplifiers are very badly designed. Even if it does occur, since the ear is not very concerned about the relative phases of harmonic components (see section 3.5) the effect is not very serious. We shall see in section 9.4.5 that under certain circumstances—particularly where transients are involved—the ear does take some account of phase and under these conditions phase distortion might be a serious problem.

The loudspeaker itself is often a limiting factor in a reproducing system, and in particular, if it has very small physical dimensions, it is incapable of radiating at very low frequencies. In some small modern transistor radios the combined response of the system and the speaker

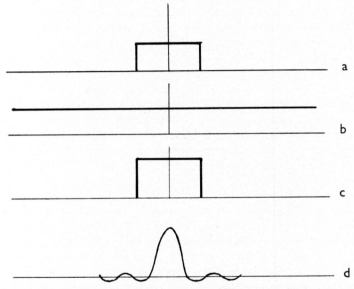

Figure 9.7 (a) Frequency-response characteristic. (b) Frequency-space representation of a pulse of infinitesimal duration. (c) Product of (a) and (c). (d) Transform of (c)—the convolution of the pulse with the transform of (a). Apart from scale this is identical with the transform of (a) and represents the wave emerging from the system of response-characteristic (a) when pulse of infinitesimal duration is fed into it.

falls to zero at relatively low frequencies. How then do they reproduce recognisable speech and music? The explanation depends at least partially on combination tones and aural harmonics produced partly in the ear and partly in the system (see section 8.4). Suppose, for example, that the sound of a bassoon is being reproduced at a basic pitch of 100 c.p.s. Harmonics occur at all integral multiples of 100 c.p.s., of different amplitudes of course, but, even if all those below the fifth harmonic at 500 c.p.s. were to be eliminated by the response characteristic, the remaining higher harmonics—600, 700, 800, etc.—would all produce difference tones with each other of 100, 200, 300 c.p.s., etc. In other words, even though the low frequencies are not reproduced by the system they are replaced by the resultant combination tones and aural harmonics. This sort of compensation also works for high-frequency cut-off, the missing harmonics being supplied by summation tones and aural harmonics. It is in fact quite possible to recognise speech sounds when passed through a filter eliminating all frequencies outside a single octave. It is important to notice, however, that this sort of argument cannot apply to the transient components. Sum and difference tones arising from regularly-spaced components which themselves fit into a harmonic series do not arise in the same way when the spectrum of the sound involved is continuous. Extra terms do come in, but they do not replace those lost in the reproduction system. Let us consider, for example, a system having the unlikely response characteristic shown in Fig. 9.8(a) and its effect on a signal consisting of a single pulse. The resulting spectrum in a linear system would be identical except for magnitude with the response characteristic, but after passing through a square-law system the result (see section 8.4) would be the self-convolution of the response characteristic which is shown in Fig. 9.8(b). It can be seen that some higher- and-lower-frequency terms have been introduced but the transform of Fig. 9.8(b) back into time-space is certainly not a single pulse (see also section 9.4.5).

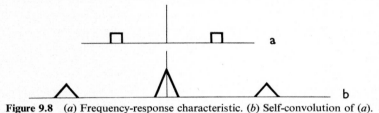

Figure 9.8 (a) Frequency-response characteristic. (b) Self-convolution of (a).

It will be clear from this discussion that it is relatively straightforward to design a reproduction system to deal satisfactorily with harmonic and other periodic components in a sine wave, but the successful reproduction of the transient components, which plays such an important part in the tonal quality of musical instruments, presents very considerable difficulties.

9.4 The mechanism of hearing

9.4.1 Introduction

Finally, in our study of the intermediate influences on the quality of sound between generation at the source and perception by the brain we must consider the hearing process itself. One or two subjective phenomena have already been mentioned, but it is now necessary to make a more logical survey of the whole process of hearing. We shall first look briefly at the construction of the ear—though the reader is referred to physiological textbooks for more detail. We shall then consider the established properties of the ear, such as sensitivity, the relation between stimulus and sensation, and their explanations in terms of some of the earlier theories of hearing. Many of the more subtle properties of the ear and brain, however, cannot be explained by the early ideas, and after surveying the nature of these problems we shall consider some recent theories. From time to time in the last 100 years or so it has been claimed that the mechanism of hearing is completely understood, but it has now become clear that that is far from true, and even the most recent suggestions fall short of a complete explanation of all the observed phenomena. In such a short section it is clearly impossible to give a full statement either of the problems or of their solutions, and we shall have to be content with a brief outline of both.

9.4.2 The construction of the ear

The ear consists of three main portions. The outer ear is merely a conical opening several centimetres long terminating in a membrane—the tympanum or drum—which completely closes the passage. In the human ear the pinna—the external structure which forms the visible part of the ear—is of little use in hearing, but in some animals, for example horses, deer, and certain dogs, the whole pinna can be oriented and possesses distinctly directional properties; it in fact acts as directional matching transformer to assist in changing the sound waves of high amplitude and low pressure into waves of slightly smaller amplitude and higher pressure. The waves fed to the drum cause it to vibrate and this vibration is then transmitted to the middle ear which is an almost-closed chamber.

The middle ear contains a very tiny bone linkage attached to the rear side of the drum at one end and to another membrane—the oval window—at the other. This lever linkage acts as a matching transformer which still further reduces the amplitude and increases the forces associated with the vibration. The chamber of the middle ear is not in fact completely closed, otherwise variations in the external atmospheric pressure would cause damage to the delicate drum. A narrow tube—the eustachian tube—links the middle ear to the atmosphere via nose and throat cavities, and thus permits equalisation of the pressure. The effect of non-equalisation—temporary deafness—can be experienced when a nose or throat infection causes blockage of the eustachian tube, or when a sudden change in the external pressure cannot be followed rapidly by the pressure in the middle ear.

Finally, the inner ear itself contains the cochlea in which the sound waves become converted into nerve impulses. The human cochlea is a remarkably fascinating organ. It is in the form of a spiral tube resembling a snail shell which if unwound would be about 3 cm. long, varying in diameter from about 2 mm. at the outer end to about $\frac{3}{4}$ mm. at the inner; the spiral has $2\frac{3}{4}$ turns. The tube is divided lengthwise into three parts—the basilar membrane divides it almost exactly into two halves of semi-circular cross-section, the canal on one side is known as the scala vestibuli and that on the other side contains a further membrane—Reissner's membrane—which divides it into two unequal parts—the smaller is known as the cochlear canal and the larger the scala tympani. The basilar membrane carries the organ of Corti which is the actual detecting device and carries nerve hairs which extend into the liquid filling the canals. The oval window, which forms the inner end of the middle ear linkage, is the entrance to the scala vestibuli. When the vibrations caused by a sound are transmitted to the oval window via the drum and the middle ear linkage, a wave is produced in the canal liquid and on the basilar membrane itself, and it is believed that relative motion of the nerve hairs in the liquid gives rise to the stimulus of the aural nerve.

The constants of the ear are more-or-less fixed; the only adjustment under control of the owner is the tension of the drum, and even this is quite involuntary and merely permits the drum to adapt to different hearing conditions.

9.4.3 Basic properties of the ear

The ear is capable of converting vibrations in the air surrounding the subject into a recognisable signal in the brain over a wide range of frequencies and intensities. There are, of course, wide personal variations, but an average human being can assign a definite tonal quality to a sound when its frequency is higher than about 18 c.p.s. The precise point is

difficult to establish because it is impossible to listen to a note of this type without introducing aural harmonics, and it is never quite clear when the tone is due to the fundamental or
to one or more of these additions. The upper limit is between 10,000 and 20,000 c.p.s. and
varies considerably with age as well as with other personal factors. The sensitivity to noises of
low intensity varies with frequency; it reaches a maximum between about 1000 and 3000
c.p.s., and falls both at the low- and high-frequency ends of the range. In the most sensitive
region the minimum amplitude of pressure variation in a sound wave which can be detected
as a definite signal is about 2×10^{-4} dynes per sq. cm.; the maximum amplitude which can
be tolerated without discomfort is about 5×10^{3} dynes per sq. cm. There are thus two
thresholds; the lower is the threshold of hearing, and the higher is the threshold of pain or
feeling. The threshold of pain falls above and below 1000 c.p.s., and hence the range of
amplitudes to which the ear can respond is considerably smaller at high and low frequencies
than in the centre of the range.

The enormous range of sensitivity ($1,000:1$ in frequency and $10^{7}:1$ in pressure amplitude)
compared with that of a physical instrument makes it important to examine the form of the
sensitivity relationship. In general it is found that the relationship between a physical
stimulus and the corresponding physiological sensation follows the same kind of law whatever the stimulus and sensation concerned. It was first studied by E. H. Weber (1825) for
weights placed on the hand. An observer was blindfolded and asked to respond when he
became conscious of the addition of a weight; it was found that he was acutely conscious of
very small weights placed directly on his hand but, if already carrying a considerable load,
a much greater increase was necessary before the addition could be detected. Weber formu-
lated the law which bears his name, and which can be stated as "the increase in stimulus
necessary to produce a given increase in sensation is proportional to the pre-existing stimulus". In mathematical terms it becomes $ds = k\dfrac{dW}{W}$, where ds is the minimum perceptible
increase in sensation, dW is the weight causing it, and W the total weight already present.
Fechner extended this idea into what is now known as the Weber-Fechner law by integrating
this expression to give $s = K \log W$. It is of course the logarithmic character of this law
which enables the ear to cover such a vast range in intensity. The logarithmic law of pitch
was introduced at an early stage in the book when we saw that the interval of one octave,
which sounds to the ear to span the same interval whether at low or high frequencies, always
involves the *multiplication* of the frequency by 2. Thus 64 c.p.s. is an octave above 32 c.p.s.,
but 1,024 c.p.s. is still only one octave above 512 c.p.s., although the differences measured in
physical terms are completely different.

We have already seen that the logarithmic relationship between pitch and frequency
makes it desirable to use logarithmic units of some kind in preparing a physical scale which
will make some sense when used in physiological experiments. The scale of cents discussed
in Chapter 8 is one such example. The same considerations apply in the intensity-loudness
relationship, and it is clearly desirable—especially if legislation is involved—to have a
physically-measurable scale of loudness which shows some degree of conformity with
physiological experience. There are two common ways of overcoming the complications
which arise from the variations in sensitivity with frequency; one is to measure the *physical*
ratio of the stimulus producing the unknown sound to that producing the minimum perceptible sound *of the same type* (i.e. if the unknown sound is a trumpet note of a certain

pitch then we must measure the ratio of the intensity of the actual trumpet sound to the minimum perceptible intensity of the same trumpet at the same pitch). This ratio, usually quoted in decibels, is termed the sensation level of the sound. (The bel and the decibel are measures of ratio used by physicists and engineers whenever physiological relationships are likely to arise. If two quantities are in the ratio $Q_1 : Q_2$ then the difference or interval between them in bels is defined as $\log_{10}\left(\dfrac{Q_1}{Q_2}\right)$ or more usually in decibels as $10 \log_{10}\left(\dfrac{Q_1}{Q_2}\right)$. The advantage of this system is that gains or losses in decibels can be added, whereas the corresponding ratios would have to be multiplied.) Thus, if a certain trumpet produces an intensity 20,000 times greater than the minimum intensity detectable by a normal observer (from a trumpet blowing the same note), its sound would be said to have a sensation level of $10 \log_{10} 20,000$ dBs, or 43 dBs.

The alternative is to match the sound by alternate listening with the sound of a pure tone of frequency 1,000 c.p.s. When they are thought to be of the same loudness the physical ratio of the intensity of the 1,000 c.p.s.-tone to the minimum perceptible intensity *for a 1,000 c.p.s.-tone* in decibels is taken as a measure of the loudness. This is then known as the equivalent loudness and is measured in units called phons. Thus, if the trumpet in the example above matched in loudness a 1,000 c.p.s.-tone, which itself had an intensity 20,000 times the minimum audible level for the 1,000 c.p.s.-tone, the trumpet would be said to have an equivalent loudness of 43 phons. It can be seen that the two scales give the same result only if one is measuring the loudness of a 1,000 c.p.s. pure tone.

The minimum difference in frequency that can be detected varies over the frequency range and is proportional to the frequency from about 500 c.p.s. upwards. In other words, $\dfrac{df}{f}$ remains constant; below 500 c.p.s. the value of $\dfrac{df}{f}$ increases considerably and depends to some extent on the way the experiment is performed. For example, if the frequency is varied sinusoidally a much greater frequency change is needed for detection than if the notes are switched abruptly (see, for example, Fletcher, 1953).

9.4.4 Early suggestions concerning the mechanism of hearing

The ideas which arose in the eighteenth and nineteenth centuries were formalised and established by Helmholtz (1877); his theory was based on the idea of resonance. The fibres of the basilar membrane were thought to be resonant vibrators which would perform a frequency analysis on the incoming sound. Thus, when a complex sound is heard, those fibres whose natural frequencies correspond to the frequency components present in the wave form would be stimulated, and hence nerves at different points along the membrane would respond. The time-varying pattern of the original wave is thus analysed into its frequency components and these are distributed to different points of the sensory mechanism; such a theory is usually termed a place theory. An alternative, in which the signals are thought to be transmitted as time variations direct to the brain, is termed a time theory.

The original place theory has much to commend it and it held sway for many years; it explains the diminution in discrimination and in sensitivity at the high- and low-frequency ends of the range by assuming that the precise range of natural frequencies covered is less than that actually detectable by the ear, and that at the ends "out-of-tune" fibres respond feebly to frequencies which are really beyond the range. It explains the insensitivity to phase in a mixture of harmonics, which was mentioned in Chapter 2, because it is claimed that the cochlea analysis transmits the relative *intensities* of the components to the brain. An experimental observation that beats are less pronounced, or even absent, if the two component tones are fed separately one to each ear, suggested that the simultaneous excitation of a single nerve is necessary for their production. Thus, on the place theory, beats should only occur if the groups of fibres near resonance are sufficiently close to stimulate the same nerve. In the last few decades the place theory has tended to give way to other suggestions. As often happens, however, the new ideas, first put forward as completely contradictory to the old ones, are now being regarded as complementary and the most recent theories involve elements of each. We shall now consider some of the properties which have to be explained by a successful theory and consider how some of the modern ideas have developed.

9.4.5 Further theories of the mechanism of hearing

Three groups of researches have provided the basis for the new approaches to the theory of the hearing process. First, physiological investigations into the purely mechanical construction of the ear have been carried out very successfully; perhaps one of the most significant contributions in this field is the work of von Békésy (see, for example, Békésy and Rosenblith, 1951). His work has shown that in fact a resonance theory is unlikely to be tenable because of the mechanical properties of the basilar membrane. He has shown that the membrane itself vibrates but that it does not behave as one would expect if it were in resonance; the phase and amplitude relations in its response do not correspond. Various other investigations of the mechanical structures have been made. For example, Onchi (1961) has constructed models of the lever linkage of the middle ear, based on physiological investigation, and then analysed the properties of the models. The second group of researches is in neurophysiology. Wever and Bray (1930*a, b, c*) and Wever (1949), for example, have described investigations of the electric potentials developed in the region of the cochlea; these potentials can be detected by probes, and it was found that for all but the loudest sounds the potential developed is proportional to the instantaneous pressure in the exciting sound wave. The part played by these potentials in the hearing process is not completely clear; it has been suggested that they may form an intermediate step between the excitation of the hairs in the cochlea and the nerve signals to the brain or they may in fact be themselves produced by the nerve signals. Galambos and Davies (1943) have studied the way in which single nerve fibres respond to acoustic stimuli, and these developments have helped considerably in setting the stage for new suggestions. Thirdly, a great many experiments in psycho-physics have been performed in attempts to obtain exact data concerning the reactions of different individuals to different sounds under controlled conditions. Numerous surveys of work done in these fields have been given, for example, by Fletcher (1953), by Allanson and Whitfield (1956) and by Licklider (1956). Before looking at the newer theories it is important to consider some more of the properties which have to be explained; many have been mentioned in passing in other parts of this book.

A successful theory must account for the recognition of pitch not only of pure tones but also of composite tones. We saw in section 8.2 that when two notes are near together in pitch the response seems to be governed by the time-space representation, and it is the envelope of the wave which is effective. When the notes are further apart the frequency-space representation seems to be more significant and the notes are heard separately. Also in Chapter 8 (sections 8.4 and 8.5) we saw how combination tones can arise if non-linearities are present in the ear. In the next chapter we shall see that for some instruments, for example the bassoon, there is practically no energy in the fundamental; it is concentrated in the higher harmonics, and yet the observer still "hears" the fundamental. All this must be explained. In the sections on formants (sections 7.2 and 7.3) we saw that the qualities of many instruments, and especially that of the human voice, are to some extent controlled by formants, but some interesting questions arise when considering simultaneous sounding of several instruments or voices. Suppose, for example, that a tenor sings a certain note to a particular vowel sound having harmonics in a low and a high formant region; if he is now joined by a contralto singing a much higher note to a vowel sound which has its low formant region in between the low and high regions for the tenor, how does the ear know which pairs of formant regions go together? An observer would certainly have no difficulty in identifying the separate voices, the pitch of the two notes and the nature of the two vowels. The interpretation of starting transients by the ear presents further problems. We saw in Chapter 6 that they are important in enabling instruments to be distinguished, but it is difficult to conceive of their detection by any form of resonance phenomenon. Investigations have shown that in listening to a pure tone the pitch can be identified by an observer in as few as five complete cycles, but in listening to a transient no such repetition occurs—does the ear divide up the transient into certain time intervals and analyse each section in turn, or does it observe directly the time variations of the wave form without preliminary frequency analysis? The pitch of a note depends chiefly on frequency, but with very loud sounds a pitch change can be heard. For example, if a pure tone of about 200 c.p.s. is sounded first quietly and then suddenly increased very considerably in loudness, most observers will gain the impression that the pitch has dropped by as much as a semi-tone. The effect seems to hold only for pure tones and is much more pronounced in the lower frequency regions of the audible range. In a complex sound, such as that of a real instrument, the higher harmonics are not appreciably affected and hence the whole note does not appear to change in pitch when the loudness is increased; this is probably a further manifestation of the "missing fundamental" effect described earlier; these are just a few of the fascinating properties of the ear and brain which have to be accounted for in any reasonable theory of hearing.

The resonance theory has already been said to be improbable on the grounds of the mechanical properties of the basilar membrane, but nevertheless some kind of place theory seems necessary. The basilar membrane responds in different ways to different tones, and it now seems probable that it performs a rough pre-sorting of the wave so that tones of different frequencies affect nerves at different parts of the membrane. It is equally clear, however, that the time aspect must also be present. In other words the signal fed to the brain by the nerves in the various localities of the basilar membrane does in fact contain the time-varying information about the original signal.† The work of Wever and Bray already mentioned supports this kind of supposition. Such a combination of the two theories would begin to explain why beats can occur for notes placed close together. The rough pre-filtering would

† George (1954) has suggested that the wave pattern is the only determining factor in the quality; he cites as evidence his experiments using tape-reversal in which he claims that the steady-state quality is modified as well as the transients.

probably lead to adjacent notes affecting the same nerve, whereas notes which are much further apart would affect different parts of the membrane. Mathes and Miller (1947) report experiments which also fit in with this idea. They showed that, if two notes are close enough together to give beats, then their relative phase *does* affect the sound heard although this is in opposition to the commonly held view that the ear is not phase-sensitive. It should perhaps be stressed that their results only apply to notes which are very close together. They contend that for such notes it is the envelope of the resultant which governs the response and they show that the degree of roughness of the sound depends mainly on whether the envelope falls to zero periodically. The same envelope idea is invoked by Schouten (1940*a*, *b*, *c*); he performed some beautiful experiments to determine why the ear "hears" a note of a certain fundamental pitch when a mixture of harmonics is sounded even though the fundamental is not in fact present. He used an optical siren, i.e. a photoelectric generator (see section 2.11), consisting of a transparent disc on which wave forms were drawn. The disc rotated and a photocell was illuminated by light passed through the disc. He studied in particular the sound generated by a pattern consisting of a regular series of sharp alternations; this, of course, gives rise to a sound very rich in harmonics. On the same disc he placed a wave form representing the peaks of the fundamental component arranged to be 180° out of phase with the pulses. Thus, by adjusting the light intensity through this portion of the disc in relation to the rest he could arrange to eliminate the fundamental entirely. He found that it made no difference to the sound of the note and concluded that, since the same effect occurs at all sound levels, the combination tones produced by the higher harmonics (see section 8.4) could not alone account for the effect. He called the low pitch heard by the ear from a collection of higher harmonics the "residue". In Chapter 4 (Fig. 4.1) we saw that a mixture of a second, fourth and fifth harmonics gives a wave form which repeats at intervals corresponding to the fundamental although the fundamental is not present. Schouten points out that if, for example, the eleventh, twelfth and thirteenth harmonics are used the resultant wave form will repeat at intervals corresponding to the fundamental frequency, but because the harmonics are so high this fundamental frequency envelope will dominate the shape of the wave. Since also the harmonics are close together they will affect the same region of nerves, and the residue or fundamental will be heard. Hoogland (1953), however, repeated some of Schouten's experiments and claimed that under certain circumstances observers reported a rise of pitch of an octave when the fundamental is removed. He claimed that the missing fundamental is supplied largely by the difference tones arising from non-linearities in the ear. Schouten has performed an interesting experiment in this connection; he raised the frequency components of a composite note from 200, 400, 600 . . . to 240, 440, 640 . . .; the difference tone is still 200 c.p.s., and hence one would still expect to hear this note. The envelope, however, would now repeat at 40 c.p.s. and so on the envelope theory one would expect to hear this note. In fact, Schouten claims that the resultant note rises by about a semi-tone! I have attempted to repeat this kind of experiment without success; I find that in the first case—with 200, 400, 600 . . . notes—the over-riding impression was of a strong 200 c.p.s.-note. With 240, 440, 640 . . ., however, the resultant effect was much less definite, and sounded like a discordant mixture of notes; the 240 c.p.s.-component certainly did not dominate and the 200 c.p.s.-component could be distinctly heard. I should hasten to point out, however, that this experiment was performed with a limited number of components and not under carefully-controlled conditions, but I include a reference to it to indicate the kind of difficulties which face the investigator in this field. One very important influence appears to be the way in which the questions to the subject are phrased. Leading questions must be strenuously avoided. It is astonishing how ready most subjects are to hear a particular note if it is suggested to them that it should be heard!

The present position can probably be summed up by saying that the mechanism of hearing up to the point of transfer to the aural nerves is fairly well understood, and that the place theory in the cochlea explains a partial pre-distribution of sound to various nerve paths. The way in which the brain deals with resulting stimuli, however, is very far from clear. It is interesting to note suggestions that, under certain circumstances, the identification of the pitch of a note may depend on the use of both ears (Huggins, 1953) and also that a new kind of place theory involving not place in the cochlea but place in the brain may be necessary (Jeffress, 1948).

9.4.6 Some supposed properties of the ear

In conclusion some mention should be made of properties claimed by various authors which are neither well defined nor clearly understood. "Absolute pitch", for example, has been widely discussed—some skilled musicians appear to have the ability to identify a note immediately or to sing a given note without reference to a standard. This kind of ability certainly exists and occurs in widely differing forms. There seems to be little conclusive evidence, however, that the property is really "absolute"; in fact, since the tuning pitch of orchestras is decided quite arbitrarily, the term "absolute" in the physical sense could not possibly apply. It is difficult to perform specific experiments because it seems that the ability is partially sub-conscious and cannot always be exercised to order under the conditions of experiment. It is clear that it is at least partly explained as a form of accurate memory. It is also possible that sub-conscious reference may be made to certain existing resonances in the cavities of the body. As an example, I can usually arrive at a fairly close approximation to the note A for tuning purposes by the rather cumbersome procedure of singing to myself the lowest note of my range—which I know is a low F and which seems to remain fairly constant—and then singing up the scale! This is certainly nothing like the possession of absolute pitch, but illustrates the way in which the existing resonances might be used. I have also met the suggestion that the property may change with time; one observer, for example, indicated that his estimates of pitch are now almost a semi-tone lower than they were some years ago, and, being aware of this, he can make a suitable correction. This observation again might support the possible use of resonances which may be expected to change with time.

A "musical ear" is another of the rather mystic properties which are difficult to define. Certainly the ability to differentiate between notes of different frequencies varies from individual to individual, and equally certainly the ability to produce (sing) a given note in tune with a standard varies considerably. Many students in elementary physics laboratories claim that they find difficulty in performing experiments in sound because they have not "got a musical ear". In my experience, however, their ability can be considerably improved with practice. The main problem is usually that they have never listened carefully to two notes which are in tune or to two notes an octave or a fifth apart, and do not really know what they are listening for. If they listen to sequences of known pairs of notes they can often improve quite rapidly their ability to differentiate between unison, octave and fifth, which are the intervals most often confused.

Lowery (1952) and Seashore (1938) have discussed the problems of musical appreciation and their relationships to physics and psychology, but, though interesting and important, such considerations lie outside the direct scope of this book.

CHAPTER 10

The Physical Characteristics of Conventional Instruments

10.1 Introduction

The theme running through this book is the physical basis of the design of musical instruments, and we have now reached a stage at which the various ideas and mechanisms which have been discussed can be reviewed in terms of their importance for conventional instruments. It would be out of place to attempt a complete history of the development of the various groups of instruments and equally so to discuss all members in great detail; attention will therefore be confined to one or two representative members of each of five groups, together with an additional section on the human voice treated as a musical instrument. References to historical and technical works are included in the Bibliography.

10.2 Bowed strings

Stringed instruments are usually divided into two groups, those played primarily by bowing and those played by plucking. In the plucked group there is no steady state; the note arises from a violent disturbance which gives rise to damped oscillations, and, in order to develop pronounced musical quality and to ensure that each note persists for a reasonable time, damping must be cut to a minimum. The softness of the player's finger used in defining the vibrating length of the string is a disadvantage, and hence instruments of this type are usually provided with metal strips which help to define the vibrating length of the string with greater precision and less damping. These strips are called frets and the whole sub-group—which includes the lute, the guitar, the mandolin, etc.—is usually distinguished from the bowed instruments by the designation "fretted". We shall concern ourselves only with the bowed group.

The modern orchestral string family consists of four members, the violin, the viola, the violoncello (or 'cello) and the double bass. Their orchestral ranges are approximately as follows:

1. Violin: 196 c.p.s. (G below middle C) to about 2,000 c.p.s.
2. Viola: 131 c.p.s. (C below middle C) to about 1,100 c.p.s.
3. Cello: 65·5 c.p.s. (two octaves below middle C) to about 700 c.p.s.
4. Double bass: about 41 c.p.s. (two octaves below the E below middle C) to about 240 c.p.s.

The range of all four instruments can be extended very considerably by skilled players using "harmonics"—higher modes of the strings introduced by lightly touching the string with the finger instead of pressing it down to the finger-board. The violin, viola and cello all have four strings, tuned a fifth apart (GDAE for the violin, CGDA for the 'cello). The double bass has four strings tuned a fourth apart (EADG). The first three differ princip-ally in scale and are largely of the same shape and construction. The precise scale factors are not preserved however, and do not relate directly to the differences in pitch. The viola, for example, is only 15 per cent larger than the violin although its pitch ratio is 2:3; the cello is only just double the size although its pitch ratio is 1:3. The double bass is signifi-cantly different in both shape and general characteristics; it is in fact closely related to the viols, which belonged to a parallel group of instruments in Elizabethan times and which had almost faded out until recent attempts to revive their popularity. The relationship of the double bass to this group is reflected in its sloping shoulders and its tuning in fourths instead of fifths. In very recent years attention has been directed to the possibility of re-scaling the violin family, and Hutchins (1962) has described the work of an informal American group known as "The Cat Gut Society" which has planned a series of eight "violins" forming a complete family all in correct scale and including the standard violin as one of its members. Their developments have been made possible by the detailed investigations initiated by Saunders (1937; 1953); some of this work will be described towards the end of this section.

Most of the rest of the section will be phrased in terms of the violin but the majority of the comments will apply equally well to the other members of the family. Figures 10.1(*a*) and (*b*) show photographs of a typical violin and cello, and Fig. 10.2 shows a transverse section of a violin. The primary tone generators are of course the strings, which are firmly attached to the tailpiece at one end and wound round pegs at the other, so that the basic pitch can be changed by altering the tension. In order that the instrument shall not be distorted by unbalanced forces the strings are made of different materials and are of different thicknesses, so arranged that the required pitches are given when the tension is about the same in all four. In modern instruments the lower strings are usually of gut or nylon wound with fine silver, aluminium or stainless steel wire to increase the mass-per-unit-length without unduly increasing the stiffness (see also section 10.5). The A-string is often of plain gut or nylon and the upper or E-string is usually a single strand of stainless steel. Fine screw ad-justors are often provided to permit more accurate tuning than is possible by the traditional "push-fit" wooden pegs in the neck. The active length of the strings is that between the bridge and the point on the finger-board at which a finger of the left hand is placed; the possible modes of vibration thus have frequencies which can be any integral multiple of the fundamental (section 2.7). The sound produced by the string alone is very weak and the necessary amplifier is supplied by the body. The body of a violin is the result of one of the most remarkable developments in the history of music. It emerged more or less in its present form in the sixteenth century and became finally stabilised by the end of the eighteenth century. As can be seen from Figs. 10.1 and 10.2 the body is a complex shape—even the thickness of the wood varies from point to point. It is usually constructed of different kinds of wood, for example a relatively soft but close-grain wood (often spruce) is used for the top plate or belly (with the grain running parallel to the strings) and a relatively hard wood (often pear or maple) with the grain running at right-angles to the strings for the back plate. The function of the bridge is to amplify as uniformly as possible throughout the range, but it is clear that an absolutely flat response is impossible. The variations in amplification at different frequencies give rise to the characteristic formants (Chapter 7), which partly account for the distinction between individual instruments and also, because of the resultant coupled system, give rise to transient effects. Leipp (1959) and Leipp and Moles (1959) have discussed the mechanism of coupling between the strings and the body via the bridge. They point out that the bridge tends to rock as the strings vibrate, and that it will rock towards the neck when the string is either raised or lowered from its mean position and away from the neck when the string regains its mean position—in other words, the rocking period is double that of the string and hence there is a tendency for the second harmonic to be emphasised.

The arched top plate of the violin has to withstand consider-

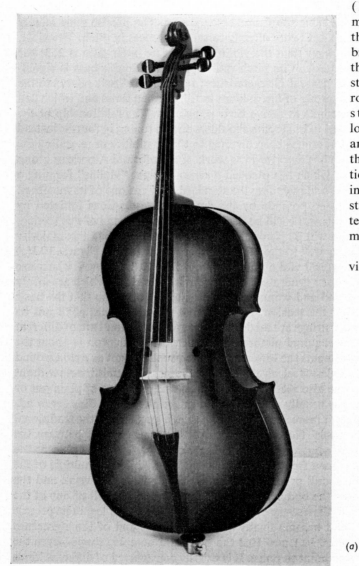

(a)   (b)

Figure 10.1   (*a*) Cello. (*b*) Violin.   (*Boosey and Hawkes.*)

able forces transmitted to it by the bridge from the strings, and, partly to strengthen it and partly to assist in distributing the vibrations of the bridge, a thick bar of wood—the bass bar—nine or ten inches long, is glued under one foot of the bridge parallel with the strings (see Fig. 10.2). A thin post of wood—the sound post—is wedged into the body near to the other foot of the bridge, and this also assists in the coupling process. Its precise location has considerable effect on the tone, and most skilled players prefer to adjust its position themselves. The mechanism of bowing was discussed in Chapter 6, and it was pointed out that the position, pressure, velocity, etc., of the bow all affect the precise quality of sound produced.

There are many myths and old wives' tales surrounding the history and construction of violins, and it is often difficult to disentangle the established facts from conjecture. Dis cussions about the value of the special varnish used by the Cremona masters whose secret appears to have been lost, of the way violin-makers selected the precise block of wood by tapping the tree, of the increase in quality of tone with age, and many other points have gone on for 200 years or so and will certainly go on for many years yet. It is only relatively recently that any concrete scientific assessment of the various factors has emerged, and the

most recent work suggests that we are beginning to establish an understanding of the nature of the important factors. The main point that emerges from recent experience is that it is now possible for modern violin-makers to produce instruments which—in the hands of a master violinist—are practically indistinguishable in tone from genuine old instruments made by such master craftsmen as Stradivarius. Comparisons have been made by highly critical audiences but there are two points which should be stressed about such experiments. They only work if the violins are played by performers of the

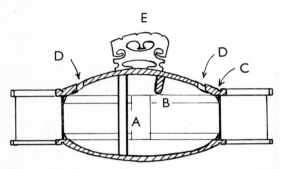

Figure 10.2 Cross-section of violin: A is the sound post, B the bass bar, C the purfling, D the f-holes and E the bridge.

very first quality, and the violinist himself is acutely aware of the differences between the violins. Perhaps the result can best be summarised as follows: with a genuine old violin made by a master craftsman a novice can produce tolerable tone quality; with a violin of standard modern manufacture a highly-skilled performer is needed to produce comparable tone.

Saunders and Hutchins have given accounts of recent work which has been done in the U.S.A. to determine the relative significance of various factors. The main concern of these researches is with the resonance of various parts of the instrument. It is necessary to couple the strings to the amplifier as efficiently as possible and a resonant frequency clearly enhances this transfer. The resonances of the cavity, however, are only part of the story; it turns out that resonances of the wood itself are even more important, and, since these resonances are not the same before the components—back, belly, sides, etc.—are assembled as when the instrument is completed, they are difficult to predict. Relations between them, however, can be found so that some estimate can be made. Saunders has introduced "loudness" curves as a means of comparing the overall effectiveness of the amplification and resonances of violin bodies. His technique involves measuring the maximum sound level that a skilled performer can produce at each successive semi-tone throughout the range. Variations of 1 to 15 dBs (section 9.4.3) in sound level for different notes on the same violin have been recorded, and variations of over 30 dBs between the maximum for one particular violin and that for another have been reported. The problem is to find which characteristic of the violin body is related to which peak, and to find at what pitch the resonances should be placed in order to achieve the most satisfactory overall result. A distinction is made between the "air tone", that is the resonance of the air cavity itself, and other resonances which appear to be characteristic of the wooden components. There appears to be only one peak due to the air cavity; it can be identified by several methods such as plugging the *f*-holes lightly with cotton-wool—only one peak disappears. Other methods of identification involve placing a filament of silk over one of the *f*-holes and noting when it is disturbed by the violent movement of the air at resonance, or filling the whole cavity with carbon dioxide which, because of the change in velocity, alters the resonant frequency. The body cavity resonance is usually round about middle C, but appears to have no overtones at all below about 3,000 c.p.s. This probably arises from the extremely complex shape. The wood resonances correspond to modes of vibration rather like those of the Chladni plate (section 2.5) and Saunders has studied possible modes by suitably-shaped metal plates. One striking result of this research is that deepening the groove round the edge of the top plate—usually filled with a thin strip of decorative wood, the purfling—leads to greatly increased loudness over the whole range. The effect of resonant strings is also discussed, and it is found that in general they reduce the total radiated energy; this may be the reason why lutes and other many-stringed instruments tend to have a weak sound. Saunders says that even the tone of a violin is louder if the three strings other than the one being played are relaxed, though this is clearly impracticable for most pieces of music. He concludes that four strings are the best compromise between adequate loudness, effective coverage of the required range, and facility in playing.

The violin group of instruments suffers from a very famous defect—the so-called "wolf" note. In most instruments—even those of the highest quality—there is one particular note at which the sound is quite different from the rest; it is difficult to hold it steady and it throbs intermittently, jumping back and forth, to higher harmonics. Raman (1918*b*) has investigated this phenomenon and showed by observing simultaneously the vibrations of the body and of the string that there is an interchange of energy between the two. In section 5.5 we saw that under certain circumstances the two components of a forced vibration can pass energy back and forth; in the case of the wolf note what seems to happen is that the fundamental of a string of a certain length coincides with a sharp resonance of the body. The energy thus passes to the body and the string ceases to vibrate at this frequency. Since the bow is still moving, however, and since the string is the primary controller of pitch (see section 6.5.1), the second harmonic of the string will take over. Once the vibration of the body in sympathy with the fundamental has died away, however, the energy is again passed back to the string at the fundamental frequency and the cycle repeats.

10.3 The woodwind

The development of woodwind instruments is almost as fascinating as that of the strings, but we shall again consider only modern instruments and confine our attention to those which are important in a modern symphony orchestra, namely the flute, clarinet, oboe, cor anglais and bassoon. In all these the primary vibrating member is the air in the pipe initiated either by edge tones or by a reed. In Chapter 2 we discussed the possible modes of vibration of cylindrical and conical pipes, and it turns out that these are the two shapes important in woodwind instruments. The change of pitch in the woodwind group is effected primarily by altering the equivalent length of the pipe by means of side holes, but in order to extend the range and to keep the number of holes reasonable it is usual to use the second and third modes in addition to the fundamental; this technique is usually known as overblowing. Benade (1959) has discussed the criteria which have to be satisfied by the bore of a pipe in order that the same set of side holes can be useful in the overblown ranges and concludes in fact that cylindrical and conical pipes are the only possible ones. Any kind of exponential horn such as is used in the brass instruments would not lead to a simple arrangement of side holes. Benade also considers the effect of the side holes and says that if they are large enough the remainder of the instrument below the bottom open hole is of little effect; it is necessary, in order to preserve a more-or-less uniform tone throughout the range, that the effective part of the pipe should have the same acoustic properties as the whole pipe. The side holes thus have to be chosen to fulfil two conditions—correct pitch of each note and uniform quality; the two necessary variables are provided by position and size.

We shall now consider each instrument in detail, beginning with the flute (Fig. 10.3). It consists of a cylindrical pipe whose effective length can be varied by opening or closing holes drilled in the walls, and which has a large hole fairly close to one end. The end nearest to the large hole is closed, but, because of the large hole in the side and of the distant open end, the tube behaves like a cylindrical pipe open at both ends and has a full series of harmonics (see section 2.8). In some models there is a slight taper, the open end being the smallest. The angle is so slight, however, that it does not affect the basic modes. Because of the full series of harmonics the flute can be overblown to give first the octave above the fundamental and then an octave plus a fifth. The initiation of the sound is by edge tones created by blowing across the single large hole, directing the air-jet from the mouth at the opposite edge. The short length of closed pipe on the opposite side of the blowing hole from the main pipe acts as a kind of matching device and affects the reflection of the standing waves set up in the tube; adjustment of its length has an effect on both the pitch and the quality. Most of the sound is radiated from the blowing hole, but it seems likely that resonance of the mouth cavity of the player also has an effect in determining the tonal quality.

The primary source of the vibrations is the edge tone and this forms a coupled system with both the pipe and the mouth cavity. The starting transient is relatively long, and there is also a high pure-noise content—the familiar "breathy" sound. The characteristics of the transient—which can be studied by slowing down a tape recording—seem to be a slow transition from the hiss of the breath to a tone in which the fundamental predominates. When blown very softly in the middle of its pitch range the amount of energy in the harmonics is very small indeed. As the strength of blowing is increased a full series of higher harmonics gradually emerges. The tone in the lowest octave is rather different from that of the higher pitches, and in fact the lowest half-dozen-or-so notes have a rich, almost reedy, quality which gradually disappears as the pitch increases. This change is characteristic of all the woodwind and arises from the influence of the formant (see section 7.2). The formant characteristic leads to an enhancement of notes at specific pitches, and, as the absolute pitch of the fundamental rises, any formant peak of lower frequency than the fundamental is of no further consequence, and hence there is a "simplification" of tone with increasing pitch. The normal range of the flute is from 261·6 c.p.s. (middle C) to about 2,093 c.p.s. The piccolo is merely a scaled-down version which is pitched an octave higher.

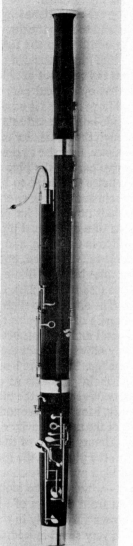

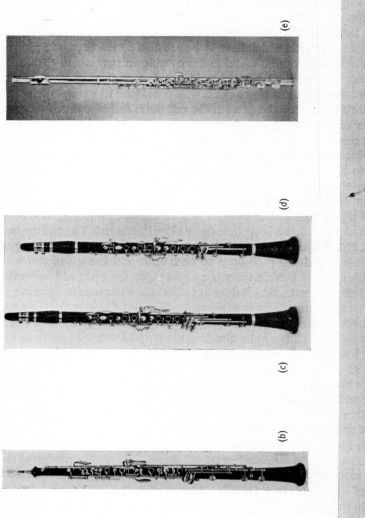

Figure 10.3 Woodwind instruments: (*a*) Cor anglais. (*b*) Oboe. (*c*) Clarinet in A. (*d*) Clarinet in B♭. (*e*) Flute. (*f*) Bassoon. (*Boosey and Hawkes.*)

The clarinet also has a cylindrical bore except for the short bell at the end, but because it is driven by a reed which behaves as a closed end from the point of view of reflection, it has only the odd-numbered harmonics (see section 2.8); the partials therefore have frequency ratios $1:3:5:7$, etc., and it overblows into its second mode of vibration at a twelfth above the fundamental (i.e. an octave plus a fifth). The absence of the even harmonics is partly responsible for the "fruity" tone of the clarinet, but the fact that it overblows at a twelfth leads to complications. In order to cover the full range of notes in the second octave a number of extra keys and holes is required, and the fingering becomes more complicated than that of a flute. There are two principal forms of clarinet in use, one is the clarinet in B♭ (Fig. 10.3(d)) and is the commonest, and the other is the clarinet in A (Fig. 10.3(c)). The use of two different instruments of not very different pitch facilitates the performance of music in different keys. The ranges are respectively 147 or 139 (D or C♯ below middle C) to about 1,500 c.p.s. Instruments of other pitches are available but are not in common use in a symphony orchestra.

The initiation of the sound in a clarinet is by means of a single beating reed (see section 6.5.4) which is held in the lips of the player. The tone varies very considerably over the range. The first mode (the so-called "chalumeau" register—a word which simply means reed and is the name of the parent instrument from which the clarinet developed) has a rich mellow quality. The second mode with frequencies three times that of the first (the clarion register) is much more brilliant in tone, and the third mode of five times the frequencies (the high register) tends to be rather squeaky. The section of the first mode lying between the octave and the twelfth—that is the region catered for by the special finger-holes in the upper part of the instrument—is rather unsatisfactory by contrast with the rest of this register except in the hands of a very skilled performer. The change from one mode to another—which in the flute is executed merely by overblowing—is not so easy on the clarinet. To assist the transition a small "speaker key"—covering a much smaller hole than the normal finger holes—is provided about half-way along the instrument, and this, when opened, influences the vibration of the pipe, and by reaction the reed, into the higher mode.

The existence of only odd harmonics gives a characteristic tone which on this basis alone should remain constant throughout the range. Formant characteristics, however, arise as in the flute with the result that the lower notes are much richer and more complex. The clarinet formant, however, is not quite so sharply defined as that of either the flute or the oboe. It is interesting to note in passing that the odd-harmonic characteristic has an influence on the harmonising possibilities of the clarinet; thus, for example, if a clarinet plays the note C and a violin the note G above, the harmonics (taking C as 1) would be as follows:

Clarinet	1		3		5		7		9		etc.	
Violin		2		4		6		8		10		etc.

Thus there are no common notes at all and the possibility of beats between harmonics if one is a little out of tune does not exist. (We are, of course, excluding the possibility that the notes are loud enough to excite aural harmonics or combination tones.) If the instruments exchanged roles, however, this condition would not arise, as shown below.

Violin	1	2	3	4	5	6	7	8	9	10	etc.
Clarinet		2				6				10	etc.

The side holes in any reed instrument have an important influence apart from simply changing the pitch. Their size and the wall thickness—which determines the size of the small cavities left when a hole is closed either by a key or a finger—have considerable effect on the formant characteristic. Unlike the flute, in which most of the radiation is from the mouth hole, in the clarinet most of the sound emerges from the side holes, and it is their properties as radiators differing at different frequencies which account for their influence. Only the two or three holes below the last closed hole influence the sound; this can be demonstrated by opening and closing the bottom one or two holes while a note in the middle of the first octave is played and noting that the effect is negligible. The bell is also of little effect for any except the lowest one or two notes, and can be removed without much effect; its purpose is in fact to act as a substitute for the side-hole radiators for the lowest notes which would otherwise differ significantly in tone from the rest of the first octave.†

The clarinet starting transient is in two portions, the first of which is the initiation of the reed vibration itself, which is usually abrupt and almost percussive, especially in the lower register; once the reed is vibrating the second part of the transient is the build-up of the vibration in the pipe, which is relatively smooth.

The oboe family is the remaining section of the woodwind to be discussed. The three principal representatives are the oboe itself, the cor anglais and the bassoon. Their ranges are

Oboe: 233 (B♭ below middle C) to 1,568 c.p.s. (Fig. 10.3(b))
Cor anglais: 165 (E below middle C) to 932 c.p.s. (Fig. 10.3(a))
Bassoon: 58 (B♭ just over 2 octaves below middle C) to 622 c.p.s. (Fig. 10.3(f)).

There is also a double bassoon of pitch roughly an octave lower still. All have a conical pipe which gives a full series of harmonics and also eliminates the fingering difficulties of the clarinet because it overblows to the second mode at an octave above the fundamental. The oboe is straight with a small bell at the open end, the cor anglais has a bulbous endpiece and is straight except for the mouthpiece (not shown in the photograph) which is bent through a small angle to enable the player to reach the lower finger keys. The bassoon is folded almost in half and the mouthpiece is bent round at right angles to the two main sections. The reed in all members of this family is a double one, of cane, fixed to a thin metal tube; it is clamped between the player's lips during performance.

The reed is of course the initiating mechanism and forms a coupled system with the pipe which ultimately determines the choice of pitch. All the members have a very characteristic tone which is defined very largely by their pronounced formant characteristics. A striking illustration of the predominance of the formant is given by Seashore (1938) for the bassoon and his diagram is reproduced in Fig. 10.4; it shows the relative level in decibels of the harmonics of various notes, and the emphasis on whichever happens to be near to the region 400–500 c.p.s. is quite obvious. The solid bars are for loud notes and the outlined bars for softly-blown notes. The frequency of the fundamental is marked for each and the small circles represent the positions of a harmonic partial which is not present.

The most interesting feature of the steady state—which emerges clearly from the lower

†An interesting demonstration of this based on a suggestion by Benade is to prepare three lengths of rubber hosepipe, the first plain, the second having three or four holes cut to represent finger-holes, and the third having a cheap tin funnel fitted in the end. The lengths are adjusted so that all three give the same note when a clarinet mouthpiece is attached and blown; the plain pipe gives a muffled tone, but the other two show signs of the characteristic "woody" tone of a clarinet.

notes in Fig. 10.5—is that the fundamental is not the strongest component and may even be almost non-existent. Usually the third and fourth, or sometimes the second and third, harmonics predominate. The ear, however, hears a fundamental of the right pitch as a result of the difference tone developed from the other harmonics whose separation in frequency is equal to that of the missing fundamental. The starting transients are also very characteristic; the initiation is percussive and has sometimes been described as a "quack" at the beginning of each note. As with the clarinet, however, once the reed vibration is initiated the build-up is relatively simple and short-lived. Saunders (1946), though confirming the weakness of the fundamental in the oboe and cor anglais, finds no evidence of formants in these and in the clarinet and flute.

10.4 The brass

The brass family differs from the woodwind group in three very important ways, each of which has a marked influence on the quality of sound produced. First, the principal way of changing pitch is by change of mode: in order that a wide variety of notes should be available the fundamental is usually made very low, and use is made of the high modes. Secondly, the initiation of the sound is by the double reed formed by the lips of the player stretched over the cup-shaped mouthpiece. Thirdly, there are no side holes and all the sound is radiated from the bell; the bell therefore has an important influence on the whole range of notes.

Three characteristic members of the family are shown in Fig. 10.5. The orchestral trumpet (Fig. 10.5(a)) has a working range from 185 c.p.s. (F# below middle C) to 1,046 c.p.s., though considerable extension above this is possible but is not continuous. The French horn (Fig. 10.5(b)) has a working range from about 61 c.p.s. (B just over two octaves below middle C) to about 700 c.p.s. The trombone (Fig. 10.5(c)) exists at three different pitches; the one illustrated is the tenor (highest pitch) and has a range from about 81 c.p.s. (E below the C below middle C) to about 520 c.p.s. The trumpet and trombone have a cylindrical bore which becomes conical towards the end and finishes almost exponentially. The horn is much more nearly conical throughout its length. Since the predominant influence in determining the pitch is the mode of vibration in the pipe it is clearly important that we should look closely at the

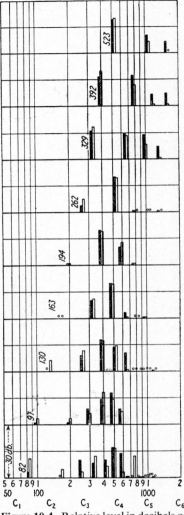

Figure 10.4 Relative level in decibels of the harmonics of various notes played on a bassoon. The solid bars are for loud notes, and the outlined bars for softly-blown notes. The frequency of the fundamental is marked for each and the small circles represent the positions of an absent harmonic partial (from *The Psychology of Music* by Seashore, 1938, McGraw-Hill Book Company. Used by permission).

(a)

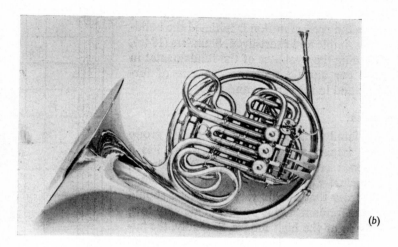

(b)

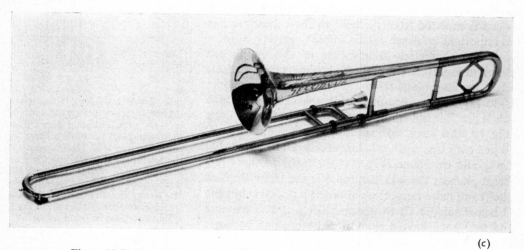

(c)

Figure 10.5 Brass instruments: (*a*) Trumpet. (*b*) French horn. (*c*) Trombone. (*Boosey and Hawkes.*)

influence of the bore. It would appear that the lips of the player form a more-or-less closed end, and one might expect that a cylindrical pipe giving only odd harmonics would not be ideally suited to an instrument based on mode-changing. Fortunately (or unfortunately!) there are complications which make the instruments satisfactory but at the same time make a clear physical understanding of their operation more difficult. In fact, the physics of the brass instruments still holds some fascinating problems which are by no means completely solved.

We shall consider first the relationship between the modes of cylindrical and conical pipes. Let us first take a cylindrical pipe closed at one end and define its fundamental frequency as 1 and compare the relative frequencies of its possible modes with those of a conical pipe of the same length (see section 2.10).

Cylindrical pipe closed at one end	1		3		5		7		9		11		13		15
Conical pipe		2		4		6		8		10		12		14	

The point to notice is that as we move to higher harmonics, the difference between successive notes on the same pipe is almost the same for both. If, therefore, we modify the length of the conical pipe slightly to make, for example, its fifth partial in tune with the fifth partial of the cylindrical pipe we find the following sequences:

Cylindrical	1	3	5	7	9	11	13	15
Conical	1·8	3·6	5·4	7·2	9	10·8	12·6	14·4

If one also bears in mind that the lips do not behave completely as a closed end, that even the trumpet becomes conical for part of its bore, and that the reed or lip frequency can "pull" the frequency of the pipe by at least a semi-tone from the natural frequency, it is possible to see why both the horn and the trumpet can give satisfactory sequences by mode-changing.

The sequence available, however, is still not sufficient for performers of music in all keys. Various devices have been used in the past to overcome this difficulty. For example, in the horn the pitch of the whole series can be lowered by inserting the hand into the bell, though this also changes the tone. Alternatively, "crooks" can be provided; these are interchangeable U-shaped sections of tubing which can be inserted as part of the main pipe in order to change its total length. In the modern versions of the three members of the brass family discussed here more effective techniques are used. In the trumpet and horn three prominent crooks are provided which can be effectively inserted or removed by the operation of three keys or pistons; they provide a lowering of pitch by a semi-tone, a tone, and a tone-and-a-half respectively, and can, of course, be used in conjunction with each other to provide larger changes. In the trombone a single very large crook is made telescopic and can slide continuously out and in; it permits the lowering of pitch by any degree up to three whole tones.

The initiation of the sounds is quite a complicated process. It is usually accepted that the lips of the player act as a double reed but their operation differs from that of the reed in an oboe since the aperture is never completely closed. The lips themselves are set into vibration by a complicated edge tone caused by the air rushing out between them. It is well known to performers and instrument makers that the shape of the mouthpiece is also very

significant, and Richardson (1929) ascribes this particularly to the production of further
edge tones when the cylindrical column of air from the lips strikes the sharp edge of the
mouthpiece cup. It is clear that, in addition, the mouthpiece acts as a matching transformer
to relate the impedance of the lips and mouth cavity to that of the bore of the instrument
(section 5.2), and that it also acts as a frame across which the lips can be stretched to assist
in controlling their tension. Cross-sections of typical trumpet, horn and trombone mouthpieces are shown in Fig. 10.6. The problem of the coupling between the lips and the pipe is
an extremely interesting one. Any experienced brass player can produce notes of a definite
pitch with the mouthpiece alone, but when the instrument itself is attached there is a
strong reaction on the lips. Modern jazz trumpeters can pull the frequency of the natural
harmonics of the pipe by an astonishing amount, but the fact remains that when a note of

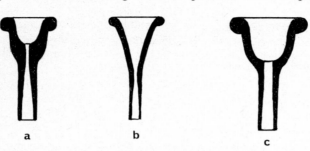

Figure 10.6 Sections through typical mouthpieces: (*a*) Trumpet.
(*b*) French horn. (*c*) Trombone.

the natural series is played the lips vibrate much more easily and the instrument seems to
actively encourage the vibration of the lips. A careful study of this coupling shows that there
are other notes—particularly with a cylindrical pipe—at which the lips vibrate especially
easily though not with quite the same vigour as at the true natural frequencies. A great
deal of thought was given to this point by the French physicist Bouasse (1929) whose work
unfortunately seems to have been largely neglected. Benade (1960) draws freely on his work
but it is hard to find a mention of his name in other textbooks on the physics of music.
Bouasse wrote in an extremely frank and racy style with many personal comments about his
contemporaries, but his researches are astonishingly complete. His so-called privileged
frequencies correspond to sub-harmonics of any of the natural frequencies of the pipe;
or, putting the statement the other way round, they correspond to overtones of the reed
which coincide with harmonics of the pipe. At the true natural frequencies, each harmonic
of the lip vibration finds a corresponding harmonic of the pipe and hence the reaction is
most vigorous.

The complex nature of the coupling between the lips, edge-tone and pipe (and also to
some extent with the vibrations of the metal walls according to some authors) leads to a
relatively complicated starting transient. Its precise form can be varied considerably by the
player from the almost explosive staccato initiation of repeated trumpet blasts to the soft
emergence of the lower notes on the French horn.

The third difference between brass and woodwind mentioned earlier arose from the
absence of the side holes. Nearly all the sound is radiated from the bell and hence the
properties of the bell itself are extremely important. It acts as a further matching transformer or radiator (section 5.2), and mathematical investigation shows that its behaviour is
highly frequency-sensitive. In general terms, the energy radiated at different frequencies
depends on the size of the bell—the larger its diameter at the open end the lower the frequencies that can be efficiently radiated. It is thus clear that the wave form radiated may be

different from that generated in the pipe itself; this is perhaps one of the most obvious ways in which a formant characteristic can arise. It can be modified by the addition of "mutes" placed in the bell; in general they diminish still further the radiation at low frequencies and also affect the reflection conditions in the pipe. The trumpet has a relatively small bell and hence its formant region tends to be high, which leads to the characteristic brilliance of its tone. The French horn on the other hand has a very large bell and consequently much lower harmonics can be radiated satisfactorily, leading to its well-known mellowness of tone.

10.5 The organ

The organ is really a complete orchestra under the control of one player and falls clearly into the category of instruments in which change of pitch is achieved by using a separate generator for each note. Most organ installations are themselves made up of several separate organs, each with its own keyboard. For example, in a so-called three-manual organ there are three manual keyboards and one pedal keyboard, and hence four

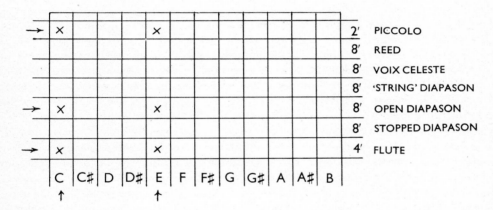

Figure 10.7 Diagrammatic representation of the layout of one octave of an organ with stops. In the figure the notes C and E are being played with the open diapason 4′ flute and 2′ piccolo stops drawn. The pipes marked *X* are thus speaking.

separate organ units. The "great" organ is controlled from the middle manual and produces all the basic organ sounds. The "swell" organ which is controlled from the upper keyboard contains a higher proportion of reed pipes, and the "choir" organ controlled from the lower keyboard contains relatively quiet pipes intended chiefly for accompanying voices. The pedal organ consists of pipes of low pitch. The swell and choir organs are each completely en-closed in a massive wooden box fitted with shutters which can be opened and closed by a pedal, thus enabling the player to change the total volume smoothly (hence the name swell). Each organ unit can be thought of as a matrix (see Fig. 10.7) in which the depression of a key admits air to a specific column and the drawing of a stop admits air to a specific row. Any pipe lying at the intersections of an open row and column will sound. All the pipes in a given row—a rank of pipes—are of the same type and produce notes of the same quality.

All the pipes in a given column produce notes of the same frequency or some integral multiple or sub-multiple of it. Thus, by pressing one key, complex notes of many different qualities but of the same basic pitch can be produced according to the combination of stops which is drawn. The multiple or sub-multiple frequency stops permit the emphasis of certain harmonics and add to the general complexity of the combination tone pattern. On most organs, to facilitate playing, certain pre-arranged groups of stops can be drawn simultaneously by operating a single pedal or piston.

Pipes which sound at the same pitch as the corresponding note on a piano are described as of 8-ft. pitch; the name refers to the approximate length of an open pipe which would correspond to the lowest note of such a series. 4-ft. and 2-ft. pipes are respectively an octave and two octaves higher, and 16-ft. and 32-ft. pipes are an octave and two octaves lower. Pipes of intermediate pitch, for example $2\frac{2}{3}$ ft. (sounding a twelfth above 8-ft. pitch) also occur, and can be used to modify the harmonic pattern when a combination of pipes is being used. Air is admitted to the various pipes by valves or pallets which were originally mechanically-linked with the keyboard (tracker action), in which case the physical layout and mechanical design follow very closely the matrix pattern illustration in Fig. 10.7. Modern organs, however, have either pneumatic or electric action, i.e. the valves are operated, often from a distant console, via pneumatic or electrical links.

There are three basic types of pipe but within each group there are wide variations of tone which arise from such factors as the material of construction (for example thin or thick wood, thin or thick metal, etc.), the ratio of bore to length (which influences the proportion of the various harmonics sustained), the air pressure, and the design of the initiating mechanism. The reader is referred to one of the many comprehensive volumes on organ design for full details. A brief outline only of the three main types will be given here. Two general points should first be made however. The organ is almost unique among musical instruments because each pipe is designed specifically to produce one note and one note only. The organ-builder thus has far more freedom to adjust the various factors under his control to give the best possible result. No compromise is necessary as with other instruments in which usually one resonant box or one reed, etc., has to operate over a wide range of pitches. This fact leads to the second general point, which is that it is debatable whether one can really talk of a "formant" for an organ. A formant as discussed up to now has been taken to be a modification of the relative harmonic amplitudes which is constant for the instrument and which remains constant whatever pitch is being played. Certainly in organ pipes of different shapes different harmonics are amplified or diminished, but by suitable scaling it is possible to maintain the same relative amplitudes at all basic pitches. The formant in other words is now a characteristic of each individual pipe and not of the whole rank, but in order to make a fair comparison with other instruments it is the rank of pipes that should be used as the basis. There is therefore a very fundamental reason for the difference in quality between, for example, a clarinet and a rank of clarinet-tone organ pipes. The acoustic properties of the swell box and of the room in which the organ is placed do however provide an overall formant applying to all pitches and all types of pipe, and until recent years relatively little attention has been paid to this important factor.

The basic member of the organ-pipe family is the open diapason. It is an open-ended pipe driven by edge tones and is usually of square cross-section, if made of wood, or circular if made of metal. A section of a typical example is shown in Fig. 10.8. It behaves as a pipe open at both ends and thus has a complete series of harmonics. The sound is radiated partly from the open end and partly from the side hole, and the final harmonic pattern of the radiated sound depends to some extent on the size of these two holes in relation to the pitch. The ratio of cross-section to length is thus a very significant factor. No adjustments are provided for the knife edge or for the jet once the organ has been installed; the pipe itself determines the pitch, and its effective length is controlled for tuning purposes either by a slot running down a short distance from the top which can be partly covered or uncovered by a bent strip of metal or, in the case of a cylindrical pipe of soft metal, by opening or closing the top of the pipe with a special conical tool. The design of the jet and the edge and the choice of "cut-up", that is the distance of the edge from the orifice, and other features of the initiating mechanism, is a highly-skilled job, and the whole tone of the pipe can be changed by relatively small modifications. When a rank of pipes has been built a procedure known as "voicing", which involves minor adjustments of this kind, has to be applied to ensure consistent quality throughout the range. Diapason pipes can be designed to give either a full rich tone or a much thinner so-called string tone; string diapasons are usually narrow in bore and operate at a higher wind pressure. If the wind pressure is increased the edge-tone of course will change in pitch, but it may be restored to its former value by increasing the "cut-up" or by introducing an obstacle (a "beard") near the jet, and this leads to the presence of higher harmonics. The edge itself can also be modified, and in fact for mellow diapason tone at low pitches the edge is sometimes covered with leather to add to the damping of higher harmonics.

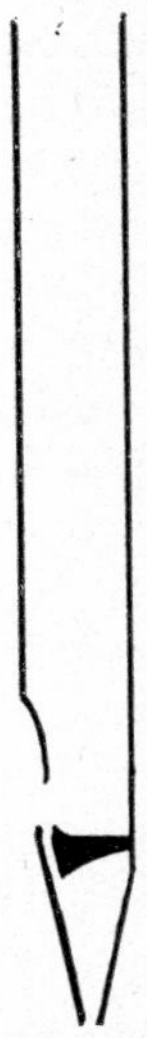

Figure 10.8 Section through an open diapason metal pipe (circular section).

Transients of diapason pipes have been studied by a number of workers and it is found that there are two distinct components. The first relatively short-lived component is the initiation of the edge-tone itself and the second component is the build-up of vibration in the pipe, in which it is often found that the harmonic content is quite different from that of the ultimate steady state. Nolle and Boner (1941b) have shown that there may be as much as 1/10th-of-a-second delay before any sign of the fundamental appears and that in the lower-pitch pipes the steady state may not be reached until more than half a second has elapsed. Pipes are sometimes specifically designed to operate in a higher mode than the fundamental. Thus a diapason pipe can be made to operate in its second mode by providing a small hole half-way along the pipe and by suitably adjusting the edge and slot (compare the speaker key of a clarinet discussed in section 10.3).

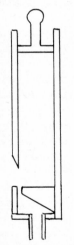

Figure 10.9 Section through a stopped diapason wooden pipe (square section).

The second characteristic member is the stopped or flute diapason (Fig. 10.9); its general construction is the same as for the open diapason except that the upper end is fully closed by a plug. Adjustment of the precise position of this plug provides the tuning mechanism.

The result is a cylindrical pipe closed at one end and therefore having only odd-numbered harmonics. The fundamental pitch is also an octave lower than that of an open pipe of the same length (see section 2.8) and the harmonic pattern has a pronounced effect on the quality. Another important influence on the tonal quality, however, is that the radiation of sound is now almost entirely in the side hole, and it is this feature which perhaps contributes more to its resemblance to an orchestral flute than the harmonic pattern which is clearly quite different. The part of the transient derived from the edge-tone initiation tends to be a little longer than for the open diapason and there is considerably more noise—the characteristic "breathy" sound—which again enhances the resemblance to the flute. Stopped diapasons are made of either wood or metal, but the metal variety usually have very much more massive walls than open diapasons of the same pitch. They are also occasionally operated in modes higher than fundamental; this is usually achieved simply by careful design of the edge and slot and an increase in wind pressure.

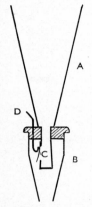

Figure 10.10 Section through reed pipe: A is the pipe, B the boot containing the reed C, and D is the reed-tuning wire.

The remaining group is the reed family—a cross-section of a typical member is shown in Fig. 10.10. The reed can be either free or beating, that is it may pass freely through the aperture or it may completely close it for some portion of each cycle. The reed is tuned by means of a spring wire which can lengthen or shorten its effective vibrating length. It is mounted on a small conical chamber called the shallot which is attached to the lower end of the pipe. A second chamber—the boot—surrounds the reed and is connected to the air supply. The reed is usually slightly curved so that it rolls on to the aperture, and an adjustment of its curvature, which is a highly skilled job, determines the rate of closure of the aperture and has considerable influence on the harmonics produced. Reed pipes are, of course, coupled systems and are usually provided with conical tubes to enhance the full range of harmonics. It is necessary to tune the pipe as well as the reed. Tuning is usually effected by the same slot device as is used in the open diapason. At very low pitches reeds are sometimes slow in starting and a special pneumatic starting device is sometimes fitted. This is just a small auxiliary bellows attached to a padded hammer arranged to strike the reed when air is admitted to the pipe in order to initiate the vibration. The diaphone (section 6.5.4) is used in some concert organs as a substitute for lower-pitched reeds because of its increased power and quicker initiation.

An interesting feature of organ construction which relates to our earlier discussion on formants can be seen if one examines the extreme upper end of the range of certain ranks of reed pipes. It will be found that the last eight or ten notes are provided by diapason-type pipes of suitable voicing without apparently creating any discontinuity of tone. The explanation is that at such high pitches the majority of the harmonics present in either reeds or diapasons are above the range of audibility; the ear is in fact providing a formant which makes all the very high pitched notes approximate to pure tones. Since high-pitched diapasons are very much easier to make than reeds the organ builder sometimes saves himself work by using this property of the ear.

Much attention has been paid to the examination of the steady state and of the transients of organ pipes largely as a prelude to the development of electronic organs (section 11.2).

For example, Trendelenberg, Thienhaus and Franz (1936), Nolle and Boner (1941a and b), and more recently Caddy and Pollard (1957), have described such work. The last-named authors showed that the transient for organ pipes depends very much on the rate of opening of the pallet, and they compared the transients of similar pipes operated by electric and by tracker action and showed significant differences. In any careful study of organ tone the noise element present becomes quite significant. Purely mechanical noise in old tracker organs can be very considerable; it is less noticeable with pneumatic action and still less with electric action, but it still exists to a significant degree and is one of the factors instantly missed in the tone of a purely electronic organ. If one stands inside the case of an organ while it is being played the amount of noise from the clicking of pallets and the hissing of air is so great that one can hardly believe that it does not completely destroy the overall musical effect. Fortunately, however, most of the noise seems to be absorbed by the case, but it is a factor which must be taken into account by organ-builders.

10.6 The piano

The organ was introduced as an instrument in which each note is produced by a separate generator, and the same is true of the piano and its earlier relations the clavichord and harpsichord. There is, however, an important difference since in the piano the amplifying device—the sound board—is common to all the notes and therefore may impose an overall formant, characteristic of the particular instrument, on all the sounds produced, whereas it was pointed out that apart from the effect of the casing there is no such overall formant for an organ. Historically, the piano may be said to be a descendant of the dulcimer, which consists of a flat sounding board over which strings are stretched to give notes of various pitches, and which is played by striking the strings with padded hammers. The psaltery, another instrument of great antiquity, resembles the dulcimer closely, but is played by plucking the strings. The psaltery was, in fact, the parent of the earliest keyboard instrument, the clavichord.

The clavichord probably developed in the twelfth century and is interesting from a physical point of view because the striking mechanism fulfils two separate functions. When a key is struck a small metal wedge (called a tangent) rises from below and not only sets the string in vibration but also remains in contact with it, thereby dividing the string into two portions and acting as a bridge. One part of the string is damped by felt or cloth interwoven with the strings, but the other part is allowed to vibrate freely. The pitch of the note thus depends on the position of striking, and in the earliest versions of the instrument two or three adjacent notes not likely to be needed together were derived from the same string by using tangents striking the string at different places. The tone is very quiet but some variation in intensity is possible by striking the keys with different degrees of violence. In the harpischord and spinet, however, no variation of loudness is possible; in these the string is set into vibration by a mechanical device which imitates the action of plucking by a plectrum. When a key is depressed the "jack" draws the string aside a certain distance and then releases it. The amplitude of vibration is determined by the distance moved, and once pre-set cannot be altered by variations in pressure on the key. The pitch is determined entirely by the string itself. The harpsichord in its various forms was a standard keyboard instrument during the sixteenth, seventeenth and eighteenth centuries, and displaced the clavichord because of its greater intensity. Instruments with two manuals which could be coupled together in various ways were developed in order to compensate to some extent for the impossibility of otherwise varying the loudness of the sound. The harpsichord itself began to be displaced by the pianoforte towards the end of the eighteenth century. The piano went back to the dulcimer principle and made use of mechanically-operated hammers which permitted both variations in loudness and retained and increased the sound level of the harpsichord. The name of the instrument reflects the importance attached to the possibility of variation of loudness. The modern form of concert grand piano became stabilised round about the middle of the nineteenth century.

The essential features—from the point of view of the physics involved—of a modern grand piano will now be outlined. The foundation of the instrument is a massive steel frame which can withstand the total force exerted by 240-odd separate strings, each operating at very high tension. The total force may in fact be as much as 30-tons weight. The strings are anchored to the frame at each end and pass over two bridges which define the active vibrating length. The peg at one end of the string can be rotated so that the tension can be adjusted for tuning purposes. One bridge is firmly fixed to the frame and the other is fixed to the sounding board and is the means by which coupling is effected. The choice of wood and the shape of the sounding board are extremely important in determining the final tone. The large number of strings for only 88 notes arises because the majority of notes have three wires tuned in unison and struck simultaneously by the hammer in order to enhance both the intensity and quality of tone. Some of the lower strings are single, but are loaded by means of a closely-wound helix of copper or alloy wire to increase the mass-per-unit-length without unduly increasing the stiffness. The strings are set into vibration by a hammer which is covered with thick compressed felt. The influence of the point of striking a string both on the resultant harmonic content and on the loudness have already been discussed (section 6.4). The complicated mechanism by which the hammer is controlled from the keyboard is a beautiful example of the craftsman's art. It has to be arranged to provide free travel of the hammer during the last portion of the movement, it has to prevent a rebound and hence the production of a double note, and it also has to enable rapid successions of notes to be played. The same mechanism also lifts a damper from the string and allows it to fall again when the key is released. The sound produced by a piano is nearly all transient; there is a violent percussive initiation followed by an exponential decay of the vibration which begins before the initial transient itself has died away. The damping, however, is relatively light compared with that of most other instruments (except the fretted stringed instruments), and during the later stages a steady wave form is developed modified only by the exponential decay.

One of the most controversial topics of musical physics in the present century has been the problem of "touch". How far can a pianist influence the tone produced by the way in which he strikes the key? A great deal has been written on the subject but some measure of agreement is beginning to emerge, and useful summaries of the basic work by Ortmann (1925), Ghosh (1936), and Hart, Fuller and Lusby (1934) are given by Seashore (1938) and by Wood (1944). More recent papers which discuss the problem are those by Báron (1958) and Young (1954). A brief account of some of the main points which have emerged will be given here.

A consideration of the mechanics of the hammer mechanism of the piano suggests that it is unlikely that the pianist can have any control over the hammer other than of the velocity with which it strikes the string. The important point, of course, is that there is no rigid link between the key and the hammer. The hammer is projected forward freely from the key mechanism just before it strikes the string, and hence at this point the pianist loses further control. Working from this basic fact it was at one time claimed that it could only result in the pianist being able to control the intensity of sound produced, and that no control of quality was possible. Musicians, however, claimed that control of quality did in fact occur. Hart, Fuller and Lusby made careful records of the sound waves produced by various pianists and also by mechanically-operated strikers, and showed that notes produced at precisely the same level of intensity on the same piano gave indistinguishable wave traces whether produced mechanically or by a pianist. The element which was ignored in the earliest discussions, but which permits some reconciliation between the views of the physicists and the musicians, is that although the velocity of the hammer is the only variable under control the velocity does in fact have an influence on other aspects of the tone than the intensity. Hart, Fuller and Lusby went on to show that enormous differences in the wave form produced by a given string when struck at different velocities can arise. In general, the higher the velocity the greater the predominance of higher harmonics. The pianist thus controls both loudness and harmonic content at the same time, though for a single note separate control of these two variables cannot be achieved. Let us consider, however, the striking of a chord consisting of several notes. It would be possible to make up the same effective loudness of the whole chord in a number of different ways. A skilled performer is quite capable of striking the different elements making up a chord with different degrees of force, and hence it should be perfectly possible to strike the same chord at the same total intensity but with different harmonic content, depending on the relative emphasis given to the different notes. Young showed that the harmonic content of a given note changes with time because the damping effect differs very considerably for the different harmonics present in a string (see also Mahajan, 1929). This fact provides a further means of tone control available to the pianist. It was explained earlier that the hammer mechanism raises the damper from the string, and the string remains undamped until the key is released. A sustaining pedal, however, is provided which raises the dampers from all the strings, and skilled use of this pedal can have considerable effect on the overall quality by determining the amount of overlap between notes. It also permits a certain amount of sympathetic vibration of other strings. There are, of course, many other elements involved in what the musician calls touch—the precise timing of sequences of notes, the almost imperceptible changes in loudness from one note to another in a sequence—but these considerations do not properly lie within the scope of physics. Finally, a brief mention should be made of the noise element which, however undesirable, forms a significant part of the piano tone; the noise of the fingers on the keys, of the hammer on the string, and of the return fall of the hammers on to felt pads, can all be heard, and, although the hearer is not usually acutely conscious of them, their absence in an electrical reproduction of the sound of a piano is immediately apparent.

10.7 The human voice

The human voice is the most fascinating of all musical instruments because of the immense variation in quality of tone that can be produced and because of the vast amount of information which can be incorporated in, and recognised from, these variations. The various hissing and percussive sounds—largely involved in the consonants—were not given much attention in the earliest researches, but the problem of vowel recognition has occupied attention since the early nineteenth century. Why is it that one can recognise a vowel sound as, for example, "ah" or "oh" whether sung by a high-pitched boy's voice or by a deep bass? What form does the modification of the basic note acquire in order to convey this extra information? Early workers discovered that each vowel was connected with a particular harmonic partial arising from a resonance of the mouth cavity, and later Helmholtz showed that some vowels involved two such resonances. In 1924 Sir Richard Paget (see Paget, 1930) showed that *every* vowel was associated with two resonances and that they are absolute in pitch, in other words they are formants and for a given vowel occur at the same pitch regardless of the basic pitch of the note being sung or of the quality of the voice. It is important to notice, however, that the resonances are not sharp; each vowel is characterised by a continuous formant which has two maximum regions. Thus the two sorts of information—the vowel sound and the pitch—can be conveyed in one wave form. The voice mechanism consists of a source of air under pressure (the lungs) feeding via a tube (the trachea) a double reed (the vocal chords) which produces the basic tone plus a rich mixture of harmonics. Control of the frequency of vibration of the chords involves changes in both tension and wind pressure. The output from the chords is thus a modulated air stream which then passes through a series of resonant cavities (larynx, pharynx, mouth, nose, etc.), some of which can be modified in order to impose the required vowel formants and some (for example, in the nose cavities) which are fixed and impose the formants that enable us to distinguish one person's voice from that of another. In addition edge-tones from the teeth and the tongue, and noise elements produced by forcing air through various constrictions, complete the resources from which voice sounds are built up.

It is interesting to notice that in whispering the resonant cavities are all adjusted as for normal speech but the feed instead of being an air stream modulated at some definite pitch by the vocal chords is instead merely white noise formed by the air passing over various obstructions. Nevertheless, the formants can be imposed on this background (see section 7.2), and hence the vowel sounds can be recognised even in the absence of a basic pitch. Various interesting demonstrations of the production of speech have been set up from time to time. Paget produced a series of plasticine models of the larynx set to correspond to various vowel sounds and fed by the output of a reed organ to provide the modulated air stream. An early electrical analogue was that developed by Dudley, Riesz and Watkins (1939), and there have been many subsequent models. Much of the recent work on speech has been made possible by the sound spectrograph (see Potter, 1946) in which a short speech sequence is recorded on a tape loop and then played over and over again through a continuously adjustable filter network. In this way a two-dimensional diagram can be provided showing the variations of harmonic content with time. Some interesting high-speed ciné photographs of the vocal chords in operation have been taken by Farnsworth (1940), and these also have played an important part in elucidating the mechanism.

There has been considerable argument about the precise relationship between the vocal chords and the resonant cavities. One theory—the so-called steady state or harmonic theory—suggests that the vocal chords produce a complex wave form containing a large number of harmonics and that the resonant cavities then select from these the ones required for a particular variable. The other theory—the transient or inharmonic theory—suggests that the vocal chords produce puffs of air and that these puffs excite the various cavities into resonance. The essential difference is that in the first theory the cavities are supposed merely to select from existing harmonics, whereas in the second the puffs are supposed to initiate resonances which need not be harmonically related. It seems likely that in fact these theories are just two ways of looking at the same thing. It can be shown that the puffs produced by the vocal chords are regularly spaced in time, in other words their wave form resembles a square wave, and it can be seen that a "complex wave form containing a large number of harmonics" is a possible frequency-space description of a regular succession of puffs in time space. The two theories are therefore probably frequency-space and time-space ways of looking at the same thing, and section 7.3 on the Fourier-transform approach to formants will further clarify the relationship between the two.

Teachers of voice production often appear to advocate completely different ways of producing good tonal quality, and there have been many fierce arguments about the relative merits of their differing methods, leading pupils to think that the basic mechanism of voice production is not at all understood. The difficulty seems to be one of language. When teachers speak of "projecting the voice to the top of the head", or some other similar descriptive phrase, these are not meant to be taken literally; they are intended to describe feelings the pupils should try to achieve in order to put the various muscles involved in the best configuration for voice production. Clearly there may be many different ways of describing what one must attempt to do, all of which may lead to the same final configuration. The same is true to a certain extent in playing other instruments. It is not easy, for example, to describe in words precisely how one should proceed in order to play a note on a trumpet. Much of the recent progress in elucidating the mechanism of voice production has arisen from work on communications systems, in which it is necessary to specify quite clearly the various elements which need to be retained in order to ensure undistorted, or at least recognisable, transmission of information.

CHAPTER 11

The New Instruments

11.1 Introduction

We have now completed the survey of the basic physical phenomena associated with the production of musical sounds and have also seen how some of them influence the sounds produced in conventional musical instruments. We can now take a brief look, by way of finale, at some of the attempts that have been made to produce new instruments. Before we consider any instrument in particular, however, it would be advisable to consider carefully the aim of producing a new instrument. In the decade before the second world war a great deal of attention was focused on the possibility of producing a purely electronic organ and great controversies raged about the musical acceptability of the product. Electronic organs have made great strides since that time, but it is still very easy to become involved in quite fierce arguments about whether they are "as good as" (whatever that may mean) a pipe organ. This kind of argument is always dangerous. If one sets out to produce an instrument which generates sounds which are completely indistinguishable, even by experts, from the tones produced by a pipe organ one is faced with an onerous task. We have seen in the earlier chapters that it is not sufficient merely to produce the correct harmonic mixtures; starting transients, formants, incidental noise, and many other factors are involved and no existing instrument succeeds perfectly. It is abundantly clear that if the aim is to produce this kind of sound then by far the cheapest way of achieving it is by means of a pipe organ! If, on the other hand, one sets out to build a *new* instrument not intended just to ape an existing one but to stand on its own feet and to permit the exploration of new tone colours and patterns, then one must agree that many of the new electronic instruments are highly successful. It seems, therefore, that anyone attempting to assess the performance of a new instrument should listen to it with an open mind and not with preconceived notions of some instrument which is being imitated, though this is an extraordinarily difficult achievement for most people. It should also be remembered that composers usually write music with specific instruments in mind, and it should not be too suprising if music written for conventional instruments sounds a little peculiar if played on new instruments, though this is not necessarily so.

One obvious way in which modern developments in physics can be harnessed in music is in the amplification of weak sounds. In Chapter 5 we saw that the need for amplification arises in most instruments, and we also saw some of the difficulties and consequences of trying to produce uniform mechanical amplification over a wide frequency range. Electrical amplification therefore offers great possibilities, and many electrified instruments have appeared, including the piano, cello, guitar, etc. The advantages are that one can control the sound level easily, thereby enabling one to practise quietly or to play in a large hall using the same degree of force on the keyboard. Also the amplifier characteristic can easily be altered, and this in fact gives one a controllable formant and hence a wider range of tone qualities.

Many composers now use technical developments in electronics to explore all sorts of new tone colours. Tape recording, for example, offers almost infinite possibilities: multiple recording or play-back with several spaced heads can be used to simulate reverberation; filters can be used to introduce formants of an unusual type; tape loops can be used to provide repetitive rhythms; smoothing and sharpening circuits, and many other tricks, have been used. Some composers generate the whole of their music synthetically by means of valve oscillators and gradually build up the complete work by successive superposition of recordings. Other composers start with natural sounds—a tap dripping into a tank of water, for example—and then modify this, altering the speed of play-back to change the pitch, altering the formant characteristics and using the same sound over and over again to create rhythmic patterns. The technical aspects of some of these developments have been discussed by Badings and du Bruyn (1958) and by Macfadyen (1964). A comprehensive survey of all electronic methods of producing music, including electronic organs, is available in the book by Douglas (1957). These are not really instruments in the sense implied at the beginning of this book however; we shall confine our attention to two groups of instruments in which the performer really "plays" without hours of preparation, and we shall also discuss briefly music generated by computers. First we shall consider electronic organs which, at least when first introduced, were designed in imitation of pipe organs, and this will be followed by a discussion of a most exciting new development and one of the few really new mechanical instruments to be produced in this century—Les Structures Sonores Lasry-Baschet.

11.2 Electronic organs

The parent of all electronic systems must have been the telharmonium (Cahill, 1897). Its tone generators were motor-driven alternators, one for each of the required frequencies; their outputs were mixed by a resistance network and fed to telephone earpieces. It turned out to be quite impracticable and uneconomic because of its enormous size, and the idea was abandoned until the advent of the thermionic valve. There are now many kinds of electronic organs, and it would be quite impossible to describe them all. In fact only three systems will be described; they are the Compton electrone, the Hammond, and the Wurlitzer organs. A necessary preliminary to the development of electronic organs was the analysis of tone of conventional instruments, and in the early stages effort was concentrated mainly on producing tones whose harmonic content could be varied. Let us consider in more detail than was given in Chapter 2 how these basic functions are performed in the selected instruments. In each example only the basic mechanisms will be described. In the most recent versions of all three many ingenious devices are included to add to the variety of tone available to the performer.

The Compton electrone (Bourn and Compton, 1932; Bourn, 1949) uses electrostatic tone-generation. The simplest model incorporates twelve identical tone-generating units, each of which produces seven notes spaced an octave apart. Each generator is fitted with a pulley of a different size and a single belt links all the generators with the driving motor. The pulley diameters are so arranged that their speeds are in the correct ratios to produce the twelve notes of the equal-tempered scale. Thus one generator produces seven C's an octave apart, the next seven C♯s and so on, so that eighty-four notes are available in all. The photograph of Fig. 11.1 shows one of the tone-generating units with the backplate removed. The backplate or stator (on the right of the photograph) carries the seven wave-form elements which are of metal on an insulating base. The black lines are the insulating material showing between the elements; the wave-form elements are bounded on one side by a wavy line and on the other side by one of the circles. The rotor (on the left of the photograph) has a series of diametrically opposite metallic sectors connected in parallel, one set

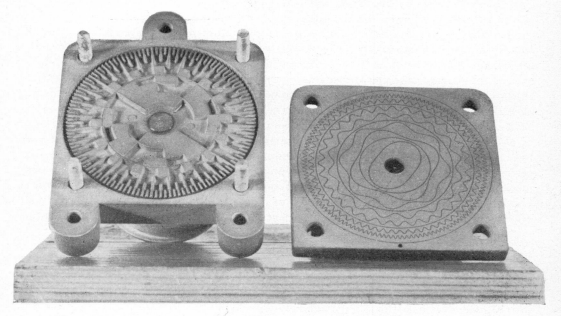

Figure 11.1   A Compton-electrone tone generator. The stator which forms the back plate is on the right and the rotor and casing on the left. (*Component by courtesy of John Compton Organ Company.*)

for each wave-form element. A further plate behind the rotor (not visible in the photograph) picks up capacitatively any signal induced on the rotor. In practice the rotor is divided into two portions, one including the three lower-pitched wave-form elements and the other the four for higher pitches; the circular insulating band can be seen in the photograph. There are thus two separate outputs—treble and bass—for each generator, and these are fed in parallel to the amplifiers. No tone is produced unless a polarising voltage is applied to one or more of the wave-form elements; the signal is then proportional to the voltage applied. This system involves high voltages, but has the advantage that there are no contacts made or broken in the actual sound circuits and hence there are no "key clicks" to be eliminated.

The required different qualities of tone are produced by mixing harmonics "borrowed" from other generators in different proportions, though of course this means that the harmonics are equal-tempered approximations and not precisely in tune. In the more advanced versions wave-form elements of much more complex shape generating particular mixtures of harmonics directly are used. These are grouped in an ingenious way so that by mixing the various complexes a wide range of useful tones can be produced. When this system is in operation the fundamental of each note is provided by a separate generator. Vibrato effects are obtained by imposing fluctuations on the belt motion by means of an oscillating auxiliary pulley; they involve principally changes in frequency. Transient effects can be simulated by means of delay networks which may give a gradual build-up or a gradual decay. Various special effects are possible, for example chimes in which the initial delay is eliminated to give a sharp rise and the final decay is considerably extended. Various compensating networks are necessary to maintain steady output under all loading conditions.

The Hammond organ, first introduced in 1934 (Hammond, 1935), uses electromagnetic tone-generation. The principle is extremely simple. Figure 11.2 is a schematic diagram of the tone-generating arrangement. The tone wheel is of steel and is about 2 in. in diameter; its profile is accurately machined to a shape which has a specific number of high points or teeth. The wheel rotates close to the tip of a magnetised rod carrying a coil, and the fluctuations in the field produced by the rotation generate currents in the coil of a frequency which depends both on the speed of rotation and on the number of teeth. The wheels are mounted in pairs, the members of

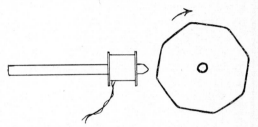

Figure 11.2 Diagrammatic representation of a Hammond tone generator.

which are driven in opposite directions from a single gear wheel. There are 48 such pairs with twelve gear-wheel sizes so that in all eight tone wheels run at each of twelve speeds. The speed ratios correspond to frequencies of the equal-tempered scale, and the eight tone wheels running at a given speed have respectively 2, 4, 8, 16, 32, 64, 128 and 192 teeth to give various octaves and harmonics of the basic notes from which suitable selections may be made. Two forms of control are available to the player. A set of harmonic controllers, one for each of nine harmonics, each of which can be set to one of eight positions including zero, can be used to experiment with new tone colours. Certain pre-set mixtures controlled by single stops are also available for combinations which are in frequent use. The draw-bars giving individual control of harmonics are calibrated so that any given combination can be noted and hence easily prepared on a future occasion. The tremulant controller is in effect a variable resistance driven by an eccentric wheel which modulates the amplitude of the total output (and not the frequency) by an adjustable amount. The remainder of the organ consists of amplifiers, filter circuits, and the necessary loud-speaker units. Again, of course, the harmonics available are the nearest notes of the equal-tempered scale and various compensation circuits are required to ensure uniform output under the varying load conditions which occur during performance.

The Wurlitzer organ is the third representative type to be described; it uses electrical oscillators as the primary source of tone. The basic tone-generating unit consists of twelve valve oscillators of the Hartley type. Each is tuned approximately by pre-set condensers to give a frequency corresponding to one of the twelve notes of an equal-tempered scale in the highest octave demanded by the keyboard. Fine tuning of each master oscillator is provided by adjustable cores in the coils. The resulting wave form contains a rich complex of harmonics and is nearer to a square wave than to a sine wave. Basic notes for the remaining four octaves covered by the keyboard are derived from the master oscillators by four successive stages of frequency dividers, each of which produces a wave form of frequency exactly half of that fed to it. Tuning of the organ is thus much simpler than if a separate oscillator were used for each individual note.

In the two organs already described in this section the required variations in tonal quality controlled by the stops are produced by synthesis from harmonic components; in the Wurlitzer organ almost the reverse process is used. The basic notes, rich in harmonics, are fed to a series of alternative filters or "shaping" circuits which modify the relative proportions of harmonics present. For "flute" tones, for example, the filter eliminates almost all but the fundamental. Ingenious circuit design makes it possible to produce percussive and non-percussive sounds. Non-percussive sounds have a relatively slow build-up and then remain constant as long as the key remains depressed; percussive sounds have a very sharp rise followed by a variable exponential decay so that piano- or guitar-like sounds can be produced. As mentioned in the introduction, such an organ can be used either to imitate existing instruments or to create new instrumental sounds not otherwise available. Various special effects are also provided; for example a vibrato effect is produced by a phase-shift oscillator working at about 6 c.p.s., the output of which can be used to modify the frequencies of the master oscillators periodically.

There are, of course, many other forms of electronic organ; the Wurlitzer company, for example, also make an organ in which the basic tone-generation is by wind-blown reeds. The primary tones are then amplified and modified electronically to produce the required volume and variation in tonal quality. In both types of Wurlitzer organ the filter, or shaping units, could be considered to impose various formants on the basic wave form.

11.3 New mechanical developments

A remarkable series of new and entirely non-electronic instruments has been developed recently by the French group founded in 1955 under the title Structures Sonores Lasry-Baschet. Their first public performance in Britain was at the York Festival in 1963, though they appeared on television on an earlier occasion. Baschet (1963) describes their method of arriving at new ideas by analysing standard musical instruments into their components— much as we have done in the earlier chapters of this book—and then assessing the possible mechanical ways of realising them. So far they have used the vibrations of rods as their primary tone-generators, but have showed great invention in their methods of amplification and of excitation.

The instruments are made from various fundamental components which can be assembled in various combinations to give different qualities and ranges. A group of the instruments is shown in Fig. 11.3. In the "cristal" (centre front in the photograph), which is the main melodic instrument in the group, the primary vibrators are short horizontal metal rods of varying length. Their frequency of transverse vibration is determined partly by the length and partly by loading with weights. At certain points along each bar a vertical glass rod about 50 cm. long is attached; this provides the initiating mechanism. The performer strokes the glass rods with wet fingers, making use of the stick-slip mechanism discussed in Chapter 6. The longitudinal motion thus produced in the glass rods in turn excites transverse vibrations in the horizontal metal rods. The resulting vibrations are analogous to

Figure 11.3 "Les Structures Sonores Lasry-Baschet". (*B.B.C. photo.*)

those of a tuning-fork—large forces associated with very small amplitude—and can be said to be high-impedance vibrations. Practically no sound is radiated unless amplifications and matching devices are introduced (see Chapter 5). All the metal rods are attached to a solid metal bar which provides coupling and a certain degree of matching. The remainder of the amplification is provided by a set of plastic air cushions which can be seen in the photograph and which behave in much the same way as the body of a violin. In fact Baschet states that he arrived at the idea as a result of a successful experiment in building a portable guitar, in which the normal body was replaced by an inflatable balloon. This instrument also carries a large number of stiff wires clamped horizontally at one end to the common bar and unsupported at the other, so that they form a metallic fringe round the front of the instrument. The various resonances in these wires provide a formant characteristic which can be pre-determined by altering the size and number of wires used. The wires also provide a certain amount of reverberation and echo. This particular instrument can be made to sound remarkably like a Baroque organ; its transient, which arises largely from the "bowing" mechanism, is a relatively smooth build-up. Two other versions of the same instrument covering lower pitch ranges can be seen at the extreme left of Fig. 11.3. They involve the same primary vibrators and initiating mechanism, but amplification and formants are provided by a series of large cylindrical resonators whose band width is broadened by introducing a relatively high damping in the coupling mechanism (see Chapter 5).

The instrument to the left of the centre with the sail-like horn radiator involves again the same basic vibrators and initiators, but the curiously-shaped sheet-metal horn gives the instrument a trombone-like tone. The instrument in the centre at the back and those on the right are percussion instruments, in which much longer metal rods are clamped to a metal frame, and horn and air-cushion amplifiers are provided; they are played by striking the rods with hammers.

11.4 Computed music

The advent of the electronic computer has provided yet another approach to the problem of producing new kinds of musical sounds. In the early days of computers a familiar party-trick was the programming of the machines to give a sequence of pulses whose periodicity varied and which on being fed to a loudspeaker could produce a crude tune. The most recent developments have progressed to the point at which the tone of a human voice or of a full orchestra can be synthesised. One typical example will be discussed; it is that described by Matthews (1961).

The actual sound generator (digital-to-acoustic converter) consists of a magnetic tape on which the successive amplitudes of the required wave form at 1/20,000-second intervals are recorded in digital form by the computer. A converter then translates this succession of numbers into a succession of pulses whose height corresponds to the numbers. This output is then fed through a filter which in effect removes the 20,000-c.p.s. component and leaves the envelope of the pulses which is the required wave form; this is fed to amplifiers and a loudspeaker. Each amplitude sample can be recorded as a four-decimal digit number and hence changes in amplitude which are quite imperceptible are possible, and in theory any wave form involving frequencies less than about 20,000 c.p.s. can be produced and heard if the computer can be made to provide the necessary number sequence. The programming operation is itself organised by the computer, so that a "score" programme can call for notes corresponding to given instruments and given pitches whose wave form characteristics have already been memorised in other sections of the machine. The "instrument" is, of course, expensive to run and not easy to operate by a composer unskilled in mathematics. However, although it may not be likely to replace a symphony orchestra for some time to come its great value in research is that it can produce small variations in sounds of accurately-determined amount. It can also produce hitherto unheard signals, and its value in psychological and related researches in music and in speech is clearly immense. Other developments in this field are described by Matthews and Guttman (1959), Rosen (1958), Hiller & Isaacson (1959), Olson, Belar and Timmens (1960), and many other workers.

Name Index and Bibliography

(Including some general works to which specific reference has not been made)

ALLANSON, J. T. & WHITFIELD, I. C.   1956. *3rd Symposium on Information Theory*. London: Butterworths.   151

ALLEN, C. H. & WATTERS, B. G.   1959. *J. Accoust. Soc. Am.*, 31, 177.   30

ANDRADE, E. N. DA C. & SMITH, F.   1931. *Proc. Phys. Soc.*, 43, 405.   9

ATTREE, V. H.   30

BACKUS, J.   1961. *J. Acoust. Soc. Am.*, 33, 806.   99

BADINGS, H. & BRUYN, J. W. DE   1958. *Phillips Tech. Rev.*, 19, 191.   179

BAINES, A.   1961. *Musical Instruments through the Ages*. London: Penguin.   10

BARBER, N. F.   1961. *Experimental Correlograms and Fourier Transforms*. Oxford: Pergamon.   —

BÁRON, J. G.   1958. *J. Acoust. Soc. Am.*, 30, 151.   110, 174

BARTHOLOMEW, W. T. 1942. *Acoustics of Music*. New York: Prentice Hall.   112, 124, 131, 135

BARTON, E. H. & BROWNING, H. M.   1918. *Phil. Mag.*, 36, 169.   71

BASCHET, F.   1963. *New Scientist*, p. 266.   71, 182

BECKETT, H. E.   See George, W. H.   89

BÉKÉSY, G. VON & ROSENBLITH, R.   1951. From Stevens, *S.S. Handbook of Experimental Psychology*. New York: Wiley.   151

BELAR, H.   See Olson, H. F.   185

BENADE, A. H.   1959. *J. Acoust. Soc. Am.*, 31, 137.   161

—— 1960. *Horns, Strings and Harmony*. New York: Doubleday.   164, 168

BERANEK, L. L.   1960. *Noise Reduction*. New York: McGraw-Hill.   48

BONER, C. P.   See Nolle, A. W.   100, 114, 171, 173

BOUASSE, H.   1929. *Instruments à Vent*. Paris: Librarie delagravie.   168

—— 1929. *Tuyaux et Resonateurs*. Paris Librarie delagravie.   168

BOURN, L. E. A.   1949 *Electronics Forum*.   30, 179

—— & JOHN COMPTON ORGAN COMPANY.   1932. *Brit. Pat.*, 403, 444.   179

BOYLE, H.   See Lloyd, L. S.   126

BRAY, C. W.   See Wever, E. G.   151

BROWN, D.   1939. *Proc. Phys. Soc.*, 51, 244.   50

BROWN, G. B.   1937. *Proc. Phys. Soc.*, 49, 493.   97, 98

—— 1938. *Science Progress*, 33, 29.   97

BROWNING, H. M.   See Barton, E. H.   71

BRUYN, J. D. DE   See Badings, H.   179

BUCHMANN, G.   See Meyer, E.   88

CADDY, R. S. & POLLARD, H. F.   1957. *Acustica*, 7, 277.   173

CAHILL, T.   1897. *Brit. Pat.*, 8725.   179

(See also Electrical World, New York 1906)

CULVER, C. A.   1956. *Musical Acoustics*. New York: McGraw-Hill.   —

DAVIS, A. H.   1934. *Modern Acoustics*. London: Bell.   32

DAVIS, H.   See Galambos, R.   151

DITCHBURN, R. W.   1955. *Optica Acta*, 1, 171.   111

DOUGLAS, A.   1957. *The Electrical Production of Music*. London: Macdonald   179

DUDDELL, W.   1900. *The Electrician*, 46, 356.   31

DUDLEY, H., RIESZ, R. R. & WATKINS, S. S. A.   1939. *Bell Labs. Mono.*, B1148   176

EWALD, P. P.   1940. *Proc. Phys. Soc.*, 52, 167.   61

FARNSWORTH, D. W.   1940. *Bell Labs. Record*, 18, 203.   176

FLETCHER, H.   1953. *Speech and Hearing in Communication*. New York: Van Nostrand.   150, 151

FOURIER, J.   1822. *Théorie Analytique de la Chaleur*.   47

FOURNIER, I. E.   1953. *L'Acoustique Musicale*. Paris: Maloirie.   111

FRANKLIN, BENJAMIN   93

FRANZ, E.   See Trendelenberg, F.   173

FRIEDLANDER, F. G.   1955.   *Proc. Camb. Phil. Soc.*, 49, 516.   90, 110

FULLER, M. W.   See Hart, H. C.   174

GALAMBOS, R. & DAVIS, H.   1943. *J. Neurophysiol.*, 6, 39.   151

GENTIL, K.   1957. *Acustica*, 7, 58.   9

GEORGE, W. H.   1954. *Acustica*, 4, 225.   88, 152

—— & Beckett, H. E.   1927. *Proc. Roy. Soc. A.*, 114, 111; 116, 115.   89

GHOSH, R. N.   1936. *J. Acoust. Soc. Am.*, 7, 254.   174

GOLDMAN, S.   1948. *Frequency Analysis, Modulation and Noise*. New York: McGraw-Hill.   —

GUTTMAN, N.   See Matthews, M. B.   185

HAMMOND, L.   1935. *Electronics*, 8, 156.   30, 181

HART, H. C., FULLER, M. W. & LUSBY, W. S.   1934. *J. Acoust. Soc. Am.*, 6, 80.   174

HELMHOLTZ, H. L. F.   1877. *On the sensations of tone*. Re-issued 1954. New York: Dover.   47, 89, 90, 117, 129, 150, 176

HIGGENS,   1777.   94

HILLER, L. A. & ISAACSON, L. M.   1959. *Experimental Music*. New York: McGraw-Hill.   185

HOOGLAND, G. A.   1953. *The missing fundamental*. Utrecht Drukkerij Fa. Schotanus en Jens.   153

HUGGINS, W. H.   1953. Air Force Research Centre Technical Report, 53-14. Cambridge, Mass.   154

HUGHES, W. & TAYLOR, C. A.   1953. *J. Sci. Inst.*, 30, 105.   50

HUTCHINS, C. M.   1962.   *Scientific American*.   157

JEANS, SIR J.   1937. *Science and Music*. Cambridge: University Press.   —

JEFRESS, L. A.   1948. *J. Comp. Physiol. Psychol.*, 41, 35.   154

JENNISON, R. C.   1961. *Fourier Transforms and Convolutions for the Experimentalist*. Oxford: Pergamon.   53, 61

KARMAN, T. VON   1912. *Gottingen Nach*, 547.   95

KAUFFMAN, W.   1895. *Ann. Physik.*, 54, 675.   89

KELLER, J. B.   1953. *Communications on Pure and Applied Maths.*, 6, 483.   90

KRIGAR-MENZEL, O. & RAPS, A.   1893. *Ann. Physik.*, 50, 444.   92

LEHR, A. 1952. *Acustica*, 2, 35. 34
LEIPP, E. 1959. *Comptes Rendus*, 249, 1474. 158
—— & MOLES, A. A. 1959. *Annales de Telecom.*, 14, 135. 158
LICKLIDER, J. C. R. 1956. *3rd Symposium on Information Theory*.
London: Butterworths. 151
LIPSON, H. & TAYLOR, C. A. 1958. *Fourier Transforms and X-ray Diffraction*
London: Bell. 61
—— See Taylor, C. A. 50
LLOYD, L. S. 1937. *Music and Sound*. Oxford: University Press. —
—— & BOYLE, H. 1963. *Intervals, Scales and Temperaments*. London:
Macdonald. 126
LOWERY, H. 1952. *The Background of Music*. London: Hutchinson. 155
LUSBY, W. S. See Hart, H. C. 174
MACFADYEN, K. A. 1964. *The Radio & Electronic Engineer*, 27, 365 179
MACLACHLAN, D. 1957. *X-ray Crystal Structure*. New York: McGraw-Hill. 61
MAHAJAN, L. D. 1929. *Ind. J. Phys.*, 4, 515. 175
MATHES, R. C. & MILLER, R. L. 1947. *J. Acoust. Soc. Am.*, 19, 780. 153
MATTHEWS, M. V. 1961. *Bell Systems Tech. J.*, 40, 677. 184
—— & GUTTMAN, N. 1959. *Proc. 3rd Int. Cong. on Acoustics*.
Amsterdam: Elsevier. 185
MEE, F. G. 1950. *Sound*. London: Heinemann. —
MERRY, F. 36
MEYER, E. & BUCHMANN, G. 1931. *Sitz. der Preuss. Adak. Wiss. Physik*.
Maths., 32, 735 88
MILBOURN, M. 1962. *Bull. Inst. Phys.*, 13, 42. 126
MILLER, D. C. 1916. *The Science of Musical Sounds*. London: Macmillan. —
MILLER, R. L. See Mathes, R. C. 153
MOLES, A. A. See Leipp, E. 158
NOLLE, A. W. & Boner, C. P. 1941a. *J. Acoust. Soc. Am.*, 13, 145. 100, 114, 173
—— 1941b. *J. Acoust. Soc. Am.*, 13, 149. 100, 171, 173
OLSON, H. F. 1943. *Dynamical Analogies*. Princeton, N. J.: Van Nostrand 32
—— 1952. *Musical Engineering*. New York: McGraw-Hill. —
—— 1957. *Acoustical Engineering*. New York: Van Nostrand. 48
——, BELAR, H. & TIMMENS, J. 1960. *J. Acoust. Soc. Am.*, 32, 311. 185
ONCHI, Y. 1961. *J. Acoust. Soc. Am.*, 33, 794. 151
ORTMANN, O. 1925. *The Physical Basis of Piano Touch and Tones*. New York: Dutton. 174
PAGET, SIR R. 1930. *Human Speech*. London: Kegan Paul. 176
PARRY, SIR H. 1930. 124
POLLARD, H. F. See Caddy, R. S. 173
POTTER, R. K. 1946. *J. Acoust. Soc. Am.*, 18, 1 and subsequent papers 48, 176
PYTHAGORAS 1, 121
RAMAN, SIR C. V. 1918a. *Studies of Bowed Strings*. Bulletin 15. Calcutta:
Indian Association for the Cultivation of Science. 90
—— 1918b. *Phil. Mag.*, 35, 493. 160
RAPS, A. See Krigar-Menzel, O. 92
RAYLEIGH, LORD. 1877. *The Theory of Sound*. Re-issued 1937.
New York: Dover. 95

RICHARDSON, E. G.   1929. *The Acoustics of Orchestral Instruments.*
    London: Arnold.   168
—— 1953a. *Sound.* 5th Edition. London: Arnold.   95
—— 1953b. *Technical Aspects of Sound.* Amsterdam: Elsevier.   96
—— 1954a. *J. Acoust. Soc. Am.,* 26, 960.   100
—— 1954b. *Acustica,* 4, 213.   106
RIESZ, R. R.   See Dudley, H.   176
RIJKE, P. L.   1859. *Ann. d. Physik.,* 107, 339.   94
ROBERTSON, J. M.   1943. *Nature,* 152, 411.   61
ROSEN, G.   1958. *J. Acoust. Soc. Am.,* 30, 201.   185
ROSENBLITH, R.   See Békésy, G. von.   151
SABINE, W. C.   1922. *Collected papers in Acoustics.* Harvard University Press.   138
SACERDOTE, G. G.   1957. *Acustica,* 7, 61.   111
SAUNDERS, F. A.   1937. *J. Acoust. Soc. Am.,* 9, 81.   157
—— 1946. *J. Acoust. Soc. Am.,* 18, 395.   165
—— 1953. *J. Acoust. Soc. Am.,* 25, 491.   157
SCHOUTEN, J. F.   1938. *Nature,* 141, 914.   50
—— 1940a. *Phillips Tech. Rev.,* 5, 286.   30, 153
—— 1940b. *Proc. Acad. Sci. Amst.,* 43, 356.   153
—— 1940c. *Proc. Acad. Sci. Amst.,* 43, 991.   153
SEASHORE, E. C.   1938. *Psychology of Music.* New York: McGraw-Hill
                                            112, 131, 155, 164, 165, 174
SMITH, F.   See Andrade, E. N. da C.   9
TAYLOR, C. A.   1960. *Bull. Inst. Phys.,* 11, 269.   —
—— & LIPSON, H.   1964. *Optical Transforms.* London: Bell.   50
    See Hughes, W.   50
    See Lipson, H.   61
THIENHAUS, E.   See Trendelenberg, F.   173
TIMMENS, J.   See Olson, H. F.   185
TRENDELENBERG, F., THIENHAUS, E. & FRANZ, E.   1936. *Akust. Zeits.,* 1, 59.   173
WALLER, M. D.   1960. *Chladni Plates.* London: Staples Press.   9
WATKINS, S. S. A.   See Dudley, H.   176
WATTERS, B. G.   See Allen, C. H.   30
WEBER, E. H.   1825. Wellenlehr.   149
WENTE, E. C.   1922. *Phys. Rev.,* 19, 333.   100
WEVER, E. G. 1949. *Theory of Hearing.* New York: Wiley.   151
—— & BRAY, C. W.   1930a. *Proc. Nat. Acad. Sci. Wash.,* 16, 344.   151
—— 1930b. *Psychol. Rev.,* 37, 365.   151
—— 1930c. *J. Exp. Psychol.,* 13, 373.   151
WHITFIELD, I. C.   See Allanson, J. T.   151
WILSON, A. J. C.   1949. *X-ray Optics.* London: Methuen.   59
WINCKEL, F.   1960. *Phänomene des Musikalischen Horens.* Berlin:
    Max Hesses.   111
WOOD, A.   1940. *Acoustics.* London: Blackie.   71, 96
—— 1944. *The Physics of Music.* London: Methuen (6th edition 1962). vii, 174
YOUNG, R. W.   1954. *Acustica,* 4, 259.   174
YOUNG, T.   1784. *The Principal Phenomena of Sounds.*   117

Index of References to Demonstration Experiments

General Index